THE STEVENSON LIBRARY
OF EDWIN J. BEINECKE

VOLUME THREE

*Original Romanticized Portrait of Stevenson
Drawn from life in charcoal at Bournemouth
by John Singer Sargent*

IN THE BEINECKE COLLECTION

A
STEVENSON LIBRARY

Catalogue

OF A COLLECTION OF WRITINGS
BY AND ABOUT
ROBERT LOUIS STEVENSON
FORMED BY
EDWIN J. BEINECKE

COMPILED BY
GEORGE L. McKAY

VOLUME THREE
AUTOGRAPH LETTERS BY
ROBERT LOUIS STEVENSON
AND HIS WIFE

NEW HAVEN
YALE UNIVERSITY LIBRARY
1956

To

Linda L. Beinecke

PREFACE

THE autograph letters described in this volume, together with those that remain to be catalogued, form a large and important part of the Beinecke Collection. While the Collection contains nearly a thousand letters written by Stevenson himself and about three hundred by his wife, it possesses also hundreds of letters written to him by members of his family, his friends and others, and letters about him. In this third volume are described only letters by Stevenson and his wife; it is planned to provide in a succeeding volume a catalogue of the other letters in the Collection.

The first large group of autograph letters by Stevenson that Mr. Beinecke acquired was one containing nearly two hundred and fifty letters written to his closest and most trusted friend, Charles Baxter. In 1906 Baxter deposited this collection in the Savile Club of London of which he and Stevenson were members. Mr. Beinecke, also a member of the Club, purchased the collection from that institution in the 1930's. Another large group of letters came from Austin Strong, son of Stevenson's stepdaughter, Isobel. The first part of this group was acquired just before the beginning of World War II, other portions from Mrs. Strong at later dates. Since the war a fine batch of letters which Stevenson wrote to his intimate friend, Sidney Colvin, and which was formerly owned by Francis Peabody, was added to the Beinecke Collection. Within the last two years an interesting group of letters which Stevenson wrote to Charles Scribner and to Edward Livermore Burlingame, editor of *Scribner's Magazine*, was purchased from the Scribner firm, Stevenson's principal American publishers. Besides the letters by Stevenson, this group includes carbon copies of many handwritten and typewritten letters to Stevenson by Scribner, Burlingame and the firm.

Letters played a very important part in the lives of Stevenson and his circle, a more important part, one would suppose, than in the lives of a comparable group today. The fact that Stevenson spent his adult life in places farther and farther removed from his native Edinburgh (in London, Paris and vicinity, the French Riviera, Davos, Bournemouth, Saranac Lake, California, Hawaii and other Pacific islands, Sydney and finally Samoa) made letter writing imperative. When he sailed from London in August, 1887, to spend the remaining seven years of his life in America and the Pacific, he left in Britain most of his relatives, friends and other correspondents. Nearly all this travelling was in search of health, and in the Adirondacks and the Pacific he found a measure of health that was almost unbelievable to the invalid of Davos, Hyères, Nice and Bournemouth, who had passed through one serious illness after another for years. Stevenson found that he could not safely remain in Scotland, and the climates in some other parts of the world affected him adversely. Even if his health had been good, however, it is hard to imagine him settled in one place all his days.

Although wandering about the face of the earth seemed a necessity, distances of thousands of miles did not make him forget his friends, and a voluminous correspondence between the Pacific and Britain continued until the end of his life. In the invalid days on the European Continent and in Bournemouth many of Stevenson's letters contain long passages about his health. In them he also described the weather, what he ate and drank, the people he met. The more interesting letters and passages are devoted to the states of his mind, the books he read and those he wrote. As to recording the everyday events of life in the European days, he was perhaps not as good a reporter as his wife. But when he came to America and the Pacific he wrote many very long letters giving full accounts of many aspects of his life.

Stevenson and his wife failed to date most of the letters

by them in this Collection. A few of the envelopes in which they were mailed have been preserved and from these the dates of posting have been obtained and recorded. Some of the recipients of the letters, e.g. Stevenson's mother, Baxter, Burlingame and Scribner, often dated them. If no date has been left us by the writer, the recipient or the post office, it has nearly always been possible to assign an approximate date and sometimes an exact one from events mentioned in an undated letter, from the kind of stationery used, and from other evidence. Dates at the beginnings of entries which are not transcriptions of dates written by the authors of the letters or an amanuensis are printed within brackets. In cataloguing a collection which contains so many undated items, it was felt necessary to record the opening words of each letter in order to identify it beyond question.

Stevenson usually addressed his life-long friend, legal adviser and literary agent, as "Baxter," "Charles," or "C. B." Occasionally in the 1880's he saluted him as "Johnson" or "Thomson"; such letters Stevenson usually signed as "Thomson," "Thamson," "Johnson" or "Johnstone." Colvin he usually addressed as "My dear Colvin," or occasionally "S. C." Fanny Stevenson usually greeted the latter as "Dear Custodian." Henley was sometimes "My dear lad." Stevenson greeted his wife with quite a number of epithets, often "Dear fellow." Mrs. Sitwell was occasionally "Dear Madonna." Isobel Strong was sometimes "Teuila." Mrs. R. L. S. addressed her mother-in-law as "Mrs. Stevenson" during the life of R. L. S.; after his death she became "Aunt Maggie." Samuel Lloyd Osbourne, Stevenson's stepson, was usually referred to in the letters of R. L. S. and his wife as "Sam" until about the end of the Bournemouth period after which he was called "Lloyd." In the Stevenson letters as edited by Colvin the name "Sam" has invariably, it would seem, been changed to "Lloyd." Mrs. R. L. S. was sometimes referred to as "Cassandra" particularly by her father-in-law.

The earliest signature in Stevenson's hand here recorded (1856) is written as: "R. L. B. S." (i.e. Robert Lewis Balfour Stevenson). Until 1866 or 1867 he signed a number of letters to his father or mother: "R. Stevenson." Beginning in 1868 he often signed letters: "R. L. Stevenson," and between 1871 and 1873 there are several to Baxter and Colvin signed "Louis Stevenson." By the mid-70's it was usually "Robert Louis Stevenson" or "R. L. S." To his wife he usually signed himself as "Louis" or "R. L. S." but to his parents and friends he was almost never "Louis." He was a great inventor of aliases, such as "The Beroomed Stevenson," "Bold Bob Boltsprit," "Drucken Au'ra," "The Inspired Bard," "The Man," "The Man in the Moon," "The Meagre Living Pen," "Nine Pounds," "penitent thief," "The Real Mackay." Fairly often his letters had no signature at all. Mrs. R. L. S. usually signed her letters "Fanny V. de G. Stevenson," "F. V. de G. S.," or "Fanny."

In each entry in this third volume the attempt has been made to indicate where each letter was first published, if published at all. The compiler is not at all positive that each letter designated as Unpublished has actually never been in print. The word Unpublished has been used to mean: not published so far as known to the compiler. Most of the letters by Stevenson and his wife that have seen the light in books, periodicals and dealers' and auction catalogues have been published only in part. The numbers of lines which have not appeared in print of these partly published autographs have regularly been indicated. It is a pleasure to mention here a work that has been in preparation during the compiler's work on this third volume, viz. *RLS: Stevenson's Letters to Charles Baxter*, edited by DeLancey Ferguson and Marshall Waingrow. In this volume many letters which have here been indicated as Unpublished will be published in full, and there is the possibility that publication of this new volume of letters may antedate by a few days publication of this third volume.

As in the first two volumes of this Catalogue matter

which has been transcribed verbatim is set in roman type, and information in the compiler's words is in italics. It will be found that there are numerous errors and inconsistencies in spellings, punctuation, etc., in transcribed material; and fewer, it is hoped, in the material set in italics. The title, Sir, has not been used in recording the names of James M. Barrie, Sidney Colvin, Edmund William Gosse, Henry Norman or Herbert Beerbohm Tree, because these correspondents were all knighted many years after Stevenson's death, in 1913, 1911, 1925, 1915 and 1909 respectively.

The compiler wishes to record his grateful appreciation of assistance received in the preparation of this third volume from Mr. Beinecke, Mr. James T. Babb, Librarian of Yale University, Miss Marjorie G. Wynne, Librarian of the Rare Book Room, and Mr. Marshall Waingrow, Instructor in English in Yale University.

GEORGE L. MC KAY

New York
March 23, 1956

xi

CONTENTS

AUTOGRAPH LETTERS BY ROBERT LOUIS STEVENSON
TO

AUTOGRAPH LETTERS BY
MRS. ROBERT LOUIS STEVENSON
TO

ILLUSTRATIONS

ABBREVIATIONS

LFF   Letters of Robert Louis Stevenson to his Family and Friends
        . . . London   Methuen and Co. . . . 1899. 2 vols.
VL   Vailima Letters being Correspondence Addressed by Robert
        Louis Stevenson to Sidney Colvin   November, 1890—Oc-
        tober, 1894 . . . Chicago   Stone & Kimball   M DCCCXC V.
        2 vols.

PART TWELVE

LETTERS BY
ROBERT LOUIS STEVENSON

2629

[*August, 1887*]. Skerryvore [*Bournemouth*]. Dear Allen, Thanks for yours. We are all on the move and the decline and fall. *Signed:* Robert Louis Stevenson. *3 pp. Unpublished.*

2630

[*Summer, 1891*]. Vailima. Dear Mr Angus, You can use my letter as you will. *Signed:* Robert Louis Stevenson, *and* R. L. S. *1 p. Published in LFF, Vol. 2, pp. 232–233. Stevenson agrees to write a preface. He writes about Knox, Burns and Fergusson.*

R.L.S. TO WILLIAM AND THOMAS ARCHER

2631

Oct 17th 1888. Taiti. Dear Archer, Though quite unable to write letters, I nobly send you a line signifying nothing. *Signed:* Robert Louis Stevenson. *4 pp. With addressed envelope. Published in LFF, Vol. 2, pp. 120–121. The letter is partly addressed to William Archer's three-year-old son Thomas, to whom Stevenson gives the information that he (R.L.S.) was the best player of hide-and-seek going.*

2632

26th Nov. 1870. Edinburgh   17 Heriot Row. My dear Maud, I know I am always in debt, always owing letters. *Signed:* R. L. Stevenson. *8 pp. About 13 lines of this letter are published in The Rosenbach Company.* A Catalogue of Original Manuscripts *[etc.] . . . New York, 1933, p. 38, lot 306. Stevenson discusses a demonstration against women's rights by Edinburgh students. R.L.S. to his cousin, Maud (Balfour) Babington, wife of Professor Churchill Babington.*

2633

[*1891*]. Vailima, Upolu. My dear Baildon, This is a real disappointment. *Signed:* Robert Louis Stevenson. *3 handwritten and 2 typed pp. A copy made by Baildon for Sidney Colvin. Published in LFF, Vol. 2, pp. 219–221.*

2634

Jan. 15. 94. Vailima. My dear Baildon, Last mail brought your book and its Dedication. *Signed:* Robert Louis Stevenson. *2 pp. A copy made by Baildon for Sidney Colvin. Published in LFF, Vol. 2, pp. 317–318. Stevenson criticizes some of Baildon's writing.*

2635

Jan 30. 94. Vailima. My dear Baildon, "Call not blessed"—yes, if I could die just now, or say in half a year, I should have had a splendid time of it on the whole. *Signed:* R. L. S. *2 pp. A copy made by Baildon for Sidney Colvin. Published in LFF, Vol. 2, pp. 320–321, where parts of 2 lines of this copy are omitted. Stevenson thinks he might live to find himself* impotent and forgotten.

2636

[*August, 1893. Vailima*]. My dear Barrie, My cousin . . . Graham Balfour . . . takes to you . . . the greetings of . . . Robert Louis Stevenson. *1 p. Unpublished.*

2637

Dec. 7th 1893. Vailima Samoa. My dear Barrie I have received duly the *magnum opus* and it really is a *magnum opus*. *Signed:* Robert Louis Stevenson. *14 pp. The letter is in the hand of Isobel Strong, signed by Stevenson. Partly published in LFF, Vol. 2, pp. 311–313, where about 38 lines of the autograph are omitted. Stevenson writes about Barrie's* The Window in Thrums, *and about other books recently read by R. L. S.*

2638

[*1894? Vailima*]. Dear Barrie. I will not say anything about your hand, because my own is so damnable. *Unsigned. 2 pp. About 5 lines of this letter are published in Edith B. Tranter.* First Editions and Autograph Manuscripts of American and English Authors . . . Auction Sale . . . *New York, 1952, p. 106; about 35 lines of the autograph are omitted in this catalogue. Stevenson mentions his work on* St. Ives *and* Weir of Hermiston.

2639

[*October 31, 1871. 17 Heriot Row, Edinburgh*]. My dear Baxter, Thursday the 16th is the important day. *Signed:* Louis Stevenson. *1 p. Written on black-bordered stationery with motto:* Coelum non Solum. *Partly dated by R.L.S.'s mother. Unpublished. An invitation to a party celebrating R.L.S.'s twenty-first birthday.*

2640

[*November, 1871 ? Edinburgh*]. My dear Baxter, If you cannot bring down my copy tonight *in propria*, I shall call for it tomorrow. *Signed:* Louis Stevenson. *1 p. Written on black-bordered stationery with motto:* Coelum non Solum. *Unpublished.*

2641

[*Early 1872 ? Dunblane?*] Mon cher Baxter, After several years of feeble and innefectual[*sic*] endeavour. *Signed:* R. L. S. *4 pp. Unpublished. R.L.S. decides to omit his third initial and to sign his first two names in full.*

2642

[*1872 ?*] Accept the enclosed and thank you. *Signed:* Robert Louis Stevenson. *1 p. Unpublished.*

2643

3rd March (or April. 1872. Thursday. [*Edinburgh*]. My dear Baxter, Like one full of new wine — and so indeed I was, for I had a cab at my disposal this lovely evening — I went and called on you. *Signed:* R. L. Stevenson Bohn. *7 pp. Unpublished. Written in Biblical style.*

2644

5th March 1872. Friday. Dunblane. My dear Baxter, By the date you may perhaps understand the purport of my letter. *Signed:* R. L. Stevenson. *8 pp. Partly published in LFF, Vol. 1, pp. 27–29, where about 39 lines of the autograph are omitted.*

Stevenson meditates on solitude, memories, nature, health, old age, etc.

2645
[March 28, 1872. Edinburgh]. My dear Baxter, Damn you for a cold hearted knave. *Signed:* Louis Stevenson. *12 pp. Written partly on black-bordered stationery. Unpublished. All but the first sentence is in archaic French. Stevenson writes among other things of Balzac's stories.*

2646
9th April 1872. Tuesday. Dunblane. My dear Baxter, I don't know what you mean. I know nothing about the standing committee of the *Spec. Signed:* R. L. Stevenson. *6 pp. Partly published in LFF, Vol. 1, pp. 29–30, where about 42 lines of the autograph are omitted. The omitted portion includes Stevenson's poem, beginning:* As Daniel, bird-alone in that far land.

2647
April 28th 1872. [*Edinburgh*]. My dear Baxter, Not being in propria able to appear before you and charm away your evil spirit. *Signature and 2 lines on recto cut away. 8 pp. Written on stationery of* 17 Heriot Row. *Unpublished.*

2648
31st October 1872. [*Edinburgh*]. My dear Baxter, I have been quite depressed all day about this rotten, curious job of yours. *Signed:* R. L. Stevenson. *7 pp. At the top of p. 1 Stevenson has written:* Private. *Written on stationery of* 17 Heriot Row. *Unpublished. He disapproves something Baxter has done to one John Forman, and asks him to make amends.*

2649
December 1872. [*Malvern?*]. Secretairy, Quite contrairy, How did the voting go? Did the presidents rule Make you look like a fool? Or were you at the head of the row? *Signed:* R. L. S. *2 pp. Unpublished.*

2650

Jan 16th 1873. Imperial Hotel, Great Malvern. My dear Baxter, Without, it rains — within, muddle o' the brains. *Signed twice:* R. L. S. *8 pp. Written on stationery of* 17 Heriot Row. *Unpublished.*

2651

Feby 2nd 1873. Sunday. [*Edinburgh*]. My dear Baxter, The thunderbolt has fallen with a vengeance now. *Signed:* R. L. Stevenson. C. I., M. A., S. B, &c. *10 pp. Written on stationery of* 17 Heriot Row. *Partly published in LFF, Vol. 1, pp. 40–41, where about 75 lines of the autograph are omitted. Stevenson writes about a row with his parents over religious beliefs, which has caused suffering to them all.*

2652

[*Cir. October 20, 1873. Edinburgh*]. My dear Charles, Le grand moment est arrivé. *Signed:* R. L. S. *3 pp. Written on stationery of* 17 Heriot Row. *Unpublished.*

2653

[*October, 1873. Edinburgh*]. My dear Baxter, I wished to say a little word to you last night. *Signed:* Robert Louis Stevenson, *and* R. L. S. *3 pp. Written on black-bordered stationery of* 17 Heriot Row. *Unpublished.*

2654

[*October 25, 1873*] Saturday. [*London*]. My dear Charles, The doctor has just told me that I have succeeded in playing the devil with myself to a singular degree. *Signed:* R L. Stevenson. *12 pp. At top of p. 1:* Private — a few! *Unpublished.*

2655

[*End of October, 1873*]. 15 Chepstow Place, Bayswater, London. My dear Charles, Your kindness put me in rather an odd little difficulty on Saturday morning. *Signed:* R. Louis Stevenson. *3 pp. Written on black-bordered stationery. Unpublished.*

2656

[*Postmarked: November 4, 1873. London*]. My dear Baxter, Please redeem my "Democratic Vistas" by W. Whitman from Wilson. *Signed:* R. L. S. *3 pp. Written on stationery of* 17 Heriot Row. *The envelope containing this postmark is not preserved. Unpublished.*

2657

[*November 15, 1873*]. Hotel du Pavillon, Mentone. My dear Charles, I feel that I ought to write to you; though after all you never write to me. *Signed:* R. L. Stevenson. *6 pp. At top of p. 1:* Private. *Written on stationery of* 17 Heriot Row. *Unpublished.*

2658

December 4th [*and*] 11th December [*1873. Mentone*]. My dear Baxter, At last I must write. I began a letter to you before but it broke miserably down. *Signed:* Robert Louis Stevenson. *12 pp. Partly published in* The Letters, *1911, Vol. 1, pp. 92–94, where about 200 lines of the autograph are omitted. Stevenson discusses his health, his idleness, his reading and the Mentone weather. He writes of one Argyll Bates, of Lord Salisbury and a private tutor to the latter's children, of a paper Baxter read at the Speculative Society.*

2659

Dec 20th 1873. Monaco. My dear Baxter, There is a large wooden chest (plain deal) in my sitting room. *Signed:* R L Stevenson. *4 pp. Unpublished.*

2660

[*January, 1874. Mentone*]. My dear Charles, I am here in a funny little society. *Signed:* Robert Louis Stevenson. *4 pp. Unpublished. Stevenson writes of the Johnstone family (Americans), Robinet, two Russian ladies and children.*

2661

[*Postmarked:* Ju 25   74. London]. Très affairé, je ne trouve pas le temps de vous écrire. *Signed:* R. L. S. *Post card. Unpublished.*

2662

[*Autumn, 1874. Edinburgh*]. Dear Charles, Cold — in house — pity . . . — not able to dine tomorrow. *Signed:* Robert Louis Stevenson. *1 p. Written on stationery containing Stevenson's monogram. Unpublished.*

2663

[*July 28, 1875. London*]. My dear Charles, damned nice of you to write. Grindlay and I were awful ill with head ache on the voyage. *Signed:* R. L. S. *4 pp. Written on* Savile Club *stationery. Unpublished.*

2664

[*Autumn, 1875. Edinburgh*]. My dear Charles, I want you to see my answers to condescendences (and d - - d condescending condescendences they were). *Signed:* R L S *and 5 monograms. 2 pp. Written on Baxter's stationery of* 11 So. Charlotte Street. *Unpublished.*

2665

[*February 29, 1876. Edinburgh*]. My dear Charles, My mother will be obliged if you will dine here on Wednesday at seven. *Signed:* Robert Louis Stevenson. *3 pp. Written on black-bordered stationery of* 17 Heriot Row. *Unpublished.*

2666

[*1876. London*]. My dear Charles, Herewith sheets of the prints (£15,00's worth) stolen from Colvin on Saturday morning. *Signed:* Robert Louis Stevenson. *1 p. Written on* Albemarle Club *stationery. Unpublished.*

2667

[*Late December, 1877*]. 5 Rue Ravignon, Paris. My dear Charles The Blow has fallen. I am swept from my native Heaths. *Signed:* Wilkins Micawber alias Robert Louis Stevenson. *2 pp. Written on* Savile Club *stationery. Unpublished.*

2668

[*December 29, 1877. Paris*]. My dear Baxter   Thanks, it's received £10. received from Messrs Mitchel and Baxter. *Signed:* R L. Stevenson. *1 p. Unpublished.*

2669

[*Spring, 1878. Paris*]. My dear Charles, I am ashamed of my silence. *Signed:* R. L. Stevenson, Duc et pair. *4 pp. Unpublished.*

2670

[*June, 1878*]. Hotel Mirabeau, Paris. My dear Charles, You see you were right. I only write to ask a service. £100 quid must be had. *Signed:* Robert Louis Stevenson. *1 p. Unpublished.*

2671

June 26th 1878. Hotel Mirabeau   Paris. My dear Charles, I thank you a thousand times for your kind promptitude. *Signed:* R L. S. *2 pp. A few lines of this letter are published in The Rosenbach Company.* A Catalogue of Original Manuscripts [*etc.*] . . . *New York, 1933, p. 38, lot* 311. *Stevenson asks:* Can a man, a British subject of age, marry an American girl (of age, *if necessary*) in Scotland?

2672

[*Early August, 1878*]. Paris. My dear Baxter. Poste Restante, Montargis, till further notice. *Signed:* R. L. S. *1 p. Unpublished.*

2673

[*Postmarked:* 28 Aout 78]. Le Puy, Haute Loire. My dear Baxter. This is the new address   Poste Restante   Le Puy   Haute Loire. *Signed:* R. L. S. *1 p. With addressed envelope and mounted stamp. Unpublished.*

2674

[*Postmarked:* 11 Sept 78]. Chez Morel, Au Monastier, Haute Loire. My dear Charles, I shall never have a more permanent address than this. *Signed:* R. L. S. *1 p. With addressed envelope and mounted stamp. Unpublished.*

2675

[*Postmarked:* 16 Sept 78. Monastier]. Dear Charles, I beg your pardon for the telegram. *Signed:* R. L. S. *1 p. With addressed envelope and mounted stamp. Note on letter in Colvin's hand:* starting on travels with a donkey 1878. *Unpublished.*

2676

[*Postmarked:* 19 Sept 78. Monastier]. Morel's. My dear Charles, Yours (with inclosures) of the 16th to hand. All work done. *Signed:* R. L. S. *1 p. With addressed envelope and mounted stamp. Published in LFF, Vol. 1, pp. 128–129, where one line of the autograph is omitted.*

2677

Oct 5th [*1878*]. Alais, Gard. My dear Charles, Le tour est fait. I received the 3 letters. *Signed:* R. L. S. *2 pp. With addressed envelope and mounted stamp. Unpublished.*

2678

[*28/10/78. 4 Earl's Terrace, Devonport Rd. Uxbridge Rd., London, W.*]. My dear Charles, What is to be done to make it clear to you? *Signed:* R. L. S. *3 pp. Dated by W. H. Henley. Unpublished.*

2679

Nov. [*29*] 1878. Friday. [*London*]. My dear Charles, You did perfectly right to send the money. *Signed:* Robert Louis Stevenson. *4 pp. Written on* Savile Club *stationery. Unpublished.*

2680

[*Early December? 1878. London*]. My dear Charles, Recd 100 quid; for which God bless you. *Signed:* R. L. S. *3 pp. Written on* Savile Club *stationery. Unpublished.*

2681

[*End of December, 1878. Edinburgh*]. Dear Charles, dear camerado, I engage you with an engagement for Saturday. *Signed:* W. Whitman. *1 p. Written on stationery of* 11 So. Charlotte Street. *Unpublished.*

2682

[*Late 1878. Edinburgh*]. My dear Charles, I hope you have got your books — I saw your letter to Henley. *Signed:* Robert Louis Stevenson. *4 pp. Written on stationery of* 17 Heriot Row. *Unpublished.*

2683

[*Spring, 1879. London*]. Dear Charles, Please excuse long silence — though it's you that owes me a letter and an apology too. *Signed:* Robert Louis Stevenson. *1 p. Written on* Savile Club *stationery. Unpublished.*

2684

[*May 19, 1879. London*]. My dear Charles, I explain nothing. Wild work, very wild, but it is a wild world. *Signed:* R. L. S. *1 p. Written on* Arts Club *stationery. Dated by Baxter. Unpublished.*

2685

Ju 9 79. London. Address chez Leopold Cernay la ville Seine et Oise. *1 p. Telegram. Unpublished.*

2686

[*Postmarked:* 14 Juin 79]. Chez Leopold Cernay-la-Ville Seine et Oise. My dear Charles, I shall call at Printing House Square on my way back about 1st July. *Signed:* R. L. S. *1 p. With addressed envelope and mounted stamp. Unpublished.*

2687

[*June 25, 1879. France*]. Address Savile Club. Am on way home. *Signed:* R. L. S. *1 p. Unpublished.*

2688

[*August 4, 1879. London*]. Dear Charles, All well. please send my last batch of letters . . . to Mr Robert Stephenson. *Signed:* R. L. S. *1 p. Written on* Savile Club *stationery. Unpublished.*

2689

[*August 6, 1879. Glasgow*]. My dear Charles, Here I am in the Glasgow, my traps aboard and the deep C, or natural B— in front of me. *Signed:* Johnson. *3 pp. Written in pencil. Unpublished.*

2690

[*August 22, 1879*]. Friday. Union Pacific Transfer Council Bluffs. Iowa. U. S. Dear boy, have been on cars since Monday and have still a week before me. *Signed:* R. L. S. *2 pp. Unpublished.*

2691

[*September 9, 1879. Monterey*]. My dear Charles Address me c/o Jos. D. Strong. Monterey. *Signed:* R. L. S. *1 p. Unpublished.*

2692

[*September 24, 1879*]. c/o Jos. D. Strong Monterey Monterey Co. Cal. My dear Charles, I write you from an angora goat ranch where I live with some frontiersmen. *Signed:* R. L. S. *4 pp. Dated by Baxter. Unpublished.*

2693

Oct. 15th [*1879*]. Monterey Monterey Co. Cal. My dear Charles, A thousand thanks for your letter, the third altogether I have received from Europe since I left. *Signed:* Robert Louis Stevenson. *2 pp. Marked:* Private & Confidential. *Unpublished.*

2694

[*November 29, 1879. Monterey*]. My dear Charles, if no money has been sent by my people in answer to that telegram, please send me £50 as before. *Signed:* R. L. S. *1 p. Unpublished.*

2695

[*January 9, 1880*]. 608 Bush Street San Francisco Cal. My dear Baxter, I received the state of account and the cheque which I herewith return endorsed. *Signed:* Robert Louis Stevenson *and R. L. S. 3 pp. Unpublished. Stevenson writes that he wishes to have his books sold in order to take care of his financial obligations.*

2696

[*January 20, 1880*]. 608 Bush Street San Francisco. My dear Charles, I see I have been unjust to you. *Signed:* Robert Louis Stevenson. *3 pp. Unpublished.*

2697

Jan. 26th [*1880*]. 608 Bush Street San Francisco Cal. My dear Charles, I am truly glad you paid back the £50; I was almost afraid it might have hurt their feelings. *Signed:* R. L. S. *2 pp. Partly published in LFF, Vol. 1, pp. 164–165, where about 20 lines of the autograph are omitted.*

2698

February 22nd [*1880*]. 608 Bush St. S. F. Cal. My dear Charles, I have received yours of Jan 29, also one containing a letter of credit. *Signed:* R. L. S. *3 pp. Unpublished.*

2699

[*April or May, 1880. East Oakland, California*]. My dear Charles, I am guilty indeed. *Signed:* The Gay Japanee. *2 pp. Unpublished.*

2700

Se 8 80. Edinburgh. I am not allowed to come can I not see you even for twenty minutes. *1 p. Telegram. Unpublished.*

2701

[*September, 1880*]. Ben Wyvis Hotel Strathpeffer. My dear Charles, enclosed is a receipt with which I know not what to do — do you? *Signed:* R. L. S. *2 pp. This letter contains the poem,* On Some Ghastly [Ghostly?] Companions at a Spa, *beginning:* That was an evil day when I. *Published in* The Letters, *1911, Vol. 2, pp. 7–8, where about 5 lines of the first paragraph and 2 lines of the poem in the autograph are omitted. The poem is printed in full in the* Collected Poems Edited . . . *by Janet Adam Smith, 1950.*

2702

[*1880? Edinburgh?*]. Share Moshew jay essayay de voo vivar, may ne pouvee pa ploo longtong demurray eesee. *Signed:*

Thamson. *1 p. Written on p. 4 of a folder of Baxter's stationery; p. 1 contains Baxter's printed address, and the printed year 188 . . . to be completed by hand. Unpublished.*

2703
[*October 28, 1880. Troyes*]. Dear Charles, herewith a cheque and the old divorce, I have been pretty seedy and am just creeping toward Davos. *Signed:* R. L. S. *3 pp. Unpublished.*

2704
[*November, 1880. Davos*]. My dear Baxter, I have had the money paid and send herewith the receipt and extract of divorce, the latter to put in my little drawer in your place of business. *Signed:* R. L. S. *1 p. Unpublished.*

2705
[*Middle November, 1880*]. Hotel Belvedere Davos Platz, Switzerland. My dear Charles, Herewith a check and F's certificate — what a piece of machinery! *Signed:* R. L. S. *1 p. Unpublished.*

2706
[*December, 1880. Davos*]. My dear Charles, Of course I have something to ask. else I would not write that is plain to the meanest capacity. *Signed:* Robert Louis Stevenson. *2 pp. Baxter has written on p. 1:* recd 11 Dec 1880. *Unpublished.*

2707
[*February, 1881. Davos*]. My dear Charles, First: business. (1) enclosed cheque. (2) herewith second note to Simp. *Signed:* R. L. S. *3 pp. Unpublished.*

2708
Fe 27 81. Davos Platz. Stop bill frisco by telegram letter. *Telegram. Unpublished.*

2709
[*1881*]. My dear Charles, It was I, as you now know who telegraphed in propria. *Signed:* R. L. S. *1 p. Unpublished.*

2710

[*March 1, 1881. Davos*]. My dear Charles, This is only a line to say why I telegraphed to stop the bill. *Signed:* R. L. S. *2 pp. Unpublished.*

2711

[*March 4, 1881. Davos*]. My dear Charles, What a solemn thing is regret, what a consequential matter is neglect. *Signed:* R. L. S. *1 p. Dated by Baxter. Unpublished.*

2712

[*March 12, 1881. Davos*]. Dear Charles, Enclosed two cheques; I fear I must ask you to send me four pounds of the total here. *Signed:* R. L. Stevenson. *2 pp. Dated by Baxter. Unpublished.*

2713

[*March, 1881*]. Dear Charles, dam proud it's so little. Baronet and Lady propose to meet us Italian Lakes. *Signed:* R. L. S. *1 p. Baxter has written at top:* received 28 Mch/ 81. *Unpublished.*

2714

[*April 26, 1881. Paris*]. My dear Charles, I have received the £10 for which I enclose the receipt. *Signed twice:* R. L. S. *1 p. Written on stationery of* Hotel Saint Roman, 5 et 7, Rue Saint-Roch. *Unpublished.*

2715

[*June 4, 1881*]. Fisher's Hotel Pitlochrie Perthshire. My dear Charles, The will seems to me to be a sweet thing. *Signed:* R. L. S., *followed by unintelligible pen strokes and the words:* Mind Gone. *2 pp. Unpublished.*

2716

[*July 8, 1881*]. Kinnaird Cottage Pitlochry Perthshire. My dear Charles, I have been writing off my fingers about this chair of Mackay's. *Signed:* R. L. S. *2 pp. Unpublished. This refers to the Chair of History in the University of Edinburgh resigned by Æneas J. G. Mackay, for which Stevenson offered himself as a candidate. See no. 1431.*

2717
Jy 22 81. Pitlochry. Weather bad & I still have cold better not come. *Telegram. Unpublished.*

2718
[*July 29, 1881. Kinnaird Cottage, Pitlochry*]. My dear Charles, I suppose you have heard that I have been ill. *Signed:* R. L. Stevenson. *2 pp. Unpublished.*

2719
[*Early August, 1881. Braemar*]. My dear Charles, Herewith a check which I have been trundling for days in my pocket for lack of energy. *Signed:* R. L. S. *2 pp. Unpublished.*

2720
Sp 8 81. Braemar. No telegram received perceive with glee that you come tomorrow. *Telegram. Unpublished.*

2721
[*October 19, 1881. Davos*]. . . . . Dear Charles, many thanks for your promptitude and kindness. *Signed:* R. L. S. *1 p. Unpublished.*

2722
Oct 19th 1881. Wednesday. Davos Platz. My dear sir, Will you be so kind as to inspect on my behalf the marriage contract of Mr & Mrs Sydney de Mattos. *Signed:* Robert Louis Stevenson. *1 p. This is a copy in the handwriting of Baxter of what R. L. S. refers to in the foregoing letter as a* wierd shot at business letter. *Unpublished.*

2723
[*November 14, 1881. Davos*]. My dear Charles, I have long been meditating a letter to you: when here came this abominable business one. *Signed:* R. L. S. *3 pp. Dated by Baxter. Unpublished.*

2724
[*November, 1881. Davos*]. My dear Charles, I enclose a cheque for thirty pound and never was anybody gladder to do so.

Signed: R. L. S. *Written on stationery with heading printed by Lloyd Osbourne:* Davos Printing Office. Managed by Samuel Lloyd Osbourne & Co. The Chalet. *Unpublished.*

2725

15 December 1881. Davos. My dear Charles, That cheque to Ruedi has been lost; for God's sake stop it and supply another. *Signed:* R. L. S. *3 pp. Published in LFF, Vol. 1, pp. 226–227, where the first 4 lines of the autograph are omitted. The date 15 has been written on the autograph in a hand other than Stevenson's; in the printed version the letter is dated December 5.*

2726

[*January, 1882? Davos*]. My dear Charles This is intolerable, but we have been very unhappy, dog ill, wife ill and the rest. *Signed:* R L. S. *4 pp. Written on stationery of* Hôtel & Pension Buol. *Unpublished. Following his signature Stevenson has written a poem of 3 stanzas titled:* Ode by Ben Johnson[*sic*], Edgar Allan Poe, and a bungler. *The first stanza begins:* Long, long ago, (It was in the Lothian Road). *The second begins:* Brash, Brash is dead. *The third:* Yet fear not we shall follow; for wherever. *The first stanza consists of 6 lines, the second of 21 lines, and the third of 14 lines. The third stanza is in the meter of the* Brashiana *sonnets, and may be regarded as one.*

2727

[*January, 1882. Davos*]. Dear Charles, no sooner yours came than down I sat and penned the enclosed. *Signed:* R. L. S. *2 pp. Unpublished. Stevenson refers to 4 Brashiana sonnets, which he numbers 1, 2, 3 and 4, the texts of which were evidently sent with this letter.*

2728

[*1882*]. Dear Charles, I've been ill and here is the result. I don't know about order [*of the* Brashiana *sonnets*]. You'll have to see. I forget about the others. Here is a hypothetical order
1. "We found him first as in the dells of May."
2. "Sir in one thing I will commend myself."
3. (the one about his being dead, "as falls the cedar," "light-

ning flash" &c.). [*beginning:* We found him and we lost. The glorious Brash].

4. "There let us often wend our pensive way."
5. "Brash, while he lived, we not deserted; nor."
6. "Alas that while the beautiful & strong."
7. (the one ending "the Caliban of God"). [*beginning:* As the great artists, at the writing desk].
8. "Who that hath walked with nature in her mirth."
9. "This gory helm the soldier must embrace"
10. "Rain that effaces epitaphs: the gale."

Of course, you edit and have my leave to reject any peace[*sic*] unworthy of his memory. A cut is under way. *Unsigned. 1 p. Written in pencil. Unpublished.*

2729
Feb 2nd 1882. Davos-Platz. My dear Charles I had written a letter to you some time back but it was, by opinion of counsel put in the fire. *Signed:* R. L. S. *2 pp. Marked:* Private & confidential. *Written on stationery of* Hôtel & Pension Buol. *Unpublished. Stevenson writes of an account and correspondence with one Robertson which he doesn't like.*

2730
[*February 6, 1882. Davos-Platz*]. My dear Charles, Will you mind raising me what you can on that hundred quid that I'm to get from Chatto. *Signed:* R. L. S. *Written on stationery of* Hôtel & Pension Buol. *Unpublished. Stevenson writes that he can stand the Buol no longer and wants to get away in spite of his and his wife's illness.*

2731
[*February, 1882. Davos-Platz*]. My dear Charles, I told you I had written a more explicit letter; I will and I can write no more. *Signed:* R L. S. *4 pp. Written on stationery of* Hôtel & Pension Buol. *Baxter has written on p. 1:* recd 14 Feb 1882. *Unpublished.*

2732
[*February 14, 1882. Davos-Platz*]. My dear Charles, For God's sake give me an answer in peace; I am quite sewn up. *Signed:*

penitent thief. *1 p. written on stationery of* Hôtel & Pension Buol. *Unpublished.*

2733
[*February 22, 1882. Davos-Platz*]. My dear Charles, Your most welcome letter has raised clouds of sulphur from my horizon. *Signed:* R L. S. *3 pp. Written on stationery of* Hôtel & Pension Buol. *Partly published in LFF, Vol. 1, pp. 228–229, where about 19 lines of the autograph are omitted.*

2734
[*March, 1882. Davos-Platz*]. My dear Charles, I meant a long while ago to write to you on two subjects: your wife and mine. *Signed:* Nine pounds, *and* A hundred and nine pounds. *3 pp. Written on stationery of* Hôtel & Pension Buol. *Baxter has written on p. 1:* recd 11 Mch/82. *Unpublished.*

2735
[*May or June, 1882. Edinburgh*]. Dear Charles, Couldn't you look down this afternoon, or at 1/2 past eight this evening and play one game of chess. I'll stand Sam Yrs R.L.S. I'm confined to the house. *1 p. Unpublished.*

2736
1st July 1882. Stobo Manse. Dear Baxter I inclose an account — no it is needless. *Signed:* R. L. Stevenson. *1 p. Unpublished.*

2737
[*July, 1882. Edinburgh*]. *In Baxter's hand:* Received Donald Nobles voucher for payment of £1.17.3. *In Stevenson's hand:* not known and not admitted R. L. Stevenson. *1 p. Unpublished.*

2738
July 28th 1882. Hotel Kingussie. Dear Charles, Please receive and act as a good father of a family. *Signed:* Robert Louis Stevenson. *1 p. Unpublished.*

2739
Oct [*10*] 1882. Tuesday. Terminus Hotel Marseilles. My dear C. B., I suppose you have heard that I have had a beas'ly time.

Signed: R. L. S. *2 pp. Unpublished. At the bottom of p. 2 is a drawing by Stevenson of a monumental tomb and 2 male figures. The tomb bears the name* C. G. Brash. *The initials may stand for* Caliban of God. *Stevenson asks about the printing of the* Brashiana *sonnets.*

2740

17th Oct. 1882. Campagne Defli, St. Marcel, Banlieue de Marseille. Dear Charles, As usual nae receipt, but I'll alloo 'at I hae gotten a cheque. *Signed:* Thamson. *2 pp. Written on stationery of* Terminus Hotel, Marseille. *Unpublished. Following the signature are 8 lines of verse beginning:* Campagne De-fli: / O me! /

2741

1st December. 82. Campagne Defli St Marcel Banlieue de Marseille. Dear Charles, This, which my wife had lost, comes to you late. *Signed:* R. L. S. *2 pp. Unpublished*

2742

[*December, 1882. Campagne Defli, St. Marcel, Banlieue de Marseille*]. My dear Charlie. I cannot say how much shocked we were to hear of your loss. *Signed:* Robert Louis Stevenson. *1 p. Unpublished. At the bottom of p. 1 and on an inside p. Mrs. R. L. S. has written a note to Mr. & Mrs. Baxter. These are notes of sympathy on the death of a child of the Baxters.*

2743

[*December, 1882. Campagne Defli, St. Marcel, Banlieue de Marseille*]. My dear Charles, I send a damned dominie's account. *Signed:* Robert Louis Stevenson. *3 pp. Unpublished. Stevenson writes about a preface he expected Baxter to write to the* Brashiana *sonnets. On a sheet accompanying this letter Stevenson has drawn a man over whom a huge candle flame extinguisher is being lowered. The man is approaching a grave stone which bears the words:* Finis Coronat Opus. *The drawing is titled:* Apotheosis of Brash.

2744

[*December, 1882*]. Campagne Defli St Marcel Banlieue de Marseille. Dear Charles, Herewith these, how shall I call them? — proofs de luxe. *Unsigned. Mostly in French. 2 pp. Unpublished.*

2745

[*December, 1882*]. Campagne Defli St Marcel Banlieue de Marseille. Dear boy, This proof would wake the dead. *Unsigned. 2 pp. Written in pencil. Unpublished. Upon receipt of a proof of the first* Brashiana *sonnet, Stevenson here suggests 3 corrections. 2 of these corrections have not been made in printed versions of the sonnet.*

2746

Jan 7th 1883. Nice. My dear Charles, Enclosed is the cheque of which I spoke to you as in a parable in my last. *Signed:* Robert Louis Stevenson. *1 p. Written on stationery of the* Grand Hotel, Nice. *Unpublished.*

2747

[*Postmarked:* 12 Janv. 83. Nice]. Dear Charles, Thanks for your good letter. *Signed:* Thomson. *4 pp. In Scots dialect. With addressed envelope and mounted stamp. Published in LFF, Vol. 1, pp. 255–256, where about 2 lines of the autograph are omitted.*

2748

[*January, 1883*]. Marseille. Dear Charles To explain my movements were impossible. *Signed:* Thamson. *1 p. Baxter has written at bottom:* recd 25 Jan 1883. *Unpublished.*

2749

11th [*March, 1883*]. Sunday. Hotel des Iles d'Or, Hyères, Var. My dear Charles, my people are away from home, and I have already written to them for money and fear it will come too late. *Signed:* R. L. S. *1 p. Unpublished.*

2750

April 21. / 83. Chalet la Solitude Hyeres Var. *4 letters in 1, the first beginning:* Dear Sir, Your undated favour of the twenty second caused me repeatedly to vomit. *Signed:* Mason, Dudley & Cutler. *The second:* Dear Sir, Enclosed please find a cheque for £45. *Signed:* R. L. S. *The third:* Dear Charles, How's that for clear & calculated? [*this is the first of 10 lines of verse*]. *Signed:* The Inspired Bard. *The fourth:* Dear Sir, In reply to your insulting and undated favour . . . I have the pleasure to inform you that I despise your bestial rancour. *Signed:* William Figg. *2 pp. Unpublished.*

2751

[*April, 1883. Hyères*]. My dear Charles. I am not a man of business. There! *Signed four times:* Twenty Pounds. *2 pp. Baxter has written at the top of p. 1:* Recd 23 April / 83. *Unpublished.*

2752

8th May: 1883. Chalet la Solitude Hyères les Palmiers: Var: France. My dear Charles. Did you not receive a cheque for £6 . . 15? *Signed:* R. L. S. *1 p. Unpublished. Partly about* Treasure Island.

2753

[*May 20, 1883. Hyères*]. Johnson Esq: Dear Sir, Enclosed, please find a recipse[*sic*] for that twenty pound ye sent me. *Signed:* Thomson. *2 pp. Dated by Baxter. Unpublished. Contains 24-line poem beginning:* O dinnae mind the drams ye drink.

2754

[*May or June, 1883*]. The Solitude Hi-ears the Pawm Trees Var. Dear Cherls, Here's a bit checky, chuckie. *Unsigned. 2 pp. Contains 32-line poem beginning:* When I was young and drouthy. *The poem is published in* To Charles Baxter 1883, *a* Christmas Greeting *folder issued in 1940 by Mr. Beinecke. See nos. 736 and 1224.*

2755

June 21st 83. Hyères. Dear Charles, I enclose two bargains which I beg you to add to my archives in the halls of Baxterium. *Signed:* R L. S. *2 pp. Written on stationery of* La Solitude. *Unpublished. Contains 16 lines of verse beginning:* Grim spirit of Finance.

2756

[*July 5, 1883*]. Clermont Ferrand Hotel de la poste. My dear Charles, Henley says, and I obey, that I am to instruct you to request Paul to inform us what has become of Tr[*avel*]s with a D[*onke*]y and an I[*nlan*]d V[*oya*]ge. *Signed:* George North. *2 pp. Self portrait on p. 2. Written on stationery of* La Solitude. *Unpublished.*

2757

20th Jul. 1883. Royat. Dear Charles Pray find inclosed cheque for £10. *Signed:* R. L. Stevenson. *1 p. Written on stationery of* La Solitude. *Unpublished.*

2758

[*Postmarked:* 7 Aout 83. Royat]. Dear C. Baxter, Blame fool! don't reduce weight like that. *Signed:* T Brash. *1 p. Written on stationery of* La Solitude. *With addressed envelope and mounted stamp. Unpublished.*

2759

[*September? 1883. France*]. Dear Baxter, Please give the bearer, one S. L. Osbourne . . . the magnificent sum of five pounds sterling. *Signed:* Robert Louis Stevenson. *1 p. Unpublished.*

2760

3 Oct 1883. Chambers — La Solitude, Hyères. My dear Charlie-over-the-whisky-and-water, Your despatch of the 1st duly to hand — Encle, ahem! Encl. *Signed:* R. L. S. *4 pp. Written on stationery of* La Solitude. *With addressed envelope marked* Private, *and mounted stamp. Unpublished. Contains drawing of both sides of a medal Stevenson says he had struck:* Strages Bankerorum; *and 24 lines of verse beginning:* "Encl," breathed the rustic maid.

886

2761

Eicht October Auchty three. Hyères. Dear Charlie over the whiskey and water, I enclose a chequie; it's aye drib-dribblin. *Signed:* Yours te-totally, Drucken Au'ra. *2 pp. Written on stationery of* La Solitude. *Unpublished.*

2762

[*October 19, 1883. Hyères*]. Cherlie over the whiskey and water Here is a checkie, ye see; Please put it down to me; And I will be Yours as he oughtee   Robert Louee. *Signed three times:* Louee, *and once:* Shakespeare (Wully). *3 pp. Written on stationery of* La Solitude. *Unpublished.*

2763

[*October, 1883. Hyères*]. Verily, verily I say unto thee, it is not those who say unto me, Encle, Encl, but those who acknowledge cheques, who enter into the Kingdom of the Cygnet. *Unsigned. 2 pp. Written on stationery of* La Solitude. *Unpublished.*

2764

[*After October 27, 1883. Hyères?*]. Here, Thomson, is a checkie I am yours Johnson . . . *4 lines written on the verso of a printed excerpt from the* Athenaeum *of October 27, 1883. Unpublished.*

2765

[*Postmarked:* 7 Dec 83. Hyères]. Toddy Vale by Kilrummer. Thomson It's done — I'm a dissenter. *Signed:* Aw Johnstone. *4 pp. In Scots dialect. Written on stationery of* La Solitude. *With addressed envelope and mounted stamp. Unpublished.*

2766

[*Postmarked:* 14 Dec 83. Hyères]. My dear Charles, What is this I hear from Henley, that you are hesitating? *Signed:* R. L. S. *2 pp. Written on stationery of* La Solitude. *With addressed envelope and mounted stamp. Unpublished.*

2767

[*December, 1883. Hyères*]. Dear Charles, I inclose a receipt with thanks. Henley of that ilk bids me explain to you Cook's

887

tickets. *Signed:* R. L. S. *1 p. Unpublished. On the verso of this is a letter to Baxter from Mrs. R. L. S.*

2768

[*1883. France*]. Dear C. B. I enclose a further bulletin of the great crash of Johnstone. *Unsigned. 1 p. Unpublished.*

2769

[*Postmarked:* 3 Mars 84. Hyères] send us for God's sake £60, and more if we have it. *Signed:* Johnston. *1 p. Written in pencil on stationery of* La Solitude. *With addressed envelope and mounted stamp. Unpublished. This is an addition to a letter by Mrs. R.L.S.*

2770

[*Postmarked:* 7 Mars 84. Hyères]. Dear Cherrels. Here is a chaquey Yours Drucken Jackey. *1 p. With addressed envelope and mounted stamp. Unpublished.*

2771

[*Postmarked:* 28 Avril 84. Hyères]. Dear Cherls. Encl. please find a cheque for £40. *Signed:* R. L. S. *4 pp. In Scots dialect. Written on stationery of* La Solitude. *With addressed envelope and mounted stamp. Unpublished. Contains 6 lines of verse beginning:* Whan first upon the alto flute.

2772

[*Spring, 1884. Hyères*]. Dear Charles Herewith the cheque. I am muckle obleeged to you for a' t's come and gane. *Signed:* Thomson, *and* D. Thomson. *3 pp. In Scots dialect. Unpublished.*

2773

[*September, 1884*]. Sunnington Rise, West Cliff Gardens Bournemouth. Dear Cherls, a checkie — very small and a bill very big. *Signed:* R. L. Stevenson. *1 p. Unpublished.*

2774

Oct 4. 1884. Wensleydale Bournemouth. My dear Charles, Herewith a chequy. I was sorry to hear of your accident.

Signed: Thomson. *1 p. Unpublished. Stevenson writes that he had a tapeworm removed from his body.*

2775

Nov. 11th [*1884*]. Bonallie Towers Branksome Park Bournemouth. My dear Charles, I beg to inform you that I have already received Colvin's interest from him directly. *Signed:* Thomson. *3 pp. With addressed envelope and mounted stamp. Partly published in LFF, Vol. 1, p. 337, where about 13 lines of the autograph are omitted.*

2776

[*Postmarked: November 13, 1884*]. Bournemouth. My dear Thomson It's a maist remarkable fac,' but nae shuner had I written yon braggin' blawin' letter . . . *Signed:* Johnson. *4 pp. In Scots dialect. The envelope containing this postmark is not preserved. Published in LFF, Vol. 1, pp. 337–338, where several words of the autograph are omitted.*

2777

Novr 16th [*1884*]. Bonallie Towers Branksome Park Bournemouth. My dear Charles, Herewith receipt and thanks. I was much surprised and vexed to hear of the death of poor Magnus. *Signed:* R. L. Stevenson. *4 pp. Unpublished.*

2778

[*Cir. January 1, 1885. Bournemouth*]. Dear Charles, I send on to these birds to make new bargains owing to the errors. *Signed:* R. L. S. *1 p. Unpublished.*

2779

[*January, 1885*]. Bonallie Tower Branksome Park Bournemouth. Dear Charles, Here's luck to you and all manner of good to all your friends and doings. *Signed:* Thomson. *1 p. Mostly in Scots dialect. Unpublished.*

2780

Jan. 27th 85. B[*onallie*] T[*ower*], B[*ranksome*] P[*ark*]. B[*ournemouth*]. Dear Charles, if Clark the printer slings you a bill, for God's sake, meet it. *Signed:* R. L. S. *1 p. Unpublished.*

2781

[*January, 1885. Bournemouth*]. Fair killed wi correspondence. *Signed:* R. L. S. *1 p. In Scots dialect. Unpublished.*

2782

30th Jan 1885. Bonallie Tower Branksome Park Bournemouth. My dear sir, I beg to remark that if in contradiction to every probability, you have returned the duplicate agreement to Messrs. Longman . . . *Signed:* Thomson, *and* R. L. S. *2 pp. Unpublished.*

2783

Fe 6 85. Bournemouth. Can you not bring down your wife with you Let us know if we may expect her. *1 p. Telegram. Unpublished.*

2784

[*March 24, 1885. Bournemouth*]. Dear Thomson, Its extrodnar; you and me in a court of Law; a place at I swure I wouldnae put ma fit in for the Queen hersel. *Signed:* Thamson, *and* Johns'one. *4 pp. In Scots dialect. Unpublished.*

2785

April 2nd 1885. Bournemouth. My dear Charles, I write out of a whorlwind. *Signed:* R. L. Stevenson. *2 pp. Unpublished. Stevenson asks Baxter to send him from 17 Heriot Row his business table.*

2786

[*Cir. April 2, 1885. Bournemouth*]. Dear Thomson. It's grand: ye have the right lilt; ye have the real fire; man, ye're a poet! *Signed:* Dauvit Johnstone. *2 pp. At top of p. 1:* For Jaikson. *Unpublished.*

2787

[*Cir. April 9, 1885. Bournemouth*]. My dear Charles, A thousand thanks for the admirable manner you have executed the task. *Signed:* R L. S. *1 p. Unpublished.*

2788

[*April, 1885. Bournemouth*]. Dear Charles, Could you oblige me with a cheque for £40? *Signed:* Thamson. *2 pp. Unpublished.*

2789

Ap 21 85. Bournemouth. Been ill shall write soon perhaps today. *1 p. Telegram. Unpublished.*

2790

Feb 14th 1886. Skerryvore Bournemouth. My dear Charles, I have at last a moment to write to you; it is already my ninth letter this mortal day. *Signed:* Robert Louis Stevenson. *4 pp. Unpublished. Stevenson informs Baxter that he wishes to dedicate* Kidnapped *to him.*

2791

[*Cir. March 6, 1886. Bournemouth*]. Dear Charles. I know not what to say about that money (I had a dam dream that I had bust up). *Signed:* R. L. S. *1 p. Unpublished.*

2792

[*Postmarked:* Jy 7 86. Bournemouth]. Dear C. B. What has the account come to from the Clarks? Suppose I came north could you take in me and my wife for a couple of days? *Signed:* R. L. S. *Beneath this signature Stevenson has drawn 3 portraits, one titled:* my intellect. *2 pp. With addressed envelope and mounted stamp. On the envelope Stevenson has written:* If I come, tell no one. R. L. S. *Unpublished.*

2793

[*End of July, 1886. Bournemouth*]. Dear Charles, Doubtless if all goes well towards the 1st of August we shall be begging at your door. *Signed:* R. L. S. *2 pp. Published in LFF, Vol. 2, pp. 39–40.*

2794

[*Postmarked:* Oc 5 86. Bournemouth]. Dear Charles, The Alan Breck has come and I am very proud of it. *Signed:* R. L. S.

1 p. With addressed envelope and mounted stamp. Unpublished.

2795
[*Autumn, 1886? Bournemouth*]. Dear Charles, 1st Herewith a bargain. *Signed:* Robert Louis Stevenson. *2 pp. Unpublished.*

2796
De 22 86. Bournemouth. When do you come Stevenson. *1 p. Telegram. Unpublished.*

2797
[*April, 1887. Bournemouth*]. Dear Baxter and Henley, I dreamed I was with you in Edinburgh last night. *Signed:* R. L. S. *1 p. Unpublished.*

2798
[*After April 21, 1887. Bournemouth*]. My dear Charles, From the enclosed papers, I gather (1) that my cousin is a very angry man and a very disagreeable correspondent. *Signed:* R. L. S. *2 pp. At top of p. 1:* Private & confidential. *Small part of text of p. 1 torn off. Unpublished. Relates to an unpleasant family matter, possibly his father's interest in the engineering business.*

2799
April 29./87. Bournemouth. My dear Charles, Thank you for yours, the first decently supportable communication I have had in this matter. *Signed:* R. L. S. *3 pp. Unpublished. More on the matter referred to in no. 2798.*

2800
My 4 87. Bournemouth. If we come north this week can you take my wife and me in. *Stevenson. 1 p. Telegram. Unpublished.*

2801
My 6 87. York. Arrive three thirty can you meet us. Louis. *1 p. Telegram. Unpublished.*

2802

[*After May 13, 1887. Edinburgh*]. Dear C. B, The book found My mother would much like to speak to you. *Signed: R. L. S. 1 p. Written on black-bordered stationery, following the death of R. L. S.'s father which occurred on May 8. Unpublished.*

2803

21 Aug 1887. London. My dear Charles, My foot is on the shore. *Signed: R. L. S. 3 pp. Written on stationery of the* South Place Hotel, Finsbury, E. C., London. *Unpublished.*

2804

[*October 20, 1887. Saranac Lake*]. My dear Charles, I see by your account (or think I see) that £30 went to Henley. *Signed: R. L. S. 1 p. Dated by Baxter. Unpublished.*

2805

[*Postmarked:* Nov 18   1887. Saranac Lake]. My dear Charles, No likely I'm going to waste a sheet of paper. *Signed twice: R. L. S. 4 pp. On black-bordered stationery. With addressed envelope and mounted stamp. Partly published in LFF, Vol. 2, pp. 73–74, where about 30 lines of the autograph are omitted.*

2806

[*Postmarked:* Dec 2 1887. Saranac Lake]. My dear Charles, This is a letter of the most disgusting nature. *Signed:* R. L. Stevenson. *2 pp. On black-bordered stationery. With addressed envelope. Unpublished.*

2807

De 6 87. Saranac Lake. Pay Henley Macaires Stevenson. *1 p. Cablegram. Unpublished.*

2808

[*Postmarked:* Dec 12 1887. Saranac Lake]. My dear Charles, Will you please send £20 to Aunt Alan for a Xmas gift from my mother. *Signed:* Thomson alias Robert Louis Stevenson. *3 pp. Partly in Scots dialect. On black-bordered stationery. With addressed envelope and mounted stamp. Published in LFF, Vol. 2, pp. 82–83.*

2809

[*December 25, 1887. Saranac Lake*]. My dear Charles, This is Christmas his day and I drink your health and your wife's, and your bairns's, with three times three. *Signature cut away. 4 pp. On black-bordered stationery. With addressed envelope marked:* Private, *and mounted stamp. Unpublished.*

2810

30 Dec. 1887. [*Saranac Lake*]. My dear Charles, I am more upset than I can well say by the collapse of the Deacon Brodie business. *Signed:* Robert Louis Stevenson. *7 pp. On black-bordered stationery. Unpublished.*

2811

[*Postmarked:* Jan 2 1888. Saranac Lake]. Dear Charles, The £19..14 was designed merely for my credit. You are the flower of Doers. *Signed:* R. L. S. *4 pp. On black-bordered stationery. With addressed envelope and mounted stamp. Partly published in LFF, Vol. 2, p. 90, where about 21 lines of the autograph are omitted.*

2812

[*Postmarked:* Jan 8 1888. Saranac Lake]. Dear Charles, This being the Saubbuth day, I bed to request you to send £10 . . . to Dr. Barnardo his homes. *Signed:* Robert Louis Stevenson. *1 p. On black-bordered stationery. With addressed envelope, marked:* Private, *and mounted stamp. Unpublished.*

2813

[*Postmarked:* Feb 21 1888. Saranac Lake]. Dear Charles, Enclosed signachers. I agree with all you propose in the mattter of the Scott letters. *Signed:* R. L. S. *1 p. Mostly in Scots dialect. On black-bordered stationery. With addressed envelope and mounted stamps. Unpublished.*

2814

Feb 25th 1888. Saranac Lake Adirondacks N. Y. U. S. A. My dear Charles, I am sorry to put you on a piece of business that will not I fear be altogether pleasant. *Signed:* Robert Louis

Stevenson. *3 pp. On black-bordered stationery. With addressed envelope and mounted stamps. Unpublished.*

2815
[*Postmarked:* Mar 13 1888. Saranac Lake]. Dear Charles, Still I pour in floods of occupation on my doer. *Signed twice:* R. L. S. *2 pp. On black-bordered stationery. With addressed envelope and mounted stamp. Unpublished. Stevenson, recently elected to the Athenaeum, would prefer not to accept membership.*

2816
[*Postmarked:* May 11 1888]. Union House, Manasquan N. J. My dear Charles, I have found a yacht and we are going the full pitch for seven months. *Signed:* Robert Louis Stevenson. *2 pp. On black-bordered stationery. With addressed envelope and mounted stamp. Partly published in LFF, Vol. 2, p. 106, where about 20 lines of the autograph are omitted.*

2817
[*Postmarked:* May 26 1888. Manasquan]. My dear Charles, I shall just have to ask you to write no more about this affair for a while. *Signed:* R. L. S. *3 pp. With addressed envelope, marked:* Private, *and mounted stamp. Unpublished. The affair referred to is about a story written by Mrs. R. L. S. which Henley said was actually Katharine de Mattos's story.*

2818
[*June 25, 1888*]. Yacht Casco, Oakland. My dear Charles, Here I am in my berth and pretty sick; I cannot recover from this affair, though crossing the continent picked me up for the time. *Signed:* Robert Louis Stevenson, *and* R. L. S. *4 pp. Unpublished. Stevenson writes further concerning the Katharine de Mattos-Henley affair, and says good-bye before sailing into the Pacific.*

2819
Sept 6th 1888. 7 A. M. Yacht Casco, at sea, near the Paumotus, with a dreadful pen. My dear Charles, Last night as I lay under my blanket in the cockpit courting sleep, I had a comic seizure.

Signed: R. L. S. *1 p. Published in* LFF, *Vol. 2, pp.* 114–115, *where several words of the autograph are omitted.*

2820

[*Postmarked:* 15 Oct 88. Papeete, Taiti]. Taiti (as ever was But then, my dear Charles, I have seen nothing of it, having been in bed ever since I left Fakarava. *Signed:* Robert Louis Stevenson. *4 pp. Partly in Scots dialect. With addressed envelope, marked:* Private, *and mounted stamp. Partly published in* LFF, *Vol. 2, p.* 117, *where about 13 lines of the autograph are omitted.*

2821

[*Postmarked:* 10 Nov 88. Papeete, Taiti]. Tautira (The Garden of the World) Otherwise called Hans-Christian-Andersen-ville. My dear Charles, Whether I have a penny left in the wide world, I know not nor shall know — till I get to Honolulu. *Signed:* R. L. S. *4 pp. With addressed envelope and mounted stamp. Published in* LFF, *Vol. 2, pp.* 122–123, *where about 6 lines of the autograph are omitted.*

2822

[*November 10, 1888*]. Tautira. My dear Charles, I forgot Mrs Mary Ann Watts and her credit on Willis & Trantern. *Signed:* R. L. S. *2 pp. Published in* LFF, *Vol. 2, p.* 123, *where about 5 lines of the autograph are omitted. Contains 16 lines of verse beginning:* Home no more home to me, whither shall I wander?

2823

Feb 8th 1889. Honolulu. My dear Charles, Here we are at Honolulu and have dismissed the yacht, and lie here till April anyway. *Signed:* R. L. S. *4 pp. Partly published in* LFF, *Vol. 2, pp.* 134–135, *where about 21 lines of the autograph are omitted.*

2824

March [8] 1889. Honolulu. My dear Charles, At last I have the accounts. *Signed:* Robert Louis Stevenson. *2 pp. With addressed envelope and mounted stamps. Partly published in* LFF, *Vol. 2, pp.* 139–140, *where about 29 lines of the autograph are omitted. Stevenson writes about amounts charged to his mother which seemed to him unjustifiable. He mentions the possibility of residing in Madeira. Mrs. R.L.S. has written an addition to this letter.*

2825

April [12] 1889. Honolulu. My dear Charles, As usual your letter is as good as a cordial. *Signed: R. L. S. 10 pp. With addressed envelope and mounted stamp. Both the letter and the envelope are marked:* Private. *Partly published in LFF, Vol. 2, pp. 150–151, where about 63 lines of the autograph are omitted. Stevenson complains about the high cost of supporting his family.*

2826

[*Postmarked:* Apr 27 1889. Honolulu]. My dear Charles, I forget if I have made my plans clear to you. *Signed: R. L. Stevenson. 2 pp. With addressed envelope and mounted stamp. Unpublished.*

2827

[*Postmarked:* May 10 1889. Honolulu]. My dear Charles, I am appalled to gather from your last just to hand that you have felt so much concern about the letter. *Signed: R. L. S. 2 pp. With addressed envelope and mounted stamp. Partly published in LFF, Vol. 2, pp. 151–152, where about 18 lines of the autograph are omitted.*

2828

[*Postmarked:* Jun 7 1889. Honolulu]. My dear Charles, The last mail we are likely to receive has come in; and I fear I am to go away with your last (pardon me) a little shirty letter for farewell. *Unsigned. 2 pp. With addressed envelope, marked:* Private, *and mounted stamps. Unpublished. In this and preceding letters to Baxter Stevenson complains about unauthorized publication of one or more of his letters.*

2829

June 16th 1889 [*and*] June 18th [*and*] 19th. Honolulu. My dear Charles, Herewith a certified copy of my new will necessitated by fresh risks and obligations. *Signed: R. L. S. 2 pp. Unpublished.*

2830

Dec 28th [*1889*]. Apia Samoa. My dear Charles, By a providential error on the part of the postmaster I received yours of 3rd June on my arrival here. *Signed:* R. L. Stevenson. *5 pp. Signature cut away, but recovered after many years and restored to the letter. Partly published in LFF, Vol. 2, pp. 172–175, where about 47 lines of the autograph are omitted.*

2831

Februar den 3en 1890. Dampfer Lübeck zwischen Apia und Sydney. Hooray for the Deutscher Lloyd! My dear Charles, I have got one delightful letter from you, and heard from my mother of your kindness in going to see her. *Signed:* R. L. S. *4 pp. Written on stationery of* Norddeutscher Lloyd Bremen. *Partly published in LFF, Vol. 2, pp. 177–178, where about 56 lines of the autograph are omitted. Contains the poem,* To My Old Comrades, *beginning:* Do you remember — can we e'er forget? *(35 lines). In LFF and in the* Collected Poems Edited by Janet Adam Smith, *1950, one line of the autograph poem is omitted and 2 lines (not in the autograph) are added. Stevenson writes that his purchase of 314½ acres of land above Apia means a great deal to him.*

2832

[*March 7, 1890. Sydney*]. My dear Charles, I did not send off the enclosed before from laziness. *Signed:* Robert Louis Stevenson. *4 pp. Written on stationery of the* Union Club, Sydney. *Partly published in LFF, Vol. 2, pp. 183–184, where about 19 lines of the autograph are omitted. As a result of his illness in Sydney Stevenson writes:* I am sure I shall never come back home except to die.

2833

March 12th [*1890. Sydney*]. My dear Charles, Enclosed please find a libel: you perceive I am quite frank with my legal adviser. *Signed:* Robert Louis Stevenson. *2 pp. At top of p. 1:* Private & confidential. *Unpublished. With this letter was sent the text of the Father Damien pamphlet.*

2834

[*March 20, 1890. Sydney*]. My dear Doer, You will receive along with this a document in which you are a trustee. *Unsigned. 2 pp. Unpublished. Principally about Harry J. Moors.*

2835

[*Received*] Ap 10 90. Sydney. Return Islands four months home September. *1 p. Cablegram. Unpublished.*

2836

[*Postmarked:* Ap 10 90. Sydney]. My dear Charles, I have been quite knocked over: go back to islands four months, pick up again. *Signed:* R. L. S. *2 pp. With addressed envelope. Unpublished.*

2837

[*Postmarked: May 20, 1890. Samoa*]. Janet Nichol [*sic*] at sea off Upolu. My dear Charles, This is to let you [*know*] to wit, that the voyage has had the old effect [*i.e. it improved his health*]. *Signed:* Louis. *2 pp. The envelope containing this postmark is not preserved. Unpublished.*

2838

[*August, 1890*]. Hotel Sebastopol Noumea. My dear Charles, I have stayed here a week while Lloyd and my wife continue the voyage in the Janet Nicoll. *Signed:* Robert Louis Stevenson. *4 pp. Partly published in LFF, Vol. 2, pp. 191–194, where about 42 lines of the autograph are omitted.*

2839

[*Postmarked:* 14/10 90] . . . Vailima Apia Samoa. My dear Charles, Good morning to you from a new address. *Signed twice:* R. L. S. *2 pp. With addressed envelope, marked:* Private, *and mounted stamp. Unpublished.*

2840

November 6th 1890. [*Vailima*]. My dear Charles, I have drawn on you today at 30 days in favour of H. J. Moors for £200. *Signed:* R. L. S. *1 p. Unpublished.*

2841

[*December 6, 1890. Samoa*]. My dear Charles, I wonder if you ever receive any of my letters; I see you miss many; and I have myself lost so much that I now take the precaution of registering. *Signed twice: R. L. S. 5 pp. Dated by Baxter. Unpublished. Stevenson expresses his anger at Henley's failure to call on the former's widowed mother when she returned to Edinburgh, and sends drafts of two notes for Henley breaking off the friendship.*

2842

[*January 26, 1891. Sydney*]. My dear Charles, Caught on the hop by mail. *Signed: R. L. S. 2 pp. Dated by Baxter. Unpublished. About family business affairs in Edinburgh.*

2843

[*Postmarked: March 11, 1891*]. S S Lübeck, at sea. My dear Charles, Perhaps in my old days I do grow irascible: "the old man virulent" has long been my pet name for myself. *Signed: R. L. S. 2 pp. The envelope containing this postmark is not preserved. About one-fifth of this letter is published in LFF, Vol. 2, p. 219, where about 41 lines of the autograph are omitted. Much of the omitted portion is about Henley.*

2844

[*March, 1891. Tutuila, Samoa*]. My dear Charles, I have had to draw a bill on you for £150. This was suddenly forced on me by a rise in silver on the beach. *Unfinished and unsigned. 2 pp. Written on stationery of the* Consulate General of the United States of America, Apia. *Unpublished. Stevenson writes of a visit to Tutuila, where he has gone with the American consul.*

2845

June 20 1891. Sunday. Vailima. My dear Charles Your hand was a welcome sight. But I think in the pressure of arrears, you must have let a point slip. *Signed: Robert Louis Stevenson, and R. L. S. 6 pp. With addressed envelope and mounted stamps. Registered. Unpublished. Stevenson writes about work on* The Wrecker, *and suggests how the property rights in plays pro-*

jected in the old days should be divided between him and Henley.

2846
August ?th (16th?) 91. Saturday. [*Vailima*]. My dear Charles, Yours received with the account to my huge relief. *Signed twice:* R. L. S. *2 pp. Unpublished.*

2847
Sept 15th [*1891. Vailima*]. My dear Charles, I drew another bill on you yesterday for £250. *Signed:* Robert Louis Stevenson Dilapidator. *1 p. With addressed envelope and mounted stamps. Registered. Unpublished.*

2848
Oct 14th [*1891. Vailima*]. My dear Charles, This is painful-doery with a warrant. *Signed:* R. L. S. *1 p. Baxter has written at the top:* Received 15 Nov 1891. *Partly published in Maggs Bros.* Autograph Letters and Historical Documents, *London, 1954, Catalogue No. 823, p. 60, where about 16 lines of the autograph are omitted. Stevenson sends the manuscript of* The Beach of Falesá, *and discusses serial and book publication and the amounts he expects to receive from the publishers.*

2849
Nov 91. [*Vailima*]. Dear Charles, I have just written one enclosure with an eye to Henley. *Signed:* R L. S. *2 pp. Partly published in* The Letters, *1911, Vol. 3, pp. 309–311, where about 35 lines of the autograph are omitted.*

2850
[*December, 1891. Vailima*]. My dear Charles, No word from you, and there need be little in mine. *Signature cut away and presented by Baxter to the Speculative Society. 1 p. Unpublished.*

2851
[*December? 1891. Vailima*]. My dear Charles. 1st As to Henley, I am quite willing to put myself entirely in his hands as to

publications, non publication, and whole or partial publication. *Signature cut away. 1 p. Unpublished.*

2852

Jan 2nd 92. [*Vailima*]. Dear Charles, I am at work on a short tale The Go-Between which I estimate at 30,000 words. *Signed twice:* R. L. S. *3 pp. Unpublished.*

2853

Jan 31st 92. [*Vailima*]. My dear C B. I had a strange rambling dream about you last night; in which I am sorry to say you figured in a divorce court and turned out to be the heir of a Highland family. *Unsigned. 2 pp. Unpublished. About* The Beach of Falesá, *and about Henley.*

2854

[*March 30, 1892. Vailima*]. My dear Charles, Herewith the documents signed. *Signature cut away, and presented by Baxter to the Academy. 1 p. Unpublished. Stevenson worries about his finances.*

2855

[*April 28, 1892. Vailima*]. My dear Charles, I have just written the dedication of David Balfour to you, and haste to put a job in your hands. *Signed:* R. L. S. *1 p. Published in* The Letters, *1911, Vol. 4, pp. 36–37, where 2 lines of the autograph are omitted. Stevenson asks Baxter's help in preparing maps to illustrate* David Balfour.

2856

[*May, 1892. Vailima*]. Dear Charles, No time remains to me till the mail goes. I send you this list of copies for the Samoa History. *Signed:* R. L. S. *1 p. Unpublished.*

2857

June 20th 1892. Vailima Plantation Upolu Samoa. My dear Charles: Yours of 29th April to hand. *Signed:* R. L. Stevenson. *1 p. The letter is in the hand of Isobel Strong, signed by Stevenson. Unpublished. Asking Baxter to draft a codicil to the will of Mrs. R. L. S.*

2858

[*July 18, 1892*]. Vailima Plantation Upolu Samoan Islands. My dear Charles—Enclosed is the slip filled up. I shall try to remember the set of Samoan stamps. *Signed:* Robert Louis Stevenson. *6 pp. The first 2 pp. and most of p. 3 are in the hand of Isobel Strong, the remainder in Stevenson's hand. Partly published in LFF, Vol. 2, pp. 256–257, where about 31 lines of the autograph are omitted.*

2859

Aug 11th 1892. Vailima. My dear Charles—Herewith please receive a considerable portion of David Balfour. *Signed:* Robert Louis Stevenson, *and* R L S. *4 pp. The letter is in the hand of Isobel Strong, signed by Stevenson. Unpublished.*

2860

Sept. 12th 1892. [*Vailima*]. My dear Charles, Herewith David, Chap XXII to XXVII. The end should come next mail, about as much again. *Signed:* R. L. Stevenson. *4 pp. Unpublished. Stevenson and his mother between them propose to contribute £1,200 to a new wing to* Abbotsford, *i.e. Vailima.*

2861

Oct. 7th 1892 [*and*] Oct. 10th Vailima Samoan Islands. My dear Charles—The deuce and all—here have been nearly two months and not a word from you. *Signed:* R. L. Stevenson, *and* R. L. S. *4 pp. The letter is in the hand of Isobel Strong, signed by Stevenson. Unpublished. Stevenson writes that he expects Arthur Claxton to bring a libel suit against him.*

2862

[*October 10, 1892. Vailima*]. My dear Charles, You are advised that Mrs Sitwell will be buying a cloak for Fanny and will draw on you for not over £6. Yours ever Robert Louis Stevenson. *1 p. Unpublished.*

2863

Nov. 4th 1892. Vailima Plantation Samoan Islands—South Seas. My dear Charles: The luck that pursues us is extraordinary. *Signed:* R. L. S. *6 pp. Mostly in the hand of Isobel Strong.*

Finished and signed in Stevenson's hand. Unpublished. Steven-
son writes that he is less annoyed by the possible libel action.

2864
Dec. 1st 1892. Vailima Upolu Samoan Islands. My dear
Charles—I am sending off by this mail a bill for seven hundred
pounds in favor of the German firm. *Signed:* Robert Louis Stevenson. *6 pp. The letter is in the hand of Isobel Strong, signed*
by Stevenson. It is accompanied by: Second Thought—I wish
Pitcairn's Criminal Trials. *Signed:* Robert Louis Stevenson.
2 pp., in the hand of Graham Balfour, signed by Stevenson.
About a fourth of the 8 pp. are published in LFF, Vol. 2, pp.
273–274, where about 107 lines of the autograph are omitted.

2865
Dec 5th [*1892. Vailima*]. Dear Charles—Here is the Devil's
news — it seems our Oct. mail has been destroyed by fire crossing the plains. *Unsigned. 1 p. Mostly in the hand of Isobel*
Strong. Finished in Stevenson's hand. Unpublished.

2866
Dec 28th 1892. [*Vailima*]. My dear Charles, Your really decent
letter to hand. And here I am answering it to the merry note
of the carpenter's hammer. *Signed twice:* R. L. S., *and once:*
Robert Louis Stevenson. *2 pp. Partly published in* The Letters,
1911, Vol. 4, pp. 137–138, where about 20 lines of the autograph
are omitted. Contains 8 lines of verse, beginning: O sovereign
of my Cedercrantz.

2867
Jan 8th 1893. Vailima. My dear Charles I have just had a turn
of influenza. *Signed:* Robert Louis Stevenson. *3 pp. The letter*
is in the hand of Isobel Strong, signed by Stevenson. Marked
by him: Private & Confidential!!!! *Unpublished. Stevenson*
proposes that in case of his death his letters be called in from
the recipients by Baxter, that Graham Balfour select those to be
published, and that the latter be edited by Sidney Colvin.
Stevenson writes: I protest wholly against any idea of a biography.

2868

[*January 8, 1893. Vailima*]. Dear Charles, Three letters from you this month. Well done, thou good and faithful. *Signed:* R. L. S. *1 p. Dated by Baxter. Unpublished.*

2869

[*March 1, 1893. Vailima*]. My dear Charles, I have had the influenza, as I believe you know. *Unsigned. 2 pp. Dated by Baxter. Partly published in* The Letters, *1911, Vol. 4, pp. 147–148, where it is dated February, 1893, and about 18 lines of the autograph are omitted. Largely about* The Schooner Farallone, *i.e.* The Ebb Tide.

2870

[*April 16, 1893, and*] April 17th [*Vailima*]. My dear Charles, Yours of 22nd Feb and 16th March to hand. *Signed:* R. L. Stevenson. *5 pp. The letter is partly in the hand of Isobel Strong, and partly in Stevenson's, signed by him. A small portion is published in LFF, Vol. 2, pp. 285–286, where about 141 lines of the autograph are omitted. Stevenson expresses dissatisfaction with Scribners.*

2871

[*June 17, 1893, and*] Sunday 18th June. [*Vailima*]. My dear Charles, I had no idea last month of the extent of your calamity. *Signed:* Robert Louis Stevenson. *2 pp. Unpublished. Stevenson refers apparently to the loss of Baxter's wife and to Baxter's financial reverses.*

2872

[*July 19, 1893. Vailima*]. My dear Charles, I return herewith Arnot (which unfortunately I already possessed) and Balfour's letters, to see what you can get for them. *Signature cut away. 2 pp. Dated by Baxter. Partly published in LFF, Vol. 2, p. 300, where about 44 lines of the autograph are omitted. Stevenson writes much about his financial prospects.*

2873

Aug 14th 1893. Vailima Samoa. My dear Charles — Yours of 7th July to hand — All quite satisfactory. *1 p. Bottom of letter.*

including signature if any, torn away. The letter is in the hand of Isobel Strong. Unpublished.

2874

[*September, 1893. Vailima, and S. S. Mariposa en route to Honolulu*]. My dear Charles, Herewith goes my will to you. Will you please send us a copy of Fanny's? *Signed:* R. L. S. *1 p. Postmarked San Francisco, September 23, 1893. Published in* The Letters, *1911, Vol. 4, pp. 208–209, where about 3 lines of the autograph are omitted.*

2875

[*October 25, 1893, Honolulu*]. My dear Charles, Sorry that I have not been able to keep my promise, and have spent all this extra money! *Signed:* R. L. S. *1 p. Dated by Baxter. Written on stationery of Sans Souci, Waikiki, Honolulu. Unpublished. With this Stevenson enclosed a letter from one James Hunter of Edinburgh who has decorated and sent to Stevenson a copy of Underwoods, asking help from Stevenson. R. L. S. asks Baxter to do something for Hunter.*

2876

[*November 6, 1893. Apia, Samoa*]. Dear Charles, Of course let John Horne Stevenson have a proof of the introduction. *Unsigned. 1 p. Dated by Baxter. Unpublished.*

2877

[*December 6, 1893. Vailima*]. "Oct. 15 1685, at Privy Council, George Murray . . . did . . . obtain a clandestine order . . . My dear Charles, the above is my story. *Signature cut away. 2 pp. Dated by Baxter. Partly published in LFF, Vol. 2, pp. 309–310, where about 26 lines of the autograph are omitted. About* Heathercat, *and about Stevenson's mother.*

2878

[*December 6, 1893. Vailima*]. Dear C. B. I had near forgotten. *Unsigned. 1 p. Unpublished. Asking Baxter to bind some R. L. S. titles in elegant manner and send them to Henry Henderson.*

2879

Jan. 1st 1894. Vailima. My dear Charles I am delighted with your idea. *Signed: R. L. S. 5 pp. The letter is in the hand of Isobel Strong, signed by Stevenson. Postscript (4 lines) in Stevenson's hand. Partly published in LFF, Vol. 2, pp. 316–317, where about 87 lines of the autograph are omitted. Mostly about the* Edinburgh Edition *of Stevenson's works.*

2880

[February 28, 1894. Vailima]. Dear Charles, The mail coming four days too late. *Signed: R. L. S. 2 pp. Dated by Baxter. Unpublished.*

2881

March 26th 1894. Vailima Samoa. My dear Charles 1. Received bills of lading for Wynand Lockink and wine from No 17. *Signed: R. L. S. 4 pp. The letter is mostly in the hand of Isobel Strong, partly in Stevenson's, signed by him. Unpublished.*

2882

April 17th 1894 [*and*] April 20th. Vailima. My dear Charles: St. Ives is now well on its way into the second volume. *Signed: R. L. S. 5 pp. The letter is mostly in the hand of Isobel Strong, partly in Stevenson's, signed by him. Partly published in LFF, Vol. 2, pp. 326–327, where about 62 lines of the autograph are omitted.*

2883

[Cir. May 18, 1894]. Vailima Samoa. My dear Charles — I have received Melville's report and the very encouraging documents that he encloses. *Signed: R. L. Stevenson. 7 pp. The letter is mostly in the hand of Isobel Strong, partly in Stevenson's, signed by him. Partly published in LFF, Vol. 2, pp. 328–330, where about 95 lines of the autograph are omitted. Contains the 13-line poem:* To My Wife I dedicate this Edinburgh Edition of my works. I see rain falling and the rainbow drawn. *In spite of this title Stevenson writes that* It was not intended for the E E, but for the Justice Clerk [*i.e.* Weir of Hermiston] when it should be finished.

2884

June 18th [*1894*]. Vailima. My dear Charles Your long and interesting letter of May 14th duly come to hand, but alas not the dummy. *Signed: R. L. S. 5 pp. The letter is in the hand of Isobel Strong, and signed by Stevenson. Unpublished. Much of this is about the* Edinburgh Edition.

2885

[*July, 1894. Vailima*]. My dear Baxter, I have received the balloon books from your bookseller, and I must say he is a daisy. *Signed once: R. L. Stevenson, and twice: R. L. S. 8 pp. The letter is mostly in the hand of Isobel Strong, partly in Stevenson's, signed by him. Unpublished. Accompanied by 1 p. of questions in Baxter's hand and answers in Stevenson's. Stevenson authorizes Baxter to pay Henley £5 a month when necessary.*

2886

Aug 12th 1894. [*Vailima*]. My dear Charles   All previous points approved. *3 pp. The bottom of p. 3, which may include an additional portion of the letter and Stevenson's signature, is torn off. The letter is in the hand of Isobel Strong. Unpublished.*

2887

[*August, 1894. Vailima*]. My dear Charles, I have thought well of the matter, and I judge thus. *Signed: R. L. S. 3 pp. Partly published in LFF, Vol. 2, pp. 352–353, where the letter is dated September, 1894, and about 22 lines of the autograph are omitted. Partly about the death of Charles Baxter's father.*

2888

Sept 9th 1894 [*and*] Sep. 10th [*Vailima*]. Dear Charles, 1st Thanks for books received. *Signed: Robert Louis Stevenson. 2 pp. The letter is partly in the hand of Isobel Strong, and partly in Stevenson's, signed by him. Unpublished. Stevenson is much pleased to learn that Baxter plans to visit him in Vailima.*

2889

[*October 10, 1894. Vailima*]. Dear Charles, I am sorry; you have chosen the worst season in the year for Samoa. *Signed: R. L. S. 2 pp. Dated by Baxter. Unpublished.*

2890

Nov. 4th 1894. [*and*] 26th. Vailima Samoa. My dear Charles: This will be my last letter to you until I shall have the pleasure of greeting you at Apia. *Signed:* R. L. Stevenson. *8 pp. The letter is mostly in the hand of Isobel Strong, partly in Stevenson's, signed by him. Unpublished. Baxter has written at the top of p. 1:* My last letter from R. L. S. C. B.

2891

[*1890*]. Dear Mr Bishop, The point on which I am most frankly inclined to join issue with you is the clothing. *Signed:* Robert Louis Stevenson. *2 pp. With addressed envelope. Unpublished. Stevenson writes about morality, depopulation, etc. in the South Sea islands.*

R.L.S. TO RICHARD DODDRIDGE BLACKMORE

2892

[*Postmarked:* 19. IV. 82. Davos]. My dear Sir. I should have written long since to thank you for your very great kindness. *Signed:* Wogg Stevenson. *3 pp. With addressed envelope. The letter is mostly in the hand of Mrs. R.L.S., purporting to have been dictated by the Stevenson dog, Wogg. Unpublished. Wood engravings and verses by Stevenson, printed by Lloyd Osbourne, were sent with this letter.*

2893

[1892]. Vailima Plantation Samoan Islands — To the artist who did the illustrations to Una. Dear Sir, I only know you under the initials G. B., but you have done some exceedingly spirited and satisfactory illustrations to my story "The Beach of Falesá." *Signed:* Robert Louis Stevenson. *2 pp. The letter is in the hand of Isobel Strong, signed by R.L.S. Published in an unidentified periodical (1892?), where about 4 lines of the autograph are omitted.*

2894

[*April or May, 1888*]. c/o Charles Scribner's Sons, 743 Broad-way, New York City, U. S. A. [*Written at Saranac Lake*]. My dear Mrs Burgess, From a spot in the Adirondack Mountains, where we have passed a winter of incredible cold but fair health, I write to you at last. *Signed:* Robert Louis Stevenson, *and* R. L. S. *4 pp. Partly published in George M. Williamson.* Catalogue of the . . . Collection of First Editions [*etc.*] . . . Sold . . . January 30 . . . 31, 1908 . . . The Anderson Auction Company . . . *New York* [*1908*], *p. 105, where about 20 lines of the autograph are omitted.*

2895

[*October? 1887. Saranac Lake*]. My dear Mr Burlingame, Your title is too c . . . on my part. *Signed:* Robert Louis Stevenson. *2 pp. Unpublished. Stevenson writes of his satisfaction with his home at Saranac Lake, and discusses possible titles for an article.*

2896

[*Autumn? 1887. Saranac Lake*]. Dear Mr Burlingame, I send you herewith a set of verses by Mr Henley which I think very remarkable. *Signature cut away. 1 p. Unpublished. Stevenson suggests that Henley's verses be published in* Scribner's Magazine *and that he (R.L.S.) write prose to accompany them.*

2897

[*Autumn, 1887. Saranac Lake*]. Dear Mr Burlingame. Union. I have telegraphed to you this morning finally to suppress this line. *Signed:* Robert Louis Stevenson. *3 pp. Written on blackbordered stationery. Unpublished. Stevenson writes about* Confessions of a Unionist, *which was intended for* Scribner's Magazine *of January, 1888, but was not published until 1921; and of* The Master of Ballantrae.

2898

[*November, 1887. Saranac Lake*]. Dear Mr Burlingame Herewith the proof, which I trust will put your printers on their mettle. *Signed:* Robert Louis Stevenson. *2 pp. Written on blackbordered stationery. Unpublished. Stevenson complains of the printers'* making hay of my punctuation; *and suggests that Charles Warren Stoddard be asked to write for* Scribner's Magazine.

2899

[*Postmarked:* Dec 6 1887. Saranac Lake N. Y.] Dear Mr Burlingame, Thank you for your promptitude about the Hanging Judge. *Signed:* Robert Louis Stevenson. *4 pp. On p. 1:* Private & Confidential. *With addressed envelope and mounted stamp.*

Published in LFF, *Vol. 2, pp. 75–76, where 2 lines of the autograph are omitted. R.L.S. expresses his chagrin at learning that he is guilty of a* breach of an agreement *in making a bargain with S. S. McClure for the serial publication of a story after having signed an agreement with Scribners affecting this and other stories.*

2900

[*December, 1887. Saranac Lake*]. My dear Mr Burlingame Well, well, we shall call it over; only I trust I shall behave better in future. *Signed:* R. L. S. *2 pp. Unpublished. Stevenson refers to his error in making the bargain with S. S. McClure. He lists titles (or contents) of 12 prospective chapters of* The Master of Ballantrae.

2901

[*Winter, 1887–1888. Saranac Lake*]. Dear Mr Burlingame, The revise seemed all right, so I did not trouble you with it. *Signed:* Robert Louis Stevenson. *1 p. Unpublished. Stevenson writes of* The Lantern-Bearers.

2902

[*Winter, 1887–1888. Saranac Lake*]. Dear Mr Burlingame, Herewith number 4. I think it rather a Buster myself. *Signed:* R. L. S. *1 p. Written on black-bordered stationery. Unpublished.*

2903

[*1887 or 1888. Saranac Lake*]. Dear Mr Burlingame, Just what you want. I place all reliance in you. *Signature cut away. 1 p. Written on black-bordered stationery. Unpublished.*

2904

[*Postmarked:* Jan 6 1888. Saranac Lake N. Y.] Dear Mr Burlingame, Please send off Mr Henley's verses to him at once. *Signed:* Robert Louis Stevenson, *and* R. L. S. *4 pp. Written on black-bordered stationery. Published in* LFF, *Vol. 2, pp. 90–92, where 20 lines of the autograph are omitted. Stevenson writes of articles for* Scribner's Magazine *and* The Master of Ballantrae.

2905

Jan 18th [*1888. Saranac Lake*]. Dear Mr Burlingame, I cannot think what has happened to my correspondence with your firm. *Signed:* Robert Louis Stevenson. *1 p. Unpublished. Stevenson sends an article which he asks Scribners* to publish in the earliest possible number, displacing all the rest.

2906

[*January? 1888. Saranac Lake*]. Dear Mr Burlingame, Herewith is a tale of my wife's, which I hope you may like. *Signed:* Jasper Honeycomb Better known, however, as Jack Dunck. alias Christopher P. Heyrick alias R. L. S. alias an ass . . . Peter Malone . . . *3 pp. Written on black-bordered stationery. Unpublished. Stevenson mentions a possible row with Howells. He writes:* Here lie the bones of R.L.S. His wits are with the Lord, I guess.

2907

[*February, 1888. Saranac Lake*]. Dear Mr Burlingame, 1. of course then don't use it. Dear Man, I write these to please you: not myself. *Signed:* Robert Louis Stevenson. *3 pp. On black-bordered stationery. Photostat. Published in* LFF, *Vol. 2, pp.* 95–96. *Stevenson writes:* I dislike this battle of the dollars; I feel sure you all pay too much here in America; and I beg you not to spoil me any more.

2908

[*February? 1888. Saranac Lake*]. Dear Mr Burlingame, All right. Many thanks. I hope you have Durrisdeer long since. *Signed:* Robert Louis Stevenson. *3 pp. Written on black-bordered stationery. Unpublished. Stevenson writes about* Scribner's Magazine, *and mentions his articles,* Pulvis et Umbra *and* Gentlemen.

2909

[*Spring? 1888. Saranac Lake*]. My dear Mr Burlingame, Can anything be done with this? *Signature cut away. 1 p. Unpublished. Stevenson writes of some difficulty about a package of books.*

2910

[*Postmarked:* Apr 12 1888 Saranac Lake N. Y.] My dear Burlingame, I hope to leave here Monday. *Signed:* R. L. S. *2 pp. With addressed envelope and mounted stamp. Unpublished. Stevenson writes about an article with which he has had trouble.*

2911

[*Summer, 1888. Pacific Ocean*]. My dear Burlingame. Wrong Box. Explicit valde feliciter. *Unsigned. 2 pp. Unpublished. Stevenson writes about* The Wrong Box, The Master of Ballantrae *and* Ticonderoga.

2912

[*Postmarked: October 15, 1888. Taiti*]. Dear Burlingame. Herewith the end of part VI. *Signature cut away. 3 pp. Envelope containing above postmark not retained. Unpublished. Stevenson asks Burlingame to have a typewritten copy made of* The Game of Bluff *(i.e.* The Wrong Box) *and sent to him.*

2913

[*November? 1888. Pacific Ocean*]. Dear Burlingame, Send me please to care American Consul Honolulu Bourget's[?] expedition and Men of Henry the Trader. at once not a moment R. L. S. *1 p. Notation in pencil:* Rec'd Nov. 27. *With addressed envelope, postmarked:* Nov 21 '88. San Francisco, *and mounted stamp. Unpublished.*

2914

[*Late January, 1889*]. Honolulu. My dear Burlingame, Here at last I have arrived. *Signed:* R. L. S. *14 pp. Partly published in* LFF, *Vol. 2, pp. 131–134, where 66 lines of the autograph are omitted. R.L.S. writes about William Hole's illustrations for* The Master of Ballantrae, *about* The Wrong Box, In the South Seas *and* Ballads. *He has received no money or accounts since arriving in Hawaii and has drawn a bill on Scribners in favor of A. H. Otis, captain of the yacht* Casco, *for $2,000.*

2915

[*Postmarked: March 8, 1889. Honolulu*]. My dear Burlingame. First, how small the world is! *Signed:* R. L. S. *3 pp. The en-*

velope containing this postmark has not been retained. Unpublished. Stevenson writes about Ballads, The Wrong Box *and* The Master of Ballantrae.

2916

[*March? 1889. Honolulu*]. My dear Burlingame. I came down hard; so this is to tell you I am off April 10th for four months in the islands. *Signed:* Robert Louis Stevenson. *2 pp. Unpublished. Stevenson writes that bad health has prevented a better literary output.*

2917

[*April, 1889. Honolulu*]. My dear Burlingame, This is to announce the most prodigious change of programme. *Signed:* R. L. S. *2 pp. Published in LFF, Vol. 2, pp. 145–146, where one line of the autograph is omitted. Stevenson writes of difficulty in finishing* The Master of Ballantrae, *of books to be sent him and of plans for further sailing in the Pacific.*

2918

[*Spring? 1889. Honolulu*]. My dear Burlingame, I send you herewith rough corrections on the ballads. *Signed:* Robert Louis Stevenson. *1 p. Unpublished. Stevenson writes of* Ballads *and* The Wrong Box, *and mentions* many interesting pages *in his diary.*

2919

[*Spring? 1889. Honolulu*]. My dear Burlingame, I do not want to go again into matter (which I seem to have mismanaged once) under the spur of hurry. *Signed:* Robert Louis Stevenson. *3 pp. Unpublished. Stevenson refers to a recent break in his relations with Burlingame, which now is apparently healed. He writes of* The Wrong Box *and* The Master of Ballantrae.

2920

[*Cir. May, 1889. Honolulu*]. My dear Burlingame. I I was a little puzzled by an odd phrase in your last. *Signed:* Robert Louis Stevenson. *4 pp. Unpublished. Stevenson offers Scribners* all rights in the United States *to* The Wrong Box *for $5,000. He writes of* The Master of Ballantrae, *and* Ballads *of which he* *asks for proofs in duplicate or triplicate. He writes of plans to sail in the* Equator, *and writes 4 lines of verse, beginning:* I find a point where I agree with Howells.

2921

[*Late June, 1889. Honolulu*]. My dear Burlingame, Herewith I shall return the first pp of the Wrong Box. *Signature cut away. 1 p. Unpublished. Stevenson mentions rewriting part of* The Wrong Box *and a visit to the leper colony at Molokai.*

2922

[*Summer? 1889*]. My dear Burlingame. Master [of Ballantrae] With this I trust will go the Master — proofs ready for book, end of m.s. &c. *Unsigned. 2 pp. Unpublished. Stevenson writes of* The Master of Ballantrae, The Wrong Box, *and of plans to go to Sydney.*

2923

4th Dec. 1889. Wednesday. Schooner Equator at sea. My dear Burlingame, We are now about to rise, like whales, from this long dive. *Signed:* Robert Louis Stevenson. *4 pp. Partly published in LFF, Vol. 2, pp. 170–172, where 49 lines of the autograph are omitted. Stevenson gives details of* The Wrecker, *including the titles of chapters. He describes further voyages in the Pacific.*

2924

[*February, 1890*]. S. S. Lübeck, between Apia & Sydney. My dear Burlingame, I desire nothing better than to continue my relation with the magazine. *Signed:* R. L. S. *3 pp. Published in LFF, Vol. 2, pp. 179–182. Stevenson sends the poem,* The House of Tembinoka, *with an introduction. He writes of* The Wrecker, In the South Seas, Ballads, *and a book about hostilities in Samoa.*

2925

[*February or March, 1890. Sydney*]. My dear Burlingame, Enclosed please find Tembinoka pictures. *Signed:* R. L. S. *2 pp. Unpublished. Stevenson lists the titles of some of his* Ballads *and* Songs of Travel. *He notes that some of his poems are set to music and wonders if it would be advisable to print some of the airs. The letter contains 12 lines of verse, beginning:* O what a bard I should have been.

2926

March 11th [*1890*]. Sydney. My dear Burlingame, Herewith ten chapters, or (by new figuring) five numbers, of The Wrecker. *Signed:* R. L. S. *3 pp. Unpublished. Stevenson writes of various problems in the writing of* The Wrecker.

2927

[*April, 1890*]. Str Janet Nicoll at Sea. My dear Burlingame, I shall have a chance to post this at Au[*c*]kland. *Signed:* The South-Sea-yer. *1 p. In pencil. Unpublished. Stevenson writes of sailing in the* Janet Nicoll.

2928

[*August and*] Septr 2nd [*1890. Sydney*]. My dear Burlingame, It is trusted all animosity is removed. *Signed:* R. L. S., *and* Robert Louis Stevenson. *9 pp. written on stationery of the* Union Club, Sydney. *Partly published in LFF, Vol. 2, pp. 194–195, where 83 lines of the autograph are omitted. Stevenson writes of anachronisms in* The Wrecker *and of a chapter on New York publishers. He writes of his* Ballads, *with some of which he is displeased.*

2929

[*September, 1890. Vailima*]. My dear Burlingame, I am very sorry to send you no "Wrecker" this mail. *Signed:* R. L. S. *1 p. Unpublished. Stevenson describes reminiscences written by his grandfather on a voyage made with Sir Walter Scott.*

2930

Novr 5th [*1890. Vailima*]. My dear Burlingame, Yesterday a note went to the post for you, containing no great matter. *Signed:* Robert Louis Stevenson. *2 pp. Unpublished. Stevenson writes that* The Wrecker *cannot be finished for six or more months, partly because Lloyd Osbourne has gone to England where he was to do some of the writing.*

2931

Nov 26. 1890. Vailima Apia Samoa. My dear Burlingame, I write in a hurry in answer to your last. *Signed:* Robert Louis Stevenson, *and* R. L. S. *4 pp. Unpublished. Stevenson writes about* The Wrecker *and* Ballads.

2932

[*December, 1890. Vailima*]. My dear Burlingame, By some diabolical accident, I have mislaid your last. *Signed:* Robert Louis Stevenson. *3 pp. Published in* LFF, *Vol. 2, pp. 211–212, where 3 lines of the autograph are omitted. Stevenson writes of plans for his home at Vailima, of farmering, and of articles he expects to send for* Scribner's Magazine.

2933

[*Winter? 1890–1891. Vailima?*]. My dear Burlingame, Possibly some more chapters will go to you by the same mail as this. *Unsigned. 2 pp. Unpublished. Stevenson marvels at the bulk to which* The Wrecker *has grown.*

2934

Jan. 20 (?) [*1891*]. Sydney. My dear Burlingame, Fear I have missed a letter from you. *Signed:* R. L. S. *2 pp. Unpublished. Stevenson writes of necessary changes he is making in* The Wrecker.

2935

[*Cir. February, 1891*]. My dear Burlingame, Lloyd is back and his typewriter clicks and tinkles. *Signed:* R L. Stevenson. *1 p. Unpublished.*

2936

[*Spring, 1891*]. Vailima Apia Samoa. My dear Burlingame Herewith XV, XVI and XVII [*of* The Wrecker]. *Signed:* Robert Louis Stevenson, *and* R. L. S. *2 pp. Unpublished. Stevenson asks an advance on* The Wrecker, *and sends an alteration for its* Prologue. *He writes of the birds, climate, etc. of Samoa.*

2937

May 10th [*and*] 17th [*and*] 19th 1891. [*Vailima*]. My dear Burlingame, This goes to answer some things that you have expressed and some that you are thinking. *Signed:* Robert Louis Stevenson, *and* R. L. S. *2 pp. Unpublished. Stevenson is worried that pirates may issue* In the South Seas *before copyright is secured. He gives titles to the last nine chapters of* The Wrecker.

2938

June 22nd 1891. [*Vailima*]. My dear Burlingame, Herewith two more chapters of the Wrecker. *Signed:* R. L. S. *1 p. Unpublished. Of* The Wrecker *Stevenson writes:* Chapters XVIII and XIX have been the hitches; being necessary but not obvious.

2939

[*Summer? 1891*]. My dear Burlingame, I am sorry to send only one chapter. *Signed:* Robert Louis Stevenson, *and* R. L. S. *1 p. Unpublished. Stevenson writes that he has heard that* The Wrecker *is to be issued serially in England, possibly by pirates.*

2940

October 8th 1891. [*Vailima*]. My dear Burlingame, All right you shall have the tales of my grandfather soon. *Signed:* Robert Louis Stevenson. *1 p. Published in LFF, Vol. 2, p. 237, where 13 lines of the autograph are omitted. Stevenson writes of his work later titled* Records of a Family of Engineers.

2941

[*Autumn, 1891. Vailima*]. My dear Burlingame, the time draws nigh, the mail is near due. *Unsigned. 1 p. Published in LFF, Vol. 2, pp. 238–239. Stevenson writes of final work on* The Wrecker, *and lists books which he wishes sent to him.*

2942

Nov [*? —*] 28 [*1891. Vailima*]. My dear Burlingame, The end of the Wrecker having but just come in, you will I daresay be appalled to receive . . . chapters of a new book. *Unsigned. 2 pp. Partly published in LFF, Vol. 2, pp. 242–244, where 28 lines of the autograph are omitted. Stevenson writes of* A Footnote to History, *which he wishes to have published, if necessary at* *his own expense, also of missing proof (of* The Wrecker*?) and a letter.*

2943
Jan 2nd 92. [*Vailima*]. My dear Burlingame, Overjoyed you were pleased with Wrecker, and shall consider your protests. *Signed:* R. L. Stevenson. *1 p. Published in LFF, Vol. 2, pp. 246–247. Stevenson writes of* A Footnote to History *and* The Beach of Falesá.

2944
Jan [— *and*] 30th [*1892*]. Vailima. Dear Burlinghame[*sic*] I am seized with a . . . *Signed:* Robert Louis Stevenson. *1 p. The letter, partly torn away, is in the hand of Isobel Strong, signed by Stevenson. Unpublished. R.L.S. writes of having had influenza and of his concern about the copyright of* David Balfour.

2945
Feb 1st 92. [*Vailima*]. My dear Burlingame. No copy this month. I have been down with the fa'a mai, as we call it here, the influenza. *Signed:* R. L. S. *2 pp. Unpublished. Mostly about corrections and changes in proofs of* The Wrecker.

2946
[*March, 1892. Vailima*]. My dear Burlingame. Herewith Chapters IX and X [*of* A Footnote to History]. *Signed:* R. L. Stevenson. *1 p. Published in LFF, Vol. 2, pp. 253–254, where 8 words of the autograph are omitted.*

2947
[*April, 1892. Vailima*]. My dear Burlingame, Herewith the Wrecker, all but one slip . . . found missing and the end slips not received. *Signed:* Robert Louis Stevenson. *3 pp. Unpublished. Much about* The Wrecker *and* A Footnote to History. *Stevenson writes:* I am setting up a kind of a branch family in California, *and for this purpose asks that a monthly payment of $75 be sent to a lawyer in San Francisco.*

2948

June 20th 1892. Vailima Plantation Upolu Samoa. My dear Burlingame You will have already learned that you were right as to the history of Samoa. *Signed:* Robert Louis Stevenson. *3 pp. The letter is in the hand of Isobel Strong, signed by Stevenson. Unpublished.*

2949

[*Cir. May, 1892. Vailima*]. My dear Burlingame, First of all, you have all the corrections on the Wrecker. *Signed:* Robert Louis Stevenson. *2 pp. Partly published in LFF, Vol. 2, pp. 255–256, where 36 lines of the autograph, listing names of those to receive presentation copies of* A Footnote to History, *are omitted. Of this book Stevenson writes:* I trust I am done with this cursed chapter of my career.

2950

August 1st/92. Vailima Upolu. My dear Burlingame, Herewith my grandfather. *Signed:* R. L. S. *2 pp. The letter is mostly in the hand of Isobel Strong, partly in R.L.S.'s hand, signed by him. Partly published in LFF, Vol. 2, pp. 258–259, where 37 lines of the autograph are omitted. Stevenson writes of* Reminiscences of Sir Walter Scott, Baronet. By Robert Stevenson [R.L.S.'s grandfather], *and of his dislike for W. L. Metcalf's illustrations for* The Wrecker.

2951

[*August? 1892. Vailima*]. My dear Burlingame, No word from any of you this mail. *Signed:* R. L. S. *1 p. Unpublished. Stevenson writes about* The Wrecker, David Balfour *and* The Beach of Falesá.

2952

Oct. 10 1892. Vailima Plantation Samoan Islands. My dear Burlinghame[*sic*] It is now as you see the 10th of October and there has not reached the Island of Opolu one single copy or rag of a copy of the Samoa book. *Signed:* Robert Louis Stevenson. *2 pp. The letter is in the hand of Isobel Strong, signed by Stevenson. Published in LFF, Vol. 2, pp. 266–267. Stevenson is*

displeased and embarrassed at not receiving copies of A Footnote to History.

2953

Nov. 2nd 1892. Vailima Plantation. My dear Burlinghame [*sic*]
— In the first place I have to acknowledge receipt of your munifi-
cent cheque. *Signed:* R. L. Stevenson, *and* R. L. S. *3 pp. The
letter is in the hand of Isobel Strong, signed by Stevenson. Published in LFF, Vol. 2, pp. 269–270, where 12 lines of the autograph are omitted. Stevenson complains about the mails, not
having yet received copies of* A Footnote to History.

2954

Nov. 29th 1892. Vailima Plantation. My dear Burlinghame[*sic*]
Hosanna! The footnotes have at last arrived. *Signed:* Robert
Louis Stevenson. *3 pp. The letter is mostly in the hand of Isobel
Strong, a few lines in Stevenson's hand, signed by him. Unpub-
lished. Stevenson sends an excerpt from his family papers, and
orders for books and magazines.*

2955

Jan 3rd 93. [*Vailima*]. My dear Burlingame, You have taken
me wholly at unawares. *Signed:* Robert Louis Stevenson. *1 p.
Unpublished. Stevenson declines to write an article on a specific
subject for Scribners within a ten days time limit. He lists books
that he wishes sent.*

2956

April 16th '93. Vailima. My dear Burlinghame[*sic*] You must
have expected me to be shocked by the figures in your account
to Feb. 1st. *Signed:* Robert Louis Stevenson. *2 pp. The letter
is in the hand of Isobel Strong, 2 lines and signature in Stevenson's hand. Unpublished. Stevenson asks Scribners to send an
offer to Charles Baxter for the American copyright of* David
Balfour. *He writes:* I should not think it fair to myself to sacri-
fice any more of my books upon such terms *as Scribners offered.*

2957

April 16th '93. Vailima. My dear Burlingame You must have
expected me to be shocked by the figures in your account of

Feb 1st, and you will be quite prepared for a change of basis. *Typesigned:* Robert Louis Stevenson. *1 p. Copy of Stevenson's letter, typed by Lloyd Osbourne. Unpublished.*

2958
[*May, 1893. Vailima*]. My dear Burlingame, I wrote by last mail definitively. *Signed:* Robert Louis Stevenson, *and twice:* R. L. S. *1 p. Unpublished. Stevenson deplores the poor sales of* The Wrecker *in the States. He repeats his request that a lump sum payment for* David Balfour *be arranged with Charles Baxter.*

2959
June 12 1893. Vailima Plantation South Seas. My dear Bur-linghame[*sic*] Many thanks for your letter of May 16th. *Signed:* R. L. Stevenson. *2 pp. The letter is in the hand of Isobel Strong, signed by Stevenson. Unpublished. He writes:* We shall have no more royalties from the States. A sum down will have to be agreed upon for every book you shall publish in future.

2960
Aug. 14th 1893. Vailima Samoa. My dear Burlingame — I am very glad to know our business is satisfactorily settled. *Signed:* Robert Louis Stevenson. *3 pp. The letter is in the hand of Isobel Strong, 3 lines and signature in Stevenson's hand. Unpublished. R.L.S. orders books and writes about the Samoan war.*

2961
[*September, 1893*]. My dear Burlingame, This is to introduce to you my cousin Mr Graham Balfour. *Signed:* Robert Louis Stevenson. *1 p. Unpublished.*

2962
Octr 16 1893. [*Honolulu*]. My dear Burlingame, Will you please send me something as definite as you can find as to the American privateers of 1812–14? *Signed:* Robert Louis Steven-son. *1 p. Written on stationery of* Sans Souci, Waikiki, Honolulu. *Unpublished. Stevenson requests background material for St. Ives.*

2963

October 24 1893. [*Honolulu*]. My dear Burlingame, Here is
a book I shall require quam primum: Mémoires d'un conscrit de
1808 par L. F. Gille. *Signature cut away. 1 p. Written on stationery of* Sans Souci, Waikiki, Honolulu. *Unpublished.*

2964

[*1893. Vailima*]. My dear Burlingame, Well, to be sure and 't is
a beautiful book. *Signed:* Robert Louis Stevenson. *1 p. Addition
on p. 2 torn off. Unpublished. Stevenson feels that he cannot
use the title* Northern Lights *for the book which was later published as* Records of a Family of Engineers.

2965

Jan 29th 1894. Vailima Samoa. My dear Burlinghame[*sic*] The
books are all to hand except the most important of all. *Signature
cut away. 3 pp. The letter is in the hand of Isobel Strong except
for 6 lines in Stevenson's hand. Unpublished. Stevenson repeats his request for Gille's* Mémoires d'un conscrit de 1808;
and orders other books.

2966

July 8th 1894. Vailima Samoa. My dear Burlinghame[*sic*] You
surprise me very much by your sudden recurrence to the old
idea now four years old of a renewal of the series of essays.
Signed: Robert Louis Stevenson, *and* R. L. S. *3 pp. The letter
is in the hand of Isobel Strong, signed by Stevenson. Unpublished. R.L.S. writes:* I doubt if I could write essays now; I
doubt . . . whether I should find I wanted to.

2967

Oct 9th '94. Vailima. My dear Burlingame Please I must put
off until next month giving you an answer. *Signed:* Robert Louis
Stevenson, *and* R. L. S. *3 pp. The letter is in the hand of Isobel
Strong, except for 3 lines and signatures in Stevenson's hand.
Unpublished. Stevenson orders books, and writes:* P. P. S.
Second thoughts I'll have a try, if I bust. I'll send one article
and you shall say if you like it.

R.L.S. TO RICHARD HETHERINGTON
CARRUTHERS

2968

[*N.d., Vailima*]. My dear Carruthers, I was able to make a poor show of Longmans. *Signed:* R. L. S. *2 pp. Unpublished. Stevenson mentions cutting brush for three hours.* Carruthers the lawyer *is mentioned in one of Stevenson's letters to Colvin as being present at the Stevensons' Christmas dinner in 1890.*

R.L.S. TO CONRAD CEDERCRANTZ

2969

April 14th 1892. Vailima. Sir, When I wrote to you some time
ago, I was still in hopes that you might be able to explain and
I more or less to endorse your policy in these islands. *Unsigned.
1 p. At the top Stevenson has written:* Private draft and very
unsatisfactory. *Unpublished.*

2970

Sept 13th 1892. Vailima. Sir, I learn from the British half-caste,
Charles Taylor, that you are in quest of information as to my
dealings with Mataafa. *Signed:* Robert Louis Stevenson. *2 pp.
Partly printed in Edith B. Tranter.* First Editions and Autograph
Manuscripts of American and English Authors ... Auction Sale
... *New York, 1952, p. 100, where 21 lines of the autograph are
omitted. A stern letter about Stevenson's efforts to maintain
peace in Samoa, and a protest against threats of deportation
made to Charles Taylor.*

2971

[*December, 1890. Vailima*]. My dear Tamate, I had looked forward to meeting you with a pleasure that I should find it hard to exaggerate. *Signed:* Robert Louis Stevenson, *and* R. L. S. *4 pp. A few lines of this letter are printed in The Rosenbach Company.* A Catalogue of Original Manuscripts [*etc.*] . . . *New York, 1933, p. 41, lot 321. A farewell letter in which Stevenson expresses regret that he cannot see Chalmers before the latter's departure.*

2972

Dec 26th 1893. Vailima. Dear Mr Chatfield, Believe me thoroughly, that I have always done you justice in the matter of your political opinions. *Signed:* Robert Louis Stevenson. *3 pp. Photostat of the original in The Mitchell Library, Sydney. Unpublished. Stevenson writes that his relations with Chatfield* must remain essentially external and distant, *but* they need be none the less agreeable for that. *In* A Footnote to History, *p. 224, Stevenson refers to Chatfield without mentioning his name as a* man who had been discharged. *Stevenson may have done an unjustified injury to Chatfield.*

2973

Dec 1st 1894. [*Vailima*]. Dear Mr Chatfield. I beg to reinclose Consul Stuebel's letter and to congratulate you on a piece of evidence which is irrefragable in itself as far as it goes. *Signed:* Robert Louis Stevenson. *2 pp. Photostat of the original in The Mitchell Library, Sydney. Unpublished.*

2974

[*October, 1890. Sydney*]. Dear Mr Chatto, The letter to Dr Hyde [*i.e. the* Father Damien *letter*] is yours, or any man's. I will never touch a penny of remuneration. *Signed:* Robert Louis Stevenson, *and* R. L. S. *4 pp. Written on stationery of the* Union Club, Sydney. *Partly published in John A. Spoor.* . . . Library . . . Part II . . . Public Sale . . . *New York, 1939, p. 88, lot 852.*

2975

October 1st 1892. [*Vailima*]. Sir, I have to offer you my regret that I did not do earlier what I find I must do now. *Signed:* Robert Louis Stevenson. *2 pp. Unpublished. The text of this letter is repeated in Stevenson's letter to Sidney Colvin dated October 8, 1892. Stevenson writes:* In the future there can be no relations between you and me, *and refers to Claxton as* one of those men with whom I must either definitely break or cease to respect myself.

2976

September 16th 1873. Tuesday [*and*] next day. [*Edinburgh*]. My dear Colvin, I have just been having a long talk with my father. *Signed:* Louis Stevenson, R. L. S., *and* L. *9 pp. Unpublished. Stevenson writes of difficulties with his father, and about sending a manuscript to Macmillan & Co. He wants Colvin's opinion of the manuscript and writes that he* can stand honesty.

2977

Sept 23rd 1873. Edinburgh. My dear Colvin, I am so glad you think something could be made of roads. *Signed:* Robert Louis Stevenson, *and* L. *Unpublished. Stevenson writes of his essay on* Roads, *etc., stating that* it is so hard to write anything that is really fit for cold black and white printing. *He also writes:* I have had a very bad time of it with my father.

2978

[*October, 1873. Edinburgh*]. My dear Colvin, I am sorry to say that I have a little overworked myself. *Signed:* Louis Stevenson. *4 pp. Written on stationery of* 17 Heriot Row. *Dated by Colvin. Unpublished. Colvin's help is asked in matters connected with Stevenson's intended application for admission as a student at one of London's Inns of Court.*

2979

[*October 16, 1873*]. Thursday. [*Edinburgh*]. My dear Colvin, I am at my wits' end about this abominable form of admission. *Signed:* Louis Stevenson, *and* L. S. *4 pp. Written on stationery of* 17 Heriot Row. *Partly printed in* The Letters, *1911, Vol. 1, p. 79, where about 24 lines of the autograph are omitted. Stevenson writes that he would not come to London for the legal examination except that he needs a moment of escape from the unpleasantness with his parents.*

2980

[*November, 1873*]. Hotel du Pavillon, Menton. My dear Colvin, All right. I shall come. *Signed:* R. L. Stevenson. *3 pp. Written on stationery of* 17 Heriot Row. *Dated by Colvin. Stevenson writes of a proposed visit by him and Colvin to Monaco.*

2981

[*December 1, 1873*]. Hotel du Pavillon, Menton. My dear Colvin, I hope you have thought of the possibility of a quarantine. *Signed:* Robert Louis Stevenson, *and* R. L. S. *4 pp. Written on stationery of* 17 Heriot Row. *Stevenson has dated this:* Nov. 1st. *Colvin, however, has drawn a line through* Nov. *and dated the letter as above. Unpublished. Stevenson writes of a 17-days quarantine in some places on account of cholera in Naples.*

2982

[*January, 1874*]. Friday [*and*] Saturday. [*Mentone*]. My dear Colvin — Thank you very much for your note. *Signed:* Robert Louis Stevenson. *6 pp. Partly printed in* The Letters, *Vol. 1, pp. 110–111, where 19 lines of the autograph are omitted. Stevenson writes about a cloak which Colvin has suggested to him as a desirable purchase.*

2983

[*January, 1874. Mentone*]. My dear S C, I suppose this will be my last note then. *Signed:* Robert Louis Stevenson. *8 pp. Partly printed in* The Letters, *1911, Vol. 1, pp. 112–114, where about 28 lines of the autograph are omitted. Stevenson writes about the* convention *followed in writing a story,* The Bottle, *which was afterwards abandoned.*

2984

[*January —, and 12, 1874. Mentone*]. My dear Colvin, I write to let you know that my cousin may possibly come to Paris before you leave. *Signed:* Robert Louis Stevenson. *4 pp. Partly printed in* The Letters, *1911, Vol. 1, pp. 109–110, where 18 lines of the autograph are omitted. Stevenson writes an interesting characterization of his cousin, R. A. M. Stevenson.*

2985

[*January*] 13th [*1874*]. Tuesday [*and*] Wednesday. [*Mentone*]. My dear Colvin. I told you I did not hear on Monday. *Signed:* Robert Louis Stevenson. *6 pp. Unpublished.*

2986

[*January, 1874. Mentone*]. My dear Colvin, the bird of Paradise has arrived duly. *Signed:* Robert Louis Stevenson. *4 pp. Unpublished. A jovial letter in which Stevenson writes of working on* Ordered South.

2987

[*January, 1874. Mentone*]. Latine scribere mihi nunc jucundum est. *Signed:* Robert Louis Stevenson. *4 pp. Unpublished. In this letter Stevenson has written about 22 lines of Latin; he states that he has nearly finished a complete draft of* Ordered South.

2988

[*January, 1874. Mentone*]. My dear Colvin, I have been so stupid you must pardon my silence. *Signed:* Robert Louis Stevenson. *6 pp. Unpublished. Stevenson mentions Colvin's having met R. A. M. Stevenson in Paris, about working on the essay on Walt Whitman, about drinking champagne given him by Pretty-well Lang, about being kept from sleeping by the champagne or food that did not agree with him, and about Robinet and an Army doctor named Lewins.*

2989

[*January, 1874. Mentone*]. My dear Colvin, many thanks for your adorable children. *Signed:* Robert Louis Stevenson. *2 pp. Unpublished. Stevenson asks Colvin to send him books about women of the sixteenth century, about Geneva, Calvin, and other subjects.*

2990

[*January, 1874. Mentone*]. My dear Colvin, Yesterday's was to catch the Post. *Signed:* Robert Louis Stevenson, *and* R L. S. *2 pp. Unpublished. Stevenson writes of a possible article about John Knox and women.*

2991

[*February? 1874. Mentone*]. My dear Colvin, write by all means to my parents. *Signed:* Robert Louis Stevenson. *4 pp. Partly published in Henry A. Colgate.* The Stevenson Library . . . *New York, 1928, p. 37, where about 35 lines of the autograph are omitted. Stevenson states that he is unfit for work and has physical difficulty in writing.*

2992

[*End of April, 1874. Hotel St. Romain, Paris*]. My dear Colvin, I am a great deal better, but still have to take care. *Signed:* Robert Louis Stevenson, *and, three times:* R. L. S. *4 pp. Partly published in* The Letters, *1911, pp. 128–129, where about 27 lines of the autograph are omitted. Stevenson writes about work on his article on Victor Hugo; and expresses regret at not going to Göttingen to study law.*

2993

[*Spring, 1874. Edinburgh*]. My dear Colvin Here is a scratch of a pen for you. V. Hugo going on slowly and not well. *Signed:* R. L Stevenson. *2 pp. Written on stationery of* 17 Heriot Row. *Unpublished. Stevenson writes:* My father . . . insists on my passing for the Scotch Bar . . . I do not like Edinburgh.

2994

[*May, 1874*]. Swanston Lothianburn Edinburgh. All right. I'll see what I can do. *Signed:* Robert Louis Stevenson. *2 pp. Partly published in* The Letters, *1911, Vol. 1, p. 131, where 7 lines of the autograph are omitted. Stevenson writes about doing a review of Lord Lytton's* Fables in Song, *and mentions his interest in becoming a member of the Savile Club.*

2995

[*May or June, 1874. Edinburgh*]. My dear Colvin, God bless you for Sully. *Signed:* Robert Louis Stevenson. *2 pp. Unpublished. Stevenson regrets that he has lost the proof of his article for the* Cornhill Magazine, *and that he lacks ten guineas to pay dues to the Savile Club.*

2996

[*June, 1874*]. Friday. [*Edinburgh*]. My dear Colvin I am seedy — very seedy, I may say. *Signed:* Robert Louis Stevenson. *3 pp. Partly published in* The Letters, *1911, Vol. 1, p. 145, where about 9 lines of the autograph are omitted.*

2997

[*Early summer, 1874. Scotland*]. My dear Colvin, many thanks.
I have recd the 15 quid, also Portfolio proof. *Signature cut
away. 3 pp. Written on stationery bearing Stevenson's monogram. Unpublished. Stevenson mentions articles of his for two
magazines and a cruise he is about to take.*

2998

[*Summer, 1874. Edinburgh*]. My dear Colvin, Many thanks for
your letter. *Signed:* Robert Louis Stevenson. *3 pp. Unpublished.
Stevenson writes of work on his essays on Victor Hugo and
John Knox. His cousin Bob has gotten diphtheria.*

2999

[*Summer ? 1874. Edinburgh*]. My dear Colvin, Same result
again. Either my children must stay as they are, and be printed
as they are, or they must not be printed at all. *Signed:* R L S.
3 pp. Unpublished. Stevenson writes: I think I hate my maker
and all he has made more utterly than ever I did before. *The
letter is in three parts, written at three different times, the last
dated:* Wednesday.

3000

[*1874? Edinburgh*]. My dear Colvin, enclosed is a P. O. O for
£9 . . 12: £1.5 for you; and £8 for the Clubs. *Signed:* Robert
Louis Stevenson. *3 pp. Written on stationery of the* Speculative
Society's Hall. *About 9 lines of this 28-line letter are printed in
The Rosenbach Company.* A Catalogue of Original Manuscripts
[*etc.*] . . . *New York, 1933, p. 38, lot 308. Stevenson writes that
he* developed, as before, a phenomenal capacity for taking
strong drink without noticing the quantity or being at all
affected by it.

3001

Sept. 4th 1874. Swanston. My dear Colvin, I was awfully both-
ered to get your note and its bad news. *Signed:* Robert Louis
Stevenson. *1 p. Unpublished. Stevenson writes:* I am trying my
new copying paper. *This appears to be a carbon copy. He is
disturbed by Colvin's bad health.*

938

.

3002

[*September, 1874*]. Barmouth [*Wales*]. Pay no attention to this, for I am a wanderer and stranger here. *First 4 pp. of letter. Written on stationery bearing R.L.S.'s monogram. Unpublished. Stevenson writes of his love of smoking; and his long hair, a* regimen *which does not* agree so well with me as it did with Samson.

3003

[*November, 1874. Edinburgh*]. My dear Colvin, thank you and God bless you for ever. *Signed:* Robert Louis Stevenson, *and* R L. S. *3 pp. Published in* The Letters, *1911, Vol. 1, pp. 163–164, where about 4 lines of the autograph are omitted. Stevenson writes about Japanese prints sent him by Colvin.*

3004

[*January, 1875. Edinburgh*]. My dear Colvin, Forgive my bad correspondence. I am bilious, they tell me; and damned lazy, I know. *Signed:* Robert Louis Stevenson, *and* R L S. *4 pp. Written on stationery of* 17 Heriot Row. *Unpublished.*

3005

[*January, 1875. Edinburgh*]. My dear Colvin. The Devil – I have worked too hard. *Signed:* Robert Louis Stevenson, *and* R. L. S. *8 pp. Written on stationery of* 17 Heriot Row. *Partly published in* LFF, *Vol. 1, pp. 84–85, where about 66 lines of the autograph are omitted. Stevenson writes:* Bad passion is, after all, better than bad, and sham, composure.

3006

[*January, 1875. Edinburgh*]. My dear Colvin, thanks for your letter. I too am in such a state of business that I know not when to find time to write. *Signed:* Robert Louis Stevenson. *6 pp. Published in* The Letters, *1911, Vol. 1, pp. 177–179, where one line of the autograph is omitted. Stevenson lists twelve stories by him in different stages of completion. Three, he thinks, are* capital. *None of these stories apparently was ever published.*

3007

[*January or February, 1875*]. Friday ? [*Edinburgh*]. I say Colvin, your Titian is no end, and has pleased my mother as much as me. *Signed three times:* Robert Louis Stevenson. *4 pp. Unpublished. Stevenson states that he is* a damned bad writer.

3008

[*1875. Edinburgh or Swanston*]. My dear Colvin, Here's a note at last. I suppose I shall take all your damned corrections, when I come to the proof. *Signed:* R. L. S. *1 p. Unpublished. Stevenson writes about an unidentified story on which he is working.*

3009

[*June, 1875*]. Swanston Lothianburn. My dear Colvin, I am a devil certainly; but write I cannot. *Signed:* Robert Louis Stevenson. *4 pp. Published in* The Letters, *1911, Vol. 1, pp. 186–187, where 7 lines of the autograph are omitted. Stevenson writes that he is in a* humour of a sunny equanimity.

3010

[*July 7, 1875. Edinburgh or Swanston*]. My dear Colvin, thanks for your pencilations. *Signed:* R L S. *1 p. Unpublished. Stevenson mentions his forthcoming examination for the bar, and his articles on Burns and Beranger. See Colvin's letter to John Walter Thomson, to whom Colvin presented this a.l.s. by Stevenson.*

3011

[*Early July, 1875. Edinburgh or Swanston*]. My dear Colvin, Wednesday the 14th is my exam. *Signed:* R L. S. *1 p. Unpublished. Stevenson writes of a letter from Leslie Stephen, and an article on Fontainebleau (printed as* Forest Notes, *May, 1876) on which R. L. S. was at work. Stevenson passed his examination for the bar at Edinburgh on July 14, earning for him the title of* Advocate.

3012

[*End of July, 1875. Edinburgh*]. My dear Colvin, herewith you receive the rest of Henley's hospital work. *Signed:* R. L. S. Advocate. *3 pp. Published in* The Letters, *1911, Vol. 1, pp. 195–*

196, *where about 4 lines of the autograph are omitted. Steven-*
son writes about Henley's poetry and his relation to it.

3013

[*Autumn, 1875*]. Swanston. My dear Colvin, Thanks. Only, why
don't you tell me, if I can get my Spring printed? *Signed:* R.
L. H. Stevenson. *4 pp. Partly published in* The Letters, *1911,*
Vol. 1, pp. 205–206, where about 16 lines of the autograph are
omitted. The Spring *referred to is Stevenson's essay on* The
Spirit of Spring, *the manuscript of which Colvin lost. Stevenson*
jokes about the Baron Rothschild.

3014

[*Autumn, 1875. Edinburgh*]. My dear Colvin, Fous ne me gom-
brennez bas — Angry with you? no. *Signed:* Robert Louis Stevenson, *and* R. L. S. *4 pp. Published in LFF, Vol. 1, pp. 110–*
111, where 2 lines of the autograph are omitted. Stevenson is
annoyed because Colvin has lost the essay on Spring *which*
Stevenson sent him.

3015

[*1875. Edinburgh*]. Dear Colvin, I have a struggle to forgive
you this time; but I do. *Signed:* Robert Louis Stevenson. *3 pp.*
In pencil. Written on stationery of the Speculative Society.
Unpublished. Stevenson states that he has temporarily given
up short stories and is working on a long one.

3016

[*Autumn, 1875. Edinburgh*]. My dear Colvin, Thanks for your
letter and news. *Signed:* Robert Louis Stevenson, *and* R L. S.
10 pp. Partly published in LFF, Vol. 1, pp. 106–108, where
about 35 lines of the autograph are omitted. Stevenson writes
about his reading and writing.

3017

[*February, 1876. Edinburgh*]. My dear Colvin I was waiting
to write to you until I got a P. O. O but my energy fails me.
Signed: R L S. *2 pp. Unpublished. Stevenson writes:* Fontainebleau lies all ready, and I can't send it off.

3018

[*February, 1876. Edinburgh*]. My dear Colvin 1°. Yes, if you would be so good as to pay £4.4 I should bless you. *Signed five times:* R. L. S. *Portrait by Stevenson of a woman at end of letter. Partly published in LFF, Vol. 1, p. 115, where about 15 lines of the autograph are omitted. Stevenson is annoyed that Leslie Stephen does not like his* Fontainebleau, *i.e.* Forest Notes.

3019

[*1876. Edinburgh*]. My dear Colvin, your Daniel Deronda is uncommonly jolly, and right. *Signed:* R. L. S. *1 p. Written on stationery of* 17 Heriot Row. *Unpublished.*

3020

[*July, 1876*]. Swanston Lothianburn. Here I am, here. and very well too. *Signed:* R. L. S. *4 pp. Written on stationery of* 17 Heriot Row. *Partly published in LFF, Vol. 1, pp. 115–116, where about 12 lines of the autograph are omitted. Largely about articles by Stevenson. On p. 4 he has written five times:* Write, there's a good soul.

3021

[*August? 1876. Edinburgh*]. My dear Colvin, I'm in sort of hiding for the nonce. *Signed:* Robert Louis Stevenson, *and* R L. S. *4 pp. Contains pen drawings, flourishes, etc. by Stevenson. Unpublished. He states:* I've written five or six chapters of a novel, *and mentions essays on which he has been working.* I'm just away, *he writes,* to canoe in Belgium & France with Simpson.

3022

[*April or May, 1877. Edinburgh*]. My dear Colvin, I'm a wicked devil. That is now my formula at the beginning of a letter. *Signed:* Robert Louis Stevenson. *4 pp. Written on black-bordered stationery of* 17 Heriot Row. *Unpublished. Stevenson writes of his essay on François Villon and of parts he will take in Jenkin's theatricals.*

3023

[*Summer, 1877. Edinburgh or Swanston*]. My dear Colvin, I have no plans just now, and can't make any. *Signed:* R. L. S. *4 pp. Unpublished. Stevenson writes about his essay on Fran-çois Villon and* A Lodging for the Night. *The letter contains six lines of verse, beginning:* The poor inhabitant below.

3024

[*August, 1877. Edinburgh*]. My dear Colvin. of course I'm a devil. and now, I was so sorry to miss you in London. *Signed:* Louis Stevenson. *2 pp. Published in LFF, Vol. 1, p. 119, where about 7 lines of the autograph are omitted. Stevenson writes about* A Lodging for the Night *and* The Sire de Malétroit's Mousetrap.

3025

[*1877? Edinburgh*]. My dear Colvin, Would you mind sending the thing back to let me have a look at it. *Signed:* Robert Louis Stevenson. *7 pp. Written on stationery of* 17 Heriot Row. *Unpublished. Stevenson mentions several articles he has written or is going to write.*

3026

[*January, 1878. Edinburgh*]. My book could have been done by this time if I had not falled seedy. *Signed:* R. L. S. *4 pp. Unpublished. Much about* An Inland Voyage.

3027

[*February, 1878*]. 29 Rue des Abesses Montmartre, Paris. Dear Colvin, recd the book. I have signed and sent off agreement with Paul [*about* An Inland Voyage]. *Signed:* R. L. S. *2 pp. Unpublished. Stevenson writes:* My father is coming, at my request, to Paris — don't be astonished, but admire my courage and F[*anny*]'s. We wish to be right with the world as far as we can; 'tis a big venture; wish us god speed.

3028

[*Early 1878. Paris*]. My dear Colvin, I am so sorry to hear you have trouble too. *Signed:* Robert Louis Stevenson. *1 p. Unpublished. Stevenson writes about Fanny's bad health, and about negotiations with Kegan Paul for publication of* An Inland Voyage.

3029
[*October, 1878*]. Alais, Gard. My dear Colvin, Your long and kind letter is received. *Signed: R. L. S. 3 pp. Unpublished. Stevenson meditates about his lot in the world.*

3030
20/1/79. Swanston Cottage. My Dear Colvin, This should be "Our dear Colvin," or "our Colvin which art in heaven." *Signed:* W. E. H & George the Pieman. *4 pp. A joint letter by Henley and R.L.S. 4 lines are in the hand of Stevenson, the rest in Henley's hand. Unpublished. About* Deacon Brodie.

3031
[*Spring, 1879*]. Swanston Lothianburn. My dear Colvin Gryt news. First what's most important. *Signed:* R. L. S. *3 pp. Unpublished. Stevenson writes about* Deacon Brodie *on which he and* W. E. Henley *have been at work. Henley has written an addition to this letter.*

3032
[*May or June, 1879*]. poems. Why? Because they want to so badly. Can you give a better reason? *1 p. of letter. To Colvin? On the back of a p. written (by R. A. M. Stevenson?) R. L. S. writes about* Travels with a Donkey, *which, he states, is through the press.*

3033
[*Summer, 1879. Edinburgh*]. My dear Colvin, I received a letter from Eger. *Signed:* R. L. S. *3 pp. On black-bordered stationery. Unpublished. Stevenson writes about an illness, about German professors, etc.*

3034
[*1879*]. Edinr My dear Colvin, My mother claims her book of extracts. *Signed:* R. L. S. *8 pp. Unpublished. Stevenson states that he has been sick and in pain. He writes:* I like solitude and

silence . . . Just now I have a perplexity, and do you know I can tell it to none of my friends . . . except Baxter.

3035

[*Early August, 1879. Greenoch?*]. Dear Colvin, The enclosed is to go to my father. I have never been so much detached from life. *Signed:* R. L. S. *2 pp. Unpublished. Written apparently just before sailing for America.*

3036

[*August, 1879*]. on board S. S. Devonia an hour or two out of New York. My dear Colvin, I have finished my story [*i.e.* The Story of a Lie]. *Signed:* R. L. S., *and* Robert Louis Stevenson. *6 pp. Partly published in* LFF, *Vol. 1, p. 144, where about 38 lines of the autograph are omitted. 8 of the lines omitted in* LFF *are printed in* The Letters, *1911, Vol. 1, p. 243. Stevenson did much writing during an uncomfortable voyage.*

3037

[*August, 1879. In an emigrant train between New York and San Francisco*]. Dear Colvin, I am in the cars between Pittsburgh & Chicago. *Unsigned. 7 pp. In pencil. Partly published in* LFF, *Vol. 1, pp. 144–146, where about 20 lines of the autograph are omitted. This letter contains the poem beginning:* Of where or how, I nothing know. *One stanza (8 lines) is omitted in* LFF.

3038

[*September, 1879. In the Coast Range, 18 miles from Monterey, California*]. Here is another curious start in my life. *Signed:* R. L. S. *2 pp. Partly published in* LFF, *Vol. 1, pp. 147–148, where about 14 lines of the autograph are omitted. Stevenson is ill on a goat ranch. He teaches reading to the ranch children.*

3039

[*Autumn, 1879. Monterey*]. My dear Colvin, I have a long letter written to you, which I do not send, because now it would be incorrect. *Signed:* R. L. S. *2 pp. Unpublished. Stevenson asks if an article by him on a camp in the Redwoods could be published in London, illustrated by Joseph Strong's sketches which Stevenson is sending. In this and other letters written since arriving in America Stevenson complains of having gotten the itch.*

3040

21st Oct. [*1879*]. Monterey ditto Co Cal. My dear Colvin, Although you have absolutely disregarded my plaintive appeals for correspondence . . . here goes again. *Signed:* R. L. S. *4 pp. Partly published in LFF, Vol. 1, pp. 148–149, where 30 lines of the autograph are omitted. Stevenson mentions working on a story,* A Vendetta of the West, *which has not been published. About Fanny's prospective divorce and marriage to him he writes:* By or before the end of January, there is some chance of all being well, in the fullest sense and the most legitimate.

3041

[*October, 1879. Monterey*]. My dear Colvin, after I had written the enclosed to Henley, I remembered he had changed, so send on all to you. *Signed:* R. L. S. *2 pp. Unpublished.*

3042

[*December, 1879. Monterey*]. Today, my dear Colvin, I send you the first part of the Amateur Emigrant. *Signed:* R. L. S. *3 pp. Partly published in LFF, Vol. 1, pp. 157–158, where 24 lines of the autograph are omitted. Stevenson writes much about* The Amateur Emigrant *and the leaflet,* Padre Dos Reales. *He states:* With my parents, all looks dead black.

3043

[*December, 1879. Monterey*]. My dear Colvin, I have been down with pleurisy but now convalesce. *Signed:* R. L. S. *4 pp. Partly published in* The Letters, *1911, Vol. 1, pp. 260–262, where about 32 lines of the autograph are omitted. Stevenson writes much about stories on which he has been at work and the possibility of getting money for them.*

3044

Dec 26th [*1879*]. 608 Bush Street San Francisco. My dear Colvin, I am now writing to you in a café waiting for some music to begin. *Signed:* R. L. S. *4 pp. Partly published in LFF, Vol. 1, pp. 160–161, where about 30 lines of the autograph are omitted. Stevenson is worried about his finances. Fanny's divorced husband has lost his job, and Stevenson must pay the living expenses of Fanny and himself living separately.*

3045

[*Winter 1879–1880. San Francisco*]. My dear Colvin, Your letter more than undoes all that you wrote before. *Signed twice:* R. L. S. *4 pp. Unpublished. Stevenson writes:* Nobody . . . would write for advice at six weeks post . . . brief or even detailed advice by letter would not help, could it come tomorrow; and long before it ever can come, Fate and Fortune or my own act shall have cut the knot.

3046

[*January 18, 1880*]. 608 Bush Street San Francisco. Cal. My dear Colvin, This is a circular letter to tell my estate fully. *Signed:* R. L. S. *8 pp. Partly published in LFF, Vol. 1, pp. 162–164, where about 20 lines of the autograph are omitted. A detailed account of Stevenson's daily life in San Francisco.*

3047

Jan 23rd [*1880*]. 608 Bush Street San Francisco. My dear Colvin, Your telegram has puzzled me greatly. What hundred pounds? *Signed:* Robert Louis Stevenson. *4 pp. Unpublished. Stevenson conjectures that £100 may be on the way from Colvin, and finishes his letter with the words:* I would honestly prefer a letter to money, Colvin.

3048

[*January, 1880*]. 608 Bush Street San Francisco Cal. My dear Colvin, I received this morning your long letter from Paris. *Signed:* R. L. S. *4 pp. Partly published in LFF, Vol. 1, pp. 165–167, where about 26 lines of the autograph are omitted. Colvin has written Stevenson that* The Amateur Emigrant *is dull. Stevenson writes much about this and says that he will write no more books of travel. He states that Fanny and he meet and dine somewhere about twice a week.*

3049

[*February, 1880*]. 608 Bush St. S. F. Cal. My dear Colvin, I received a very nice letter from you with two inclosures. *Signed twice: R. L. S. 7 pp. Partly published in* The Letters, *1911, Vol. 1, pp. 281–283, where about 51 lines of the autograph are omitted. Colvin has accused Stevenson of being vague. Stevenson answers that until he is sure of what is going to happen to him he will continue to be uncommunicative. Stevenson writes words to be engraved on his tomb, including the lines:* Home is the sailor, home from sea, and the hunter home from the hill. *This is the earliest record of any portion of Stevenson's poem,* Requiem.

3050

[*March, 1880*]. 608 Bush St. S. F. Cal. My dear Colvin, It occurs to me that as I entered into a contract to write cheerfully, you may receive my comfortable intelligence cum grano. *Signed: R. L. S. 3 pp. Partly published in LFF, Vol. 1, p. 169, where 20 lines of the autograph are omitted. Stevenson writes that Fanny is well and happy. He has been* cast down *by the fatal illness of his landlord's and landlady's four year old child.*

3051

[*Spring, 1880. San Francisco*]. Dear Colvin, When I looked over the enclosed it looked unfriendly, flat and generally unsuited to my good news. *Signed: R. L. S. 1 p. Unpublished. Having come through a physical and moral tempest, Stevenson feels that he may have neglected Colvin and other friends.*

3052

[*April, 1880*]. P. O. S. F. Cala. My dear Colvin, My dear people telegraphed me in these words: "Count on 250 pounds annually." *Signed: R. L. S. 1 p. Published in LFF, Vol. 1, pp. 171–172, where about 5 lines of the autograph are omitted. As a result of the telegram Stevenson asks Colvin to recover and return to him the manuscript of* The Amateur Emigrant. *Stevenson felt that he was dying before his recent recovery.*

3053

[*May, 1880*]. P. O. S. F. Cal. My dear Colvin, I received your letter and proof today. *Signed: R. L. S. 2 pp. Partly published in LFF, Vol. 2, pp. 172–173, where about 18 lines of the autograph are omitted. Stevenson writes of Colvin's literary ability, of plans to go into the hills after his (R.L.S.'s) marriage, of R.L.S.'s verses which are to be printed by Lloyd Osbourne.*

3054

[*May, 1880. San Francisco, and*] Calistoga, Napa County, Cala. My dear Colvin, It is a long while since I have heard from you. *Signed: R L S. 2 pp. Partly published in LFF, Vol. 1, pp. 174–176, where about 10 lines of the autograph are omitted. Stevenson writes:* I am certainly recovering fast; a married and convalescent being.

3055

[*July, 1880*]. Ben Wyvis Hotel Strathpeffer. My dear Colvin & others, one or two words. We are here. *Signed: R. L. S. 2 pp. Partly published in* The Letters, *1911, Vol. 2, pp. 6–7, where about 12 lines of the autograph are omitted.*

3056

[*November or December, 1880. Davos*]. My dear Colvin, Argument. 1. Here is another from Paul. *Signed: R. L. S. 2 pp. The last 8 lines of this letter are printed in* The Letters, *1911, Vol. 2, p. 14. Preceding this on pp. 13–14 is text purporting to be part of the same letter but different from the a.l.s. here catalogued.*

3057

[*December, 1880. Davos*]. My dear Colvin, The book is to be sold at 3/6; now is 2d enough. *Signed: R. L. S. and F. V de G. S. Unpublished. Stevenson lists the contents of his proposed book on* The Transformation of the Highlands.

3058

[*December, 1880. Davos*]. My dear Colvin, I have a letter from Paul which I enclose. *Signed: R L. S. 4 pp. Approximately the second half of this letter (19 lines) is printed in* The Letters, *1911, Vol. 2, pp. 13–14, preceding 7 printed lines taken from the letter here dated:* [*November or December, 1880*], *as though they were parts of the same letter. Stevenson writes about a proposal from Kegan Paul for cheap editions of Stevenson books published by his firm, and about conversations with John Addington Symonds.*

3059

[*Spring, 1881. Davos*]. My dear Colvin, My health is not just what it should be. *Signed:* R. L. S. *4 pp. Published in LFF, Vol. 1, pp.* 197–199, *where about 5 lines of the autograph are omitted. Stevenson writes about the bad health of Mrs. Sitwell's son, about Carlyle, etc.*

3060

[*April or May, 1881*]. Chez Siron Barbizon par Chailly Seine et Marne. Dear Colvin, I am here at last and feel much better. *Signed:* R. L. S. *1 p. Unpublished.*

3061

[*May 17 and 18, 1881. Paris*]. Professor Colvin, General. Subprofessor Stevenson, lance corporal. My dear Cantabridgians, Greeting: Unless money peters out, we shall leave tomorrow. *Signed:* R. L. S. *2 pp. Unpublished. Stevenson writes about an illness in the night and a doctor's visit at 2 a.m.*

3062

[*June, 1881*]. Kinnaird Cottage Pitlochry Perthshire. My dear S C. Great and glorious news. *Signed:* R. L. S. *6 pp. Mostly in pencil. Partly published in* The Letters, 1911, *Vol. 2, pp.* 33–34, *where about 16 lines of the autograph are omitted. Stevenson writes about his plan to apply for the Chair of History at the University of Edinburgh, and asks Colvin's help. Contains 10 lines of verse, beginning:* Your friend sincere goes forth to war.

3063

[*July, 1881*]. Kinnaird Cottage Pitlochry. My dear Colvin, I do believe I am better mind and body. *Signed:* R. L. S. *4 pp. Partly in pencil. Published in LFF, Vol. 1, pp.* 209–211, *where about 5 lines of the autograph are omitted. Stevenson writes of his current work, principally* The Merry Men, *and of testimonials received in connection with his application for the Chair of History at the University of Edinburgh.*

3064

[*August, 1881. Pitlochry*]. My dear Colvin, This is the first letter I have written this good while. *Signed: R L. S. 8 pp. In pencil. Partly published in LFF, Vol. 1, pp. 213–215, where the text is somewhat rearranged and about 16 lines of the autograph are omitted. Stevenson writes about Colvin's work on Landor, and mentions the progress of some of his own writings.*

3065

[*August, 1881. Braemar*]. My dear Colvin, Hate me as much as you like. *Signed:* Robert Louis Stevenson. *1 p. Unpublished.*

3066

[*December? 1881. Davos*]. My dear Colvin, I have not much news of my wife. *Signed: R L. S. 1 p. Written on stationery of* Hôtel & Pension Buol. *Unpublished.*

3067

[*March, 1882. Davos*]. My dear Colvin, Herewith Moral Emblems, the elephant by Fanny — the rest by me. *Signed: R. L. S. 4 pp. Partly published in the* Skerryvore Edition, Letters, *Vol. 2, pp. 83–84, where 24 lines of the autograph are omitted. Stevenson writes:* I brought home with me from my bad times in America two strains of unsoundness of mind, the first, a perpetual fear that I can do no more work — the second, a perpetual fear that my friends have quarrelled with me. *He devotes 17 lines to a description of Mrs. J. A. Symonds.*

3068

[*March? 1882. Davos*]. Dear Colvin, I have been rioting in glee about your brother [?] *Unsigned. 2 pp. Unpublished. Stevenson mentions his* Talk and Talkers, A Gossip on Romance, Treasure Island, *and Colvin's prospective work on Keats. Contains 15 lines of verse, beginning:* Gem of my native hills.

3069

[*October, 1882*]. Friday. Campagne Defli St Marcel Marseille. So proudly, I date myself, though not yet there. *Signed:* R. L. S. *3 pp. Unpublished. Stevenson describes the house into which he plans to move.*

3070

[*January or February, 1883. Nice*]. My dear Colvin, I am aware I must appear like a kind of lunatic to you. *Signed:* R L. S. *4 pp. Unpublished. Stevenson had sent a telegram and letter to Colvin apparently asking him not to come to see him and Fanny.* I felt so sure that F and I had put an unfair pressure on you.

3071

[*February, 1883*]. Hotel du Petit Louvre M— M— Marseille, aye that's it. My dear Colvin, Yes, you are right, I suppose. *Signed:* Uxorious Billy. *2 pp. Unpublished. Stevenson mentions proof of* The Treasure of Franchard *and work on* nursery verses.

3072

15 Feb. [*1883*]. Hotel du Petit Louvre Cannebiere Marseille. Dear Sir, This is to intimate to you that Mr and Mrs Robert Louis Stevenson were yesterday safely delivered of a Campagne. *Signed:* Brabazon Drum. *3 pp. Partly published in* The Letters, *1911, Vol. 2, pp. 99–100, where about 9 lines of the autograph are omitted. Stevenson tells how he got rid of the Campagne Defli house without having to pay compensation.*

3073

[*May, 1883. Hyères*]. Colvin, The attempt to correspond with you is vain. *Signed:* R. L. S. *2 pp. Published in* The Letters, *1911, Vol. 2, pp. 118–119, where about 3 lines of the autograph are omitted. Contains 6 lines of verse, beginning:* Why am I so penniless. *Stevenson lists 4 proposed titles for the collection eventually called* A Child's Garden of Verses.

3074

Oct 8th 1883. [*Hyères*]. 10,000 Pounds Reward! Whereas Sidney Colvin . . . has vanished . . . *Signed:* R. L. S. *3 pp. Written* on stationery of La Solitude. *Published in* The Letters, *1911, Vol. 2, p. 155, where about 4 lines of the autograph are omitted. Stevenson mentions books and stories on which he is working.*

3075

[*November, 1883. Hyères*]. My dear Colvin, I have been bad, but as you were worse, I feel no shame. *Signed:* R. L. S. *4 pp. Written on stationery of* La Solitude. *Partly published in LFF, Vol. 1, pp. 296–297, where about 20 lines of the autograph are omitted. Stevenson writes an epitaph for his remains to be buried in the garden of* La Solitude.

3076

9th March 1884. [*Hyères*]. My dear S. C. You will already have received a not very sane note from me. *Signed:* R. L. S. *8 pp. Written on stationery of* La Solitude. *Published in LFF, Vol. 1, pp. 306–308, where about 14 lines of the autograph are omitted. Stevenson writes about his work on* Prince Otto, *and about reading St. Augustine, Tacitus, Barbey d'Aurevilly.*

3077

[*June, 1884. Marseille*]. Dear S. C. Are these four in time? No odds about order. *Signed:* R. L. S. *2 pp. Partly published in* The Letters, *1911, Vol. 2, pp. 187–188, where about 7 lines of the autograph are omitted. Stevenson writes about poems in* A Child's Garden of Verses, *and books to be sent him.*

3078

[*July, 1884. Marseille*]. Dear S. C. I send herewith a kind of postscript to the *Child's Garden. Signed:* R. L. S. *3 pp. In pencil. Written on stationery of* La Solitude. *Unpublished.*

3079

[*July, 1884. Royat*]. My dear Colvin, I do begin to pine amain for the *Child's Garden. Signed:* J. Knox Crawford. *4 pp. In pencil. Unpublished. Deacon Brodie was to be performed in London early in July. Stevenson expresses the wish that it might succeed and get him out of his* bankruptcy.

3080

[*July, 1884. Royat*]. Dear S. C. Books received with great thanks. *Signed:* R L. S. *4 pp. Written on stationery of* La Solitude. *Published in* The Letters, *1911, Vol. 2, pp.* 188–189, *where about 3 lines of the autograph are omitted. Stevenson writes about* Deacon Brodie.

3081

[*July, 1884. Royat*]. Many daughters have done virtuously but thou excellest them all. *Signed:* Stevenson. *8 pp. In pencil. Partly published in LFF, Vol. 1, p. 321, where about 20 lines of the autograph are omitted. Stevenson writes about* Defoe, *and* Treasure Island.

3082

[*July, 1884. Royat*]. I the bloody-minded one acknowledge receipt of yours. *Signed:* Don Sanguine Spittle. *8 pp. Partly published in LFF, Vol. 1, pp.* 321–322, *where it is recorded as a continuation of the letter beginning:* Many daughters have done virtuously, *and about 43 lines of the autograph are omitted. Stevenson refers to himself as a* blind, bloodspitting, somnolent, superannuated son of a bedpost, rotten-ripe. *He compares his readers with those of Colvin.*

3083

[*July, 1884? Royat*]. come to London, stay perhaps at Richmond or your place at Sevenoaks. *Signed:* R. L. S. *Last 3 pp. of letter. Written on stationery of* La Solitude. *Unpublished.*

3084

[*November, 1884. Bournemouth*]. Dear Colvin, 1° Sorry to hear you are not better. 2° I am fair enough in my little way. *Signed:* R. L. S. *2 pp. 6 lines of this 31-line letter are printed in Edith B. Tranter.* First Editions and Autograph Manuscripts of American and English Authors . . . Auction Sale . . . *New York, 1952, p. 88. Stevenson writes:* The Body Snatcher is a thing I long ago condemned as an offence against good manners.

3085

Jan 4th 1885. Bonallie Tower Branksome Park Bournemouth. Dear S. C. I am on my feet again and getting on my boots to do the Iron Duke. *Signed: R. L. Shorthouse. 3 pp. Published in LFF, Vol. 1, pp. 346–347. Stevenson asks Colvin to send him certain books.*

3086

[January, 1885. Bonallie Tower, Bournemouth]. Dear S. C. I have addressed a letter to the G. O. M. a propos of Villainton *[i.e. Wellington]. Signed: R. L. S. 4 pp. Partly published in LFF, Vol. 1, pp. 348–349, where 8 lines of the autograph are omitted. All but one of these 8 lines are printed in* The Letters, *1911, Vol. 2, p. 226. Stevenson writes about the Duke of Wellington and information he thinks might be obtained about him.*

3087

[February, 1885. Bonallie Tower, Bournemouth]. My dear Colvin, You are indeed a backward correspondent. *Signed: R. L. S. 4 pp. Published in LFF, Vol. 1, pp. 349–350, where about 2 lines of the autograph are omitted. About Gordon's abandonment in the Soudan, and about writings by Colvin.*

3088

[1885. Bournemouth]. Dear S. C. and damn your eyes for not coming! *Signed: R. L. S. 1 p. Published in facsimile in Gertrude Hills.* Robert Louis Stevenson's Handwriting, *New York, 1940, p. 28. A forgery of the text of this letter, in 2 pp., is also reproduced in Mrs. Hills's book.*

3089

[1886. Bournemouth]. My dear S. C. I am better. We look forward to seeing you: but have no room. *Signed: R. L. S. 1 p. Unpublished.*

3090

[1886. Bournemouth]. My dear Colvin, All I can say is that next week and on, I am ready for Mrs Jenkin. *Signed: R. L. McGuckin. (minister of the Gospel.) 2 pp. Unpublished.*

3091

[*March 17, 1886. Bournemouth*]. My dear Colvin My wife says she'll copy my letter. *Signed:* R. L. S. *4 pp. Partly published in* The Letters, *1911, Vol. 2, pp. 279–280, where 27 lines of the autograph are omitted. Stevenson writes about his father and about Vergil's* Aeneid.

3092

[*Cir. June 10, 1886. Bournemouth*]. My dear Colvin, I am in bed again — bloodie jackery and be damned to it. *Signed:* R. L. S., A repentant Dankist, John Marchmont Sepulchre, William Ring (of Janes), *and* Mathieu Pierre Devis de la Banette. *4 pp. Partly published in* The Letters, *1911, Vol. 2, pp. 239–240, where about 16 lines of the autograph are omitted. Stevenson expresses a low opinion of his story titled* The Travelling Companion.

3093

[*Summer, 1886. Bournemouth*]. Dear Custodian, I sent a letter to B. D Colvangle Esq, containing a blank cheque. *Signed:* The Beroomed Stevenson. *3 pp. Partly published in Stevenson's* Collected Poems Edited . . . *by Janet Adam Smith, 1950, pp. 354 and 548, where 16 lines of the autograph are omitted. Stevenson writes:* Je ne vis que pour le piano. *Contains 4 lines of verse, beginning:* Where is now the Père Martini?

3094

Dec 14 [*1886. Bournemouth*]. My dear Colvin, This is first rate of you, the Lord love you for it! *Signed:* The Real Mackay. *4 pp. Partly published in LFF, Vol. 2, p. 47, where 24 lines of the autograph are omitted. Stevenson writes of his father, Lloyd Osbourne, and mentions his writing* The Misadventures of John Nicholson *and Scottish verse.*

3095

[*1886 or 1887. Bournemouth*]. My dear S. C. I send two papers of Jenkin's: one "Concerning Truth" . . . the other, on George Eliot's Life. *Signed:* R. L. S. *1 p. Unpublished. Stevenson thinks the first of these papers should be printed. Fleeming Jenkin died June 12, 1885.*

3096

[*1886 or 1887. Bournemouth*]. Dear Colvin, Why do we hear nothing? *Signed:* Bloody Mary. *2 pp. Unpublished. Stevenson writes:* I have lost my spectacles, and write vaguely and with itching eyeballs.

3097

[*Winter, 1886–1887. Bournemouth*]. My dear Colvin, Yours, and interesting literature, to hand. *Signed:* R L. S. *2 pp. Unpublished. Stevenson writes that his father is reading Dickens.*

3098

[*Spring, 1887. Bournemouth*]. My dear Colvin, I read Huxley and a lot with great interest. *Signed:* R. L. S. *3 pp. Published in* The Letters, *1911, Vol. 2, pp. 312–313, where about 7 lines of the autograph are omitted. Stevenson discusses the writings of Thomas Huxley and Cotter Morison.*

3099

[*Spring, 1887. Bournemouth*]. Dear Colvin, Herewith a little stave, which seems to me funny. *Signed:* Andrew Crossnyloof. Gallio. Julius Caesar. Archbishop Strupe. My Uncle Toby and The Man in the Moon. *2 pp. Unpublished. Stevenson writes:* There is . . . a touch of the rabbi . . . in you. Scrub it out, and come to the heaven of the unbeliever along with me.

3100

[*August, 1887. Bournemouth*]. My dear Colvin, Owing to change of weather, it was decided I should stay here till Saturday. *Signed:* R. L. S. *2 pp. Unpublished. Stevenson* longs after two days of solitude.

3101

Aug. 19th. 1887. Skerryvore [*Bournemouth*]. My dear Colvin, I wanted to write to you again today. *Signed:* R. L. S. *4 pp. Unpublished. Written on the last evening in Stevenson's home. He sailed from London on August 21, never to return to England. There had apparently been some unpleasantness with Colvin.* I wish we could have left with a godspeed; but if that may not be, I know you will forgive us before long.

3102

this 22nd day of August [1887]. H. M. S. Vulgarium [i.e. S. S. Ludgate Hill] Off Havre de Grace. Sir, The weather has been hitherto inimitable. *Signed:* Bold Bob Boltsprit, *and* R. L. S. *3 pp. Partly published in LFF, Vol. 2, pp. 62–63, where 7 lines of the autograph are omitted.*

3103

[*September, 1887*]. Newport. R. I. U. S A. My dear Colvin, So long it went excellent well, and I had a time I am glad to have had. *Signed:* R L S. *3 pp. In pencil. Partly published in LFF, Vol. 2, pp. 63–64, where 11 lines of the autograph are omitted. Stevenson describes his voyage to America and his reception there.*

3104

[*December 24, 1887. Saranac Lake*]. My dear Colvin, Well, I say naught of the homunculus. *Signed:* R L S. *6 pp. Written on black-bordered stationery. Published in LFF, Vol. 2, pp. 87–88, where about 8 lines of the autograph are omitted. Stevenson writes about his work on* The Master of Ballantrae.

3105

[*March, 1888. Saranac Lake*]. My dear Colvin, Fanny has been very unwell. *Signed:* R. L. S. *4 pp. Written on black-bordered stationery. Published in LFF, Vol. 2, pp. 96–97, where about 2 lines of the autograph are omitted. Stevenson writes about the cold weather, his own good health and the bad health of others.*

3106

[*March, 1888. Saranac Lake*]. My dear Colvin, I was delighted to continue to hear from you without further developments. *Signed:* Robert Louis Stevenson. *4 pp. Written on black-bordered stationery. Unpublished. Stevenson wants to present Colvin with a year's treatment by a certain medical man. He mentions his being proposed and seconded by Colvin and Henry James for membership in the Athenaeum.*

3107

April 9th!! 1888 [*Saranac Lake*]. My dear Colvin, I have been long without writing to you, but I am not to blame. *Signed: Andrew Jackson. 4 pp. Written on black-bordered stationery. Published in LFF, Vol. 2, pp. 103–104, where one line of the autograph is omitted. Stevenson writes about a mutiny novel, never published, on which he and Lloyd Osbourne were at work.*

3108

[*May, 1888. Manasquan*]. My dear Colvin, This is almost a farewell letter. I leave in five days for San Francisco. *Signed: R. L. S. 2 pp. Unpublished. Stevenson writes:* For heaven's sake, don't think my letters cold or short; I am doing the best I can.

3109

[*Cir. March, 1890. Sydney*]. My ever dear Colvin, I was over-joyed to get your long letter, and see you write so much like yourself. *Unsigned. 2 pp. Unpublished.*

3110

[*August, 1890. Sydney*]. My ever dear Colvin, I have just arrived from New Caledonia, following Fanny & Lloyd who continued on in the Janet Nicoll and were very nearly lost on the Australian Coast. *Unsigned. 13 pp. Written on stationery of the* Union Club, Sydney. *Unpublished. Stevenson defends his remaining in the South Seas against Colvin's wishes. He writes:* Since my dear wild noble father died, no head on earth, and not my wife's, is more precious to my thought than yours. *Mrs. R.L.S. has written an addition to this letter.*

3111

[*October 8, 1892. Vailima*]. to his house to be arrested. On Oct 1st finding that I was engaged to give a Sunday school address . . . *Unsigned. 6 pp. Portion of a letter beginning with p. numbered: 3. This portion of the letter is in the hand of Isobel Strong except for the last 3 lines which are in Stevenson's hand. Contains plan of room and drawing of Samoan girl. Partly published in VL, Vol. 2, pp. 70–74, where about 109 lines of this*

portion of the autograph are omitted. Stevenson writes of pros-
pective litigation involving Messrs. Moors, Claxton and Car-
ruthers; and about a party at Vailima.

3112

October 28th 1892. Nov. 2nd Sunday Nov 6th Vailima. My dear
Colvin — This is very late to begin the monthly budget. *Un-*
signed. 9 pp. Parts of 2 of the pp. have been cut away. Most
of the letter is in the hand of Isobel Strong; most of 1 p. is in
Stevenson's hand. Partly published in VL, Vol. 2, pp. [75]–
87, where about 99 lines of this portion of the autograph are
omitted. In VL, Vol. 2, pp. 78–81 are 80 printed lines, recording
a portion of this letter which is missing in the Beinecke Collec-
tion. Stevenson writes of a hearing in a mission in Apia in which
he was cross-examined for an hour and a half; a dinner and a
reading by R. L. S. at Bazett M. Haggard's house; and a stolen
pig. Isobel Strong is the author of 18 lines included in this
letter.

3113

Dec 4th [1892]. Sunday. [Vailima]. 3rd start. But now more
humbly and with the aid of an Amanuensis. *Unsigned. 4 pp. of*
a letter begun December 1 and ended December 5. This por-
tion of the letter is in the hand of Isobel Strong. The first 4
lines of it are printed in VL, Vol. 2, p. 90. The remaining 117
lines are unpublished. Stevenson writes about difficulties with
one Bierman, German Consul at Samoa, and the possibility of
his (Stevenson's) being deported.

3114

April 21st April 22 [*1893. Vailima*]. Well, Fanny *is* really better.
Unsigned. 1 p. Unpublished. In a letter to Colvin printed in
VL, Vol. 2, p. 121, Stevenson writes under date of April 16:
Several pages of this letter destroyed as beneath scorn. *The*
autograph here described is apparently one of the pp. that
Stevenson believed to have been destroyed.

3115

[*November, 1893. Vailima*]. My dear Colvin Home again; and
found all well, thank God. *Unsigned. 1 p. Partly published in*

VL, *Vol. 2, pp. 191–192, where about 8 lines of the autograph are omitted. Stevenson writes that Mrs. R. L. S. has Bright's disease.*

3116

Jan 29th 94. Vailima. My dear Colvin I had fully intended . . . to fob you off with the meanest possible letter this month. *Unsigned. First 8 pp. of letter, in the hand of Isobel Strong. Partly published in* VL, *Vol. 2, pp. [210]–212, where about 67 lines of this part of the autograph are omitted. Stevenson writes about the threat of war in Samoa.*

3117

May 8th 1891. Vailima. Dear Sir. I regret extremely to find Mr Hay proceeding in this course. *Signed:* Robert Louis Stevenson, *and* R. L. S. *3 pp. Published in the* South Seas Edition, Letters, *Vol. 3, pp. 269–270. Stevenson writes about a discharged employee of his, who is making unwarranted claims.*

3118

[*1894. Vailima*]. Dear Mr Crockett, Come, I was very angry with you, but I have not the heart to be longer. *Signed:* R. L. Stevenson. *3 pp. At top of p. 1:* Private and confidential. *6 lines of this 40-line letter are published in Edith B. Tranter.* First Editions and Autograph Manuscripts of American and English Authors . . . Auction Sale . . . *New York, 1952, p. 82. Stevenson writes of a reading public of 10,000 persons who like literature, and of 100,000* who like ink upon paper if it's interesting.

R.L.S. TO THOMAS B. CUSACK-SMITH

3119
Oct 18th 189[2. *Vailima*]. Sir, I trust you will excuse me if I intrude upon you certain considerations. *Unsigned. 4 pp. This is apparently a copy of the letter which was retained by Stevenson. Unpublished. He asks:* Whether, the [*Samoan*] government being bound to account to the ratepayers any legal duty to pay taxes can be held to survive for British subjects.

3120
May 22 1893. [*Samoa*]. Dear Mr Cusack Smith I hear that you have been complaining of advice given by me to Mataafa. *Signed:* Robert Louis Stevenson. *1 p. This is a copy in the hand of Graham Balfour, and is preceded on the same p. by a* Memorandum of a Conversation with H B M Consul T. B. Cusack-Smith, *also in Balfour's hand. Unpublished.*

3121
[*1893 or 1894. Vailima*]. Dear Sir, In the present dead-lock of Samoan affairs it has occurred to us that you may be prepared to welcome and consider any practical proposal tending to lead to peace. *Unsigned. 3 pp. Draft, in the hand of Isobel Strong. Unpublished.*

3122
June 9th '94. Vailima. Sir: I beg to lay before you the following considerations in favour of the release of the Mataafa prisoners now in Mulinuu jail. *Unsigned. 4 pp. A draft, partly in Stevenson's hand and partly in that of Isobel Strong. Unpublished.*

3123

[June, 1887. Edinburgh]. My dear Mr Dick, Many thanks for your letter and suggestions. *Signed:* Robert Louis Stevenson. *2 pp. On black-bordered stationery. Unpublished. Written soon after the death of R.L.S.'s father to the latter's chief clerk.*

3124

July 12th [*1886*]. Skerryvore [*Bournemouth*]. Dear Dr Dobell, The Gods being more long suffering, (having known more of verses and versifiers than any mere mortal) I have addressed your patron rather than yourself. *Signed:* Robert Louis Stevenson. *3 pp. On p. 2 are 6 lines of verse by and in the hand of Dr. Horace Dobell, beginning:* Silent and grand on Skerrivore[*sic*]. *On p. 3 are 5 lines of verse written in reply by R. L. S., beginning:* Hail, rare Apollo! and what thanks are due. *Signed:* R. L. S. *Partly published in* Catalogue no. 714 *issued by Bernard Quaritch Ltd., where about 5 lines of the letter proper and the verses are omitted.*

3125

[*1884?*]. Skerryvore Bournemouth. Dear Sir, I loathe inter- viewing, and I live as you see at the end of the world. *Signed:* Robert Louis Stevenson. *1 p. A few lines of this letter are printed in C. Gerhardt & Co.* Catalogue No. 47 . . . *New York,* [*1915*], *p. 17, lot 82. Stevenson consents to an interview under condi- tions.*

3126

[*Spring, 1884. Hyères*]. My dear Dowson This is an excellent hearing. "What are the principle[*sic*] characteristics of Mr Stevenson?" At present to be ill. *Signed:* Robert Louis Stevenson. *3 pp. In pencil. Written on stationery of* La Solitude. *Unpublished. To the father of Ernest Dowson.*

R.L.S. TO MRS. EHRICH

3127

[1887 or 1888. Saranac Lake]. Dear Mrs Ehrich, I am in bed and in the least gallant and the least grateful frame of mind conceivable. *Signed:* Robert Louis Stevenson. *1 p. Facsimile of the original in the Stevenson Society, Saranac Lake, N.Y. Published in Gertrude Hills.* Robert Louis Stevenson's Handwriting, *New York, 1940, p. 30. Stevenson thanks Mrs. Ehrich for cakes.*

R.L.S. TO MR. AND MRS. CHARLES S. FAIRCHILD

3128

[*September 21, 1887. New York*]. My dear Mrs Fairchild My dear Fairchild My wife is incapable of the slightest exercise of any human art. *Signed: Robert Louis Stevenson. 2 pp. Written on stationery of Hotel St. Stephen, New York. With addressed envelope and mounted stamp. Unpublished. A letter of thanks written within a few days of the Stevensons' departure from the Fairchild home in Newport.*

3129

[*September 25, 1887. New York*]. My dear Mrs. Fairchild, Honour Bright, I am not Julian Hawthorne. *Signed: Robert Louis Stevenson, and R. L. S. 4 pp. With addressed envelope and mounted stamp. Unpublished. Stevenson apologizes for his failure to pay a chemist's and another bill during his stay at the Fairchilds' home, and sends a check for $17.*

3130

[*September, 1887. New York*]. Bogue. Acer. impiger. infelix . . . *Signed: R. L. S. 2 pp. Unpublished. Stevenson sends Mrs. Fairchild the wording on the memorial plaque to his dog, Bogue. Part of this letter is perhaps missing. RLS to Mrs. Fairchild.*

3131

[*October, 1887*]. Post Office Saranac Lake Adirondacks N. Y. My dear Fairchild, I do not live in the Post Office; that is only my address. *Signed: Robert Louis Stevenson, and twice: R. L. S. 3 pp. On black-bordered stationery. Published in The Letters, 1911, Vol. 3, pp. 14–15. Stevenson asks Fairchild to send him some grapes.*

3132

[*October, 1887. Saranac Lake*]. My dear Mrs Fairchild, My wife cannot sleep at nights, nor yet can she pluck up courage to write to you herself. *Signature and one or two lines of the letter cut away. 1 p. On black-bordered stationery. Unpublished.*

3133

[*November, 1887. Saranac Lake*]. My dear Fairchild, I trust you will have received ere this a despatch which I sent to the Plattsburgh hotel keeper to forward. *Signed:* R. L. S. *2 pp. On black-bordered stationery. Unpublished. Stevenson writes of an expected visit to be made by Fairchild and of transportation difficulties.*

3134

[*November, 1887. Saranac Lake*]. My dear Fairchild, We have rooms (after a fashion) for you. *Signed:* Robert Louis Stevenson. *2 pp. Unpublished. Stevenson attempts to give information about transportation to Saranac in connection with the expected visit.*

3135

21st Dec [*1887. Saranac Lake*]. My dear Fairchild, What is your news? *Signed:* R. L. S. *2 pp. On black-bordered stationery. Unpublished. Stevenson mentions Lloyd Osbourne's having just returned from a visit to the Fairchilds. Osbourne is believed to have returned on December 25, so Stevenson has apparently misdated the letter. Stevenson refers to Fairchild's clandestine departure, so the latter evidently got to Saranac Lake.*

3136

[*September, 1890. Sydney*]. My dear Mrs Fairchild, I began a letter to you on board the Janet Nicoll on my last cruise. *Signed:* The Bohemian Crank Robert Louis Stevenson. *8 pp. Written on stationery of the* Union Club, Sydney. *Partly published in LFF, Vol. 2, pp. 200–201, where about 53 lines of the autograph are omitted. Partly published in* The Letters, 1911, *Vol. 3, pp. 182–184, where about 33 lines of the autograph are omitted. Stevenson writes of William Dean Howells's having come with the Fairchilds' daughter to the Hotel St. Stephen, New York, in September, 1887, to call on him. R.L.S. refused to see them and apologizes now for his rudeness to Miss Fairchild. He further writes:* I regret also my letter to Dr Hyde, *i.e. the open letter to the Rev. C. M. Hyde about Father Damien.*

3137

[*March, 1892. Vailima*]. My dear Mrs Fairchild, I am guilty in your sight, but my affairs besiege me. *Signed:* Robert Louis Stevenson. *8 pp. Published in LFF, Vol. 2, pp. 249–252. Stevenson writes about the nature of his life in Samoa. The Stevensons were expecting a visit from the Kiplings which did not materialize.*

3138

[*August, 1892. Vailima*]. My dear Mrs. Fairchild, Thank you a thousand times for your letter. *Signed:* R.L.Stevenson. *4 pp. Published in LFF, Vol. 2, pp. 262–264. Stevenson discusses the younger generation.*

3139

[*1893. Vailima*]. My dear Mrs. Fairchild — From the midst of war I send you the enclosed little note of peace to Howells. *Signed:* R. L. S. *2 pp. The letter is in the hand of Isobel Strong, signed by Stevenson. Unpublished.*

3140

Nov 22nd 1883. La Solitude Hyères. Var. Dear Miss Ferrier, Many thanks for the photograph. *Signed:* Robert Louis Stevenson. *4 pp. Published in LFF, Vol. 1, pp. 299–300, where 5 lines of the autograph are omitted. Stevenson records some of his reminiscences of Miss Ferrier's brother, James Walter Ferrier, who died in the preceding September.*

3141

[March 22, 1884. Hyères]. My dear Miss Ferrier, Are you really going to fail us? *Signed:* Robert Louis Stevenson. *3 pp. Written on stationery of* La Solitude. *With addressed envelope and mounted stamp. Published in LFF, Vol. 1, pp. 313–314. Stevenson urges Miss Ferrier to visit them at* La Solitude.

3142

[October, 1884. Bournemouth]. My dear Coggie, You are the sweetest of creatures. *Signed:* The Unrepentant Thief, *and* R. L. S. *4 pp. Written in pencil, on stationery of* La Solitude. *Published in Maggs Bros.* A Selection of Books [etc.] . . . Five Hundredth Catalogue . . . *1928, p. 302, where 12 lines of the autograph are omitted. Stevenson writes of his bad health, and mentions working on an answer to Henry James's* The Art of Fiction.

3143

Nov 12th *[1884].* Bonallie Towers Branksome Park Bournemouth. My dear Coggie, Many thanks for the two photos which now decorate my room. *Signed:* R. L. S. *3 pp. Published in LFF, Vol. 1, pp. 338–339, where about 8 lines of the autograph are omitted. The first 2 pp. of this letter are reproduced in facsimile in Maggs Bros. catalogue no. 565, Autumn, 1931, facing p. 111. Partly in Scottish dialect.*

3144

[December, 1884. Bournemouth]. My dear Coggie, We are very much distressed to hear of this which has befallen your family. *Signed:* R. L. Stevenson. *3 pp. Published in LFF, Vol. 1, pp.*

340–341, *where about 2 lines of the autograph are omitted. Stevenson writes of the death of Miss Ferrier's brother-in-law, Sir Alexander Grant.*

3145

[*April, 1888. Saranac Lake*]. My dearest Coggie, I wish I could find the letter I began to you some time ago when I was ill. *Signed:* Robert Louis Stevenson. *6 pp. On black-bordered stationery. Published in LFF, Vol. 2, pp. 101–103, where about 9 lines of the autograph are omitted. 2 pp. of this letter are printed in facsimile in Maggs Bros.* A Selection of Books [*etc.*] . . . Five Hundredth Catalogue . . . *1928, facing p. 302. Stevenson writes about the unpleasant weather at Saranac, and his hope to make a cruise in a yacht.*

3146

[*1872? Edinburgh*]. know that the Comptist club are at work on a complete edition of Heine. *Signed:* Louis Stevenson. *Last 4 pp. of letter. To J. W. Ferrier? Written on stationery of 17 Heriot Row. Unpublished. Stevenson writes about Heine, Spencer and the Speculative Society.*

3147

Nov. 23rd 1872. Sat. [*Edinburgh*]. My dear Ferrier, Our intentions must have been set close to each other in the infernal mosaic. *First 8 pp. of letter; the portion containing Stevenson's signature, if any, is missing. Written on stationery of 17 Heriot Row. Unpublished. Stevenson writes of his visit to Germany in the preceding summer, of a new Edinburgh suburb, of Ferrier's work on Heine, etc.*

3148

September 24th [*1874*]. Thursday. 17 Heriot Row [*Edinburgh*]. My dear Ferrier Call me all the beasts of the Apocalypse. *Signed:* R L. Stevenson. *6 pp. Unpublished. Stevenson mentions books and papers he wants to write.*

3149

April 8th [*1880*]. P. O. San Francisco. My dear Ferrier, Many thanks for your letter. *Signed:* R. L. S. *1 p. Published in* The Letters, *1911, Vol. 1, pp. 284–285. Stevenson writes of a recent illness in which he believed he nearly died.*

3150

[*Postmarked:* Nov 20 1887. Saranac Lake]. Dear Mr Gilder, We have in vain ordered some copies of the Critic here. *Signed:* Robert Louis Stevenson. *1 p. On black-bordered stationery. With addressed envelope and mounted stamp. Unpublished.*

3151

March 1st 1888. Saranac Lake. Dear Mr Gilder, I understand you dined with my wife at St Gaudens's. *Signed:* Robert Louis Stevenson, *and* R. L. S. *3 pp. On black-bordered stationery. Unpublished. Stevenson asks for the name and address of a maker of light spectacles.*

3152

[*April 1 or 2, 1888. Saranac Lake*]. Dear Mr. Gilder, I must write and thank you for the verses. *Signed:* Robert Louis Stevenson, *and* R. L. S. *3 pp. On black-bordered stationery. Unpublished.*

3153

[*1879? Edinburgh*]. My dear Gosse, I have been sharply ill again. *Unsigned. 1 p. Contains drawing of mountain scenery by R. L. S. On stationery of* 17 Heriot Row. *Unpublished. Contains 7 lines of verse, beginning:* And still to follow after hope.

3154

[*December 6, 1880*]. Hotel Belvedere Davos Platz. Switzerland. My dear Weg, I have many letters that I ought to write in preference to this. *Signed: R. L. S. 2 pp. Published in LFF, Vol. 1, pp. 188–189. Stevenson makes suggestions for Gosse's collection of* English Odes.

3155

[*Postmarked:* Ju 24 81]. Kinnaird Cottage Pitlochry Perthshire. My dear Gosse, I wonder if I misdirected my last to you. *Signed:* Robert Louis Stevenson. *2 pp. At top of p. 1:* Private. *With front of addressed envelope and mounted stamp. Published in LFF, Vol. 1, pp. 206–207. Stevenson asks Gosse to write a testimonial for him in connection with his application for the Chair of History at the University of Edinburgh.*

3156

[*Summer, 1883. Hyères*]. My dear Gosse, I have now leisurely read your volume. *Signed: R. L. S. 4 pp. Written on stationery of* La Solitude. *Published in LFF, Vol. 1, pp. 278–279, where 10 lines of the autograph are omitted. Stevenson expresses his appreciation of Gosse's* Seventeenth Century Studies.

3157

[*May 29, 1884. Hyères*]. From my bed. Dear Gosse, The news of the Professorate found me in the article of — well, heads or tails. *Signed: R. L. S. 4 pp. Partly in pencil. With addressed envelope and mounted stamp. Published in LFF, Vol. 1, p. 319. Stevenson was at this time recovering from a dangerous illness. He complimented Gosse on his appointment as Clark Reader in English Literature at Trinity College, Cambridge.*

3158

[*March 23, 1886. Bournemouth*]. My dear Gosse   Many thanks.
I am coming to town for my father's sake this trip. *Signed three
times:* R. L. S. *1 p. With addressed envelope and mounted
stamp. Unpublished.*

3159

March 31st 1887. Skerryvore Bournemouth. Sirs   I have to acknowledge your cheque for twenty pounds (£20) which I forwarded today to Charles Scribner's Sons, to whom I believe the reparation is more justly due than to myself. *Signed:* Robert Louis Stevenson, *and* R. L. S. *1 p. The letter is in Stevenson's hand, marked* Copy *at top. Unpublished. Stevenson writes in a postscript:* I shall place our brief correspondence at the disposal of the editor of the Times. *The £20 is in payment for Harpers' pirated edition of* The Merry Men and other Tales and Fables, Treasure Island, Dr. Jekyll and Mr. Hyde, *and* Kidnapped.

3160

Jan 27th 1886. Skerryvore Bournemouth. Dear Mr Henderson, I inclose a statement of how I stand with "Kidnapped." *Signed:* Robert Louis Stevenson, *and* R. L. S. *3 pp. Partly published in Sotheby & Co.* Catalogue of Valuable Printed Books [&c.] . . . Sold . . . 22nd of June, 1953, *London, 1953, p. 14, where about 27 lines of the autograph are omitted. Stevenson discusses with the editor of* Young Folks Paper *various matters connected with the publication of* Kidnapped.

3161

[*Autumn, 1878. Edinburgh*]. My dear Henley, Bosh about Bowles. He doesn't like the book and says so, not unkindly. *Signed:* R. L. S. *2 pp. Written on stationery of* 17 Heriot Row. *Published in the* Skerryvore Edition, Letters, Vol. 1, pp. 344–345. *Thomas Gibson Bowles dislikes* An Inland Voyage. *Stevenson asks Henley to spell his name* Louis, *not* Lewis.

3162

[*August 17, 1879. New York*]. Dear lad, I have passed the salt sea with comparative impunity, having only lost a stone and got the itch. *Signed:* R. L. S. *2 pp. Unpublished.*

3163

[*Late summer, 1881*]. Castleton of Braemar. My dear Henley, I believe sir that your boasted penetration halts. *Signed:* Peter Baigrey. S. J., *and with 4 other fictitious names. 3 pp. Unpublished. Stevenson devotes nearly a page to George Saintsbury.*

3164

[*February? 1883*]. Hotel du Petty Louvre Cannebiere Marseille . . . It's a strange thing, dear lad, that I should never have spoken of the "glass of whiskey." *Signed twice:* R. L. S. *4 pp. Unpublished. Stevenson writes of a play,* Autolycus at Service, *on which he was at work.*

3165

[*1883?*] Marseille. My dear Henley. I have received the magazine but cannot yet do the circket. *Signed:* Paul the Milletist. *3 pp. Unpublished. Stevenson writes about nursery rhymes,* The Silverado Squatters, *and a painting by Millet titled* Labor. *Contains 8 lines of verse, beginning:* I now am a converted man.

3166

[*Spring? 1883*]. Dear Lad, How are you? Such very long silences are in these days alarming. *Unsigned. 2 pp. Unpub-*

lished. Stevenson mentions Penny Whistles, *and writes 14 lines of verse, beginning:* Some were born for care and cumber.

3167

[*May, 1883. Hyères*]. My dear lad, The books came some time since, but I have not had the pluck to answer. *Signed:* an aching, fevered penny-journalist. *4 pp. Contains drawings. Written on stationery of* La Solitude. *Published in LFF, Vol. 1, pp. 271–272, where about 16 lines of the autograph are omitted. Contains 28 lines of verse, titled* A lytle Jape of Tusherie by A Tusher, *beginning:* The pleasant river gushes; *also 4 lines of verse, beginning:* So why should I complain.

3168

[*1883? Hyères*]. My dear Henley, If you come bring Bird's Eye. *Signed:* Robert Louis Stevenson. *4 pp. Written on stationery of* La Solitude. *Unpublished. Stevenson urges Henley to visit him and his wife in Hyères, and sends 10 lines of verse, beginning:* Come then, my Henley, from your isle of rain.

3169

[*September? 1884*]. Highcliff Hotel, Bournemouth. Dear William Ernest Hart, What is the reason of things? The Piratic and obscure Mennel came, interviewed my uncle, and then, without a word, fled. *Signed:* R L S. *4 pp. Written in pencil, on stationery of* La Solitude. *Unpublished.*

[*April, 1887. Bournemouth*]. *See Stevenson's letter to Baxter and Henley. No. 2797.*

3170

[*1887? Bournemouth?*] Dear Henley, Public reading just finished, unprecedented success, Reader in floods of tears. *Signed:* R. L. S. *3 pp. In the hand of Mrs. R. L. S., signed by Stevenson. Unpublished. Stevenson praises a new play of Henley's which he has just read in manuscript* (Mephisto?). *Mrs. R. L. S. has written an addition to this letter.*

3171

[*February, 1890*]. S S. Lübeck at sea between Apia & Sydney. Dear lad, I handed the daughter without one word to my wife. "Henley without his clothes!" cried she. *Signed:* R. L. S. *2 pp. Contains poem, beginning:* The tropics vanish; and meseems that I. *The letter is unpublished. The poem was first published in* The Scots Observer, *April 5, 1890, p. 549.*

3172

Aug 1st [*1892*]. Vailima Plantation Upolu, Samoa. My dear Henley, It is impossible to let your new volume pass in silence. *Signed:* Robert Louis Stevenson, *and* R. L. S. *1 p. Published in* LFF, *Vol. 1, pp. 257–258. Stevenson praises a volume of poetry by Henley, probably* The Song of the Sword and other Verses.

3173

[*N.d., n.p.*] Deer Sir This coms hopping to be in town tomarra as ever was in No 5 Fitzroy his dambible Square. *Signed:* Rob the Ranter. *2 pp. Unpublished.*

3174

Feb. 25th 82. Grisons Switzerland. Dear Sir, Let me thank you for your kind letter at once, and then go on to Hazlitt. *Signed:* Robert Louis Stevenson. *3 pp. Written on stationery of* Hôtel & Pension Buol. *About 10 lines of this 47-line letter are printed in Samuel Wyllis Bandler.* Selections from the Library ... Part I ... *New York [1947?], p. 99. Stevenson writes about his proposed work on Hazlitt, in which he expects help from Ireland.*

3175

[*October? 1881*]. My dear Dr Japp, I had just written this afternoon to acknowledge your first. *Signed:* Robert Louis Stevenson. *1 p. Photostat of the original in the Widener Library. Unpublished. Stevenson writes about prospective serial publication of* Treasure Island *in* Young Folks.

3176

[June or July, 1881]. Kinnaird Cottage Pitlochry Perthshire. My dear Jenkin, We think your *Griselda* most excellent. *Signed: R. L. S. 2 pp. Unpublished. Stevenson writes about versification.*

3177

[April? 1882? Paris]. My dear Jenkin, Note received. (I should explain that this is my wife who is writing, but it is I that speak). *Signed: R. L. S. 2 pp. The letter is in the hand of Mrs. R. L. S., signed by Stevenson. Unpublished. Stevenson states:* I have a genius for morality and no talent for it.

3178

[July 25, 1877]. 17 Heriot Row Edinburgh. My dear Mr Kingero, I have to thank you heartily for the trouble you have taken. *Signed:* Robert Louis Stevenson. *4 pp. Photostat, presented by Professor Sanki Ichikawa. Published in the* Skerryvore Edition, Letters, *Vol. 1, pp. 314–315, where one line of the autograph is omitted. Stevenson writes about the state of world politics.*

3179

[December 6, 1877]. 17 Heriot Row Edinburgh. Dear Mr Kingero, I should long ago have answered your letter. *Signed:* Robert Louis Stevenson. *3 pp. Photostat, presented by Professor Sanki Ichikawa. Published in the* Skerryvore Edition, Letters, *Vol. 1, pp. 325–326. Stevenson writes of French elections and of his dislike for Marshal MacMahon.*

3180

[*1886. Bournemouth*]. My dear Lang, I treated myself to your Dead Authors, by way of an unbirthday present. *Signed:* The Bard of Muttonhole, *and* R. L. S. *2 pp. Unpublished. Contains Stevenson's thoughts, mostly favorable, on Lang's* Letters to Dead Authors, *1886, and 32 lines of verse, beginning:* Dear Andrew of the brindled hair.

3181

[*August, 1890. Sydney*]. My dear Lang, I observed with a great deal of surprise and interest that a controversy in which you have been taking sides at home, in yellow London, hinges in part at least on the Gilbert Islanders. *Signed:* R. L. Stevenson. *4 pp. Written on stationery of the* Union Club, Sydney. *Printed in* The Athenaeum, *No. 3286, London, October 18, 1890, p. 516, where 14 lines of the autograph are omitted. Stevenson writes about standing stones in the Gilbert Islands.*

3182

[*August, 1892. Vailima*]. My dear Lang, I knew you would prove a trusty purveyor. The books you have sent are admirable. *Signed:* R. L. S. *1 p. Corner of letter torn off. Published in* LFF, *Vol. 2, pp. 259–260. Stevenson writes of work on* The Young Chevalier *and* Catriona.

3183

9th August 73. Saturday. Cockfield [*Rectory, Sudbury, Suffolk*]. My dear Lewis, Please excuse my writing as I have blistered my finger in cutting bread for the school feast. *Signed:* R. L. Stevenson. *8 pp. Written on stationery of* 17 Heriot Row. *Unpublished. Stevenson writes of his attempt to supervise children at a school feast.*

R.L.S. TO LADY CAROLINE BLANCHE ELIZABETH LINDSAY

3184

June 18th 1893. Vailima Plantation Samoan Islands. Dear Lady Lindsay I am very much obliged to you for sending me your books of verse. *Signed:* Robert Louis Stevenson. *2 pp. The letter is in the hand of Isobel Strong, signed by Stevenson. Unpublished. Stevenson states that he prefers Lady Lindsay's* Lyrics and other Poems *to her other verse. He writes:* My exile is final and far from painful.

3185

[October or November, 1887. Saranac Lake]. Dear Mr McClure, The Black Arrow has come, and I believe I see my way to make something of it for your purpose. *Signed:* Robert Louis Stevenson. *1 p. Unpublished. Stevenson writes about serial publication of* The Black Arrow; *and declines an offer of $10,000 a year made by Joseph Pulitzer for an essay a week from R. L. S.*

3186

November 1st 1887. Saranac Lake. Dear Mr. McClure, The next story I finish of the same character as Kidnapped, I shall place in your hands. *Signed:* Robert Louis Stevenson. *1 p. Unpublished.*

3187
July 4. 1894. [*Vailima*]. Draft of a letter in Samoan to Malietoa, King of Samoa. *Signed:* Tusitala. *1 p. Unpublished.*

3188

[*February 6, 1892. Vailima*]. Maona e, Na tala toe pepelo a Lauilo. *Signed:* Tusitala. *1 p. In Samoan. Unpublished. On 2 pp. of this folder is a letter to Stevenson written in pencil, in Samoan, by Maona.*

3189

May 22nd 1889. Kalawao [*Molokai*]. To see the infinite pity of the place. *Signed:* Robert Louis Stevenson. *1 p. Photostat. Unpublished. 8 lines of verse, addressed to the Reverend Sister Maryanne, Matron of Bishop Home, Kalaupapa, Molokai, Hawaiian Islands.*

3190

December 11th 84. Bonallie Tower Branksome Park Bourne-mouth. My dear Miss Marzials, I have been very slow to answer you. *Signed:* Robert Louis Stevenson. *4 pp. Photostat. With addressed envelope and mounted stamp (photostat). Unpub-lished. Stevenson writes of his delicate health, and of some of the things he would like to possess.*

3191

[*1874?*]. 17 Heriot Row [*Edinburgh*]. My dear Katharine, I have gone over your paper at last . . . and I have scribbled in the margin some criticisms of detail. *Signed:* Robert Louis Stevenson, *and* R. L. S. *8 pp. Written on stationery bearing R.L.S.'s monogram. Unpublished. Stevenson criticizes a paper written by his cousin, and urges her to keep on writing.*

3192

[*1882. Davos*]. My dear Katharine, Why I have been guilty of this revolting conduct . . . I shall not stop to explain. *Signed:* R. L. S. *2 pp. Published in George S. Hellman:* The True Stevenson. *Boston, 1925, p. 141. Reproduced in facsimile, facing p. 142.*

R.L.S. TO ANDREW P. MELVILLE

3193

May 18th 94. Vailima . . . Dear Sir I have the pleasure to acknowledge your memorandum and copies of correspondence in the matter of the Edinburgh Edition. *Signed:* Robert Louis Stevenson. *3 pp. The letter is in the hand of Isobel Strong, signed by Stevenson. Unpublished.*

3194

[*1883? Hyères*]. My dear Meredith the enclosed was written four months ago, let its dis-colouration testify! *Signed:* R. L. Stevenson. *2 pp. (first and last) of a 3- or 4-page letter. Written on stationery of* La Solitude. *Unpublished.*

R.L.S. TO DR. SILAS WEIR MITCHELL

3195

[*1887 or 1888. Saranac Lake*]. Dear Dr. Weir Mitchell. You are going to be interviewed on my behalf by a Mr and a Dr Lea. *Signed:* Robert Louis Stevenson. *1 p. On black-bordered stationery. Unpublished.*

3196

[*Received at Edinburgh:*] 6 – Aug. 93. San Francisco. Twelve. Stevenson. *1 p. Cablegram. To Charles Baxter's law firm, Edinburgh.*

3197

May 28th 1887. 17 Heriot Row [*Edinburgh*]. My dear Mr Mowbray, I have been puzzling my lay head over the will. *Signed:* Robert Louis Stevenson. *4 pp. On black-bordered stationery. On p. 1 in another hand this letter is labeled:* Draft. *Unpublished. Stevenson makes inquiries about provisions of his father's will.*

3198

May 28th 1887. 17 Heriot Row [*Edinburgh*]. My dear Mr Mowbray, Many thanks for your letter. *Unsigned. 1 p. Marked at top:* Copy. *On black-bordered stationery. Unpublished. Stevenson asks for another look at his father's will.*

3199

Feb 26 '88. Saranac Lake Adirondacks Mts N. Y. U. S. A. My dear Mr Mowbray We are now so long without any definite news of how we stand in money affairs that I have thought it would spare you trouble to ask Charles Baxter to enquire and to become the medium of communication. *Typesigned:* R. L. Stevenson. *1 p. A typewritten copy. Unpublished.*

3200

16 Octbre 1882. [*Marseille*]. Sir, It has come to my ears that you have lent the authority of your columns to an error. *Signed:* Robert Louis Stevenson. *2 pp. Written on stationery of* Terminus Hotel, Marseille. *Published in* LFF, *Vol. 1, pp. 251–252. A denial that James Payn is guilty of plagiarism of anything written by R. L. S.*

3201

June 6th [*1885?*] Skerryvore Bournemouth Hants. Dear Mr Niles, I wrote to you on the occasion of the Silverado Squatters as near as possible to the following effect. *Unsigned. 4 pp. Written on* British Museum *stationery. This is apparently a draft for Stevenson's files. Published in the* Skerryvore Edition, Letters, Vol. 2, pp. 265–266. *Stevenson discusses differences of view between himself and Mr. Niles of Chatto & Windus.*

3202

Nov. 12th 1885. Bournemouth. My dear Sir, My conduct is shocking indeed. *Signed:* Robert Louis Stevenson. *1 p. Partly published in an unidentified auction catalogue, lot 141, where about 4 lines of the autograph are omitted. Stevenson writes about* Markheim, *which was printed in* Unwin's Annual, *1886, edited by Henry Norman.*

3203

[*1880. California*]. Dear Sam: They are all so mean about writing, that I shall do so myself. *Signed:* ever your affectionate Doggie. Chuchu his mark. X. *2 pp. 5 lines of this 39-line letter are published in Sotheby, Wilkinson & Hodge.* Catalogue of . . . Books [*etc.*] . . . Sold . . . 23rd of July, 1914, and following Day, *p. 68, lot 566. A letter purporting to be dictated by Lloyd Osbourne's dog while the boy was away at a boarding school.*

3204

[*1880. California*]. My dear Sam. I am deputed by the crowd to write to you. *Signed:* Robert Louis Stevenson. *2 pp. In pencil. A few lines of this letter are printed in Sotheby, Wilkinson & Hodge.* Catalogue of . . . Books [*etc.*] . . . Sold . . . 23rd of July, 1914, and following Day, p. 68, *lot 570. Stevenson calls Osbourne an* asinus parvus, *writes about the dogs Chuchu and Florry, and says he is* dying for the printing press and to start my poetical works.

3205

[*April, 1881. Paris*]. My dear Sam, We are still stuck up here in Paris. *Signed:* Robert Louis Stevenson. *2 pp. Unpublished. Stevenson writes about his dog Wogg.*

3206

17th February [*1883*]. Marseille. My dear Sam, We have cut from St. Marcel. *Signed:* Robert Louis Stevenson. *2 pp. Unpublished. Stevenson writes that he considers Osbourne a very* clever boy, *but very inexact.*

3207

[*November or December, 1888*]. Tautira. My dear Lloyd, Being rather out of health and a little downcast . . . I write you this letter of directions. *Signed:* Robert Louis Stevenson. *4 pp. 17 lines of this 56-line letter are published in Edith B. Tranter. First Editions and Autograph Manuscripts of American and English Authors . . . Auction Sale . . . New York, 1952, p. 91. Stevenson gives instructions to his step-son, in case of an acci-*

dent, in respect to a possible collected edition of R. L. S.'s writings and a life of him (preferably prepared by Colvin).

3208

June 18th 1889. Honolulu. I Robert Louis Stevenson acknowledge having received as a loan from Lloyd Osbourne the sum of one thousand dollars. *Signed:* Robert Louis Stevenson. *1 p.*

3209

[*1890? Vailima*]. My dear Lloyd, I send you some proofs. The negatives of the Savage Islanders go by same mail. *Unsigned. 1 p. Unpublished. On the verso of this is a letter by Lloyd Osbourne to an unknown recipient written in 1893 (?).*

3210

29th Sept 1890. Vailima. My dear Surfeited-with-rich-food, (the literal translation of your name) I have the pleasure to write you a first epistle from Our Forest Home. *Unsigned. 4 pp. Partly published in Sotheby, Wilkinson & Hodge. Catalogue of . . . Books [etc.] . . . Sold . . . 23rd of July, 1914, and following Day . . . London, 1914, p. 72, lot 583, where 65 lines of this 87-line autograph are omitted. Stevenson writes about bird calls, the new house at Vailima, the missionary Chalmers, work on* The Wrecker, *Brander Matthews on collaboration, and ends with 12 lines of verse, beginning:* And may I too, immortal gander. *Mrs. R. L. S. has written an addition to this letter.*

3211

[*October or November, 1890. Vailima*]. My dear Loia, Last mail, as I told you, Wrecker went to Burlingame. *Signature cut away. 4 pp. Partly published in Sotheby, Wilkinson & Hodge. Catalogue of . . . Books [etc.] . . . Sold . . . 23rd of July, 1914, and following Day . . . London, 1914, p. 73, lot 585, where 76 lines of this 89-line autograph are omitted. Stevenson asks Osbourne to get him new parts for his flageolet, praises the missionary Chalmers, names the originals of some of the characters in his writings, and gives information and diagrams of the new house at Vailima.*

3212

[*Cir. 1885*] Skerryvore, Bournemouth. Dear Miss Paget, I am but just returned, and have found the dreadful and grave note. *Unsigned. 1 p. Unpublished.*

3213

Feb. 13th 1886. Skerryvore Bournemouth. Dear Mr Palmer, Thank you for your letter and book. *Signed:* Robert Louis Stevenson. *2 pp. Unpublished. Stevenson criticizes Palmer's book, After His Kind, 1886.*

3214

Dec 21st 1882. Campagne Defli St. Marcel Banlieue . . . de Marseille. My dear James Payn, I had a fine fright when my M. S. came this morning in silence. *Signed:* Robert Louis Stevenson. *3 pp. Facsimile of the original in the Huntington Library. Published in facsimile in Bradford A. Booth.* A Note on a Letter from Robert Louis Stevenson to James Payn, [*Los Angeles*], 1954. *Stevenson writes about* The Merry Men *as published in* The Cornhill *Magazine. This version contained numerous errors because it was printed before Stevenson had returned his proof.*

3215

February 4 1890. [*Dampfer*] Lübeck. My dear James Payn, In virtue of confessions in your last, you would at the present moment . . . be sick. *Signed:* R. L. Stevenson. *2 pp. Written on stationery of the* Norddeutscher Lloyd. *Published in* LFF, *Vol. 2, pp. 182–183. A jolly letter written on the way to Sydney.*

3216

[*August 11, 1894*]. Vailima Upolu Samoa. My dear James Payn I hear from Lang that you are unwell. *Signed:* Robert Louis Stevenson. *8 pp. Published in* LFF, *Vol. 2, pp. 301–303, where 6 lines of the autograph are omitted, and where the letter is dated* [*August, 1893*]. *In* The Letters, *1911, and in the* Skerryvore Edition *of Stevenson's writings the letter is dated* [*August 11, 1894*]. *Stevenson writes about a naval attack on Samoan rebels, about Payn's bad health, about piquet, etc.*

3217

[*October 9, 1891. Samoa*]. The signatories of the address are in receipt of the President's [*Pilsach's*] favour under date [*October 2*]. *Unsigned. 2 pp. Draft of letter. Published in* The Times, *London, November 17, 1891, p. 7, and in the* South Seas Edition, *Vol. 26, pp. 88–89. This draft contains 28 lines which were evidently not used in the letter sent to Baron von Pilsach, President of the Council, Samoa, and are not printed in the* South Seas Edition. *The letter sent to Pilsach was signed by R. L. S., E. W. Gurr and nine others. Surprise and dissatisfaction are expressed in this letter at remarks made in Pilsach's letter of October 2.*

3218

Dec. 16th 1892. Vailima. Sir, Your favour of the 5th current . . . requires a word of explanation. *Signed:* Robert Louis Stevenson. *1 p. Published in the* Skerryvore Edition, Letters, *Vol. 4, p. 158. Stevenson writes about a complimentary copy of* A Footnote to History *sent to Pilsach by the publishers. Pilsach was apparently annoyed by the manner in which the book was presented. With this is a copy of the letter, reworded by Stevenson and in his hand, marked:* copy.

3219

[*188–. Bournemouth?*] My dear Pollock, I have long been in a mind to write to you. *Signed:* R. L. Stevenson. *4 pp. Unpublished. Stevenson writes about the policies of the* Saturday Review.

3220

[*188–*] Tuesday. Skerryvore Bournemouth. Dear Mrs Rawlinson, On second thoughts — I will not quite trust your first — could not you and Miss Rawlinson combine pleasure for yourselves with kindness to us? *Signed:* Robert Louis Stevenson. *2 pp. Unpublished. Stevenson asks Mrs. Rawlinson and her daughter, May, to dine with him and Mrs. R.L.S.*

3221

August 7th 1889. Butaritari. Sir, In accordance with my offer made to you this morning, I set down the result of my experience during the recent week of festival. *Signed:* Robert Louis Stevenson. *1 p. Unpublished. Stevenson writes to the United States Consular Agent at Butaritari of fighting among natives of Butaritari and Makin resulting evidently from the drinking of alcoholic beverages.*

3222

[*January, 1890? Apia?*] My dear Mr Rick, Herewith the song, which you said you would like to have a copy of. *Signed:* Robert Louis Stevenson. *3 pp. Unpublished. The* song *begins:* 'Tis years since he was born.

3223

[*February? 1890*]. Sydney. Dear Mr Rick, Here is the result of my inquiries. *Signed:* Robert Louis Stevenson. *1 p. Unpublished. A report concerning money which Jim Byron had in a Sydney bank and what may have happened to it.*

3224

Nov. 4 . . . 1894. Vailima Samoa. Dear Mr. Riding I own with contrition that I am the last and worst of mankind. *Signed:* Robert Louis Stevenson. *2 pp. The letter is in the hand of Isobel Strong, signed by Stevenson. Unpublished. Sent apparently to an editor who asked Stevenson to write something for him.*

R.L.S. TO CHARLES GRAY ROBERTSON

3225
[188–?] My dear Charlie I'm a rogue and should have written you months ago. *Signed:* Robert Louis Stevenson. *This is a copy of R.L.S.'s letter in the hand of William Fowler. 2 pp. Unpublished. Stevenson gives advice about the art of writing.*

3226
[*June, 1881*]. Kinnaird Cottage, Pitlochry, Perthshire. My dear Charlie, My military aspirations lean nearer to Kriegspiel than anything else. *Signed:* Robert Louis Stevenson. *1 p. Unpublished. Stevenson mentions re-reading Robertson's book, probably* Kurum, Kabul and Kandahar, being a brief Record of Impressions in three Campaigns under General Roberts, *Edinburgh, 1881. Mrs. R. L. S. has written an addition to this letter.*

3227
Oct 25th 1885. [*Bournemouth*]. My dear Charlie, All is well that ends well. *Signed:* R. L. Stevenson. *1 p. With addressed envelope and mounted stamp. Unpublished.*

3228
Oct: 29: 1885. Skerryvore, Bournemouth. My dear Charlie, I thank you for your kind letter: a letter very honourable to you in every way. *Signed:* R. L. S. *1 p. With addressed envelope and mounted stamp. Unpublished. Mrs. R. L. S. has written an addition to this letter.*

3229
[*November 4, 1885. Bournemouth*]. My dear Charlie, John has broken down, and its place has been taken by one "Olalla." *Signed:* R- L. S. *2 pp. With addressed envelope and mounted stamp. Unpublished.*

3230
[*November? 1886. Bournemouth*]. Dear Charlie, I treat you so shamefully that you may wonder the enclosed had the power to move my conscience. *Signed:* R. L. S. *2 pp. Unpublished. Stevenson refers to letters said to have been written by one Wheelhouse, and to a map.*

R.L.S. TO ARCHIBALD PHILIP PRIMROSE, FIFTH EARL OF ROSEBERY

3231

[*Summer, 1893. Vailima*]. My dear Lord Roseberry [*sic*] I am sorry to have to trouble you with a letter as to what I know must bore you infinitely — the state of this unhappy country. *Unfinished and unsigned. 7 pp. A draft, in the hand of Isobel Strong, part of which is in duplicate. Unpublished.*

3232

[*September ? 1880. Edinburgh*]. My dear girls. We are all the wickedest people in the world. *Unsigned. 2 pp. Written on stationery of* 17 Heriot Row. *Unpublished. The letter is to Nellie van de Grift Sanchez and Isobel Strong. Stevenson refers to his wife's* busted diaphragm, *and to the first part of* The Pavilion on the Links *printed in* The Cornhill Magazine. *Mrs. R. L. S. has written an addition to this letter.*

3233

[*October, 1887. Saranac Lake*]. Tear off the above for press. I sent you yesterday a second paper. *Signed:* Robert Louis Stevenson. *1 p. The word* copy *is entered at top. At bottom:* Rec'd Oct 21. 1887. *Unpublished.*

3234

[*October, 1887. Saranac Lake*]. My dear Mr Scribner, I hope I can avoid the essays with M'Clure, and have written him to withdraw from the arrangement. *Signed:* Robert Louis Stevenson. *4 pp. At top of p. 1 in pencil:* Rec'd Oct 26 '87. *Unpublished. Stevenson writes of future Scribner editions of his books, and lists titles of books he wishes sent him.*

3235

[*October, 1887. Saranac Lake*]. My dear Mr Scribner. Dr Jekyll. I enclose you Mr Longman's letter. *Signed:* Robert Louis Stevenson, *and* R. L. S. *3 pp. At top of p. 1 in pencil:* Rec'd Oct 27 '87. *Unpublished. Stevenson asks Scribners to pay half the royalties they owe for* Dr. Jekyll and Mr. Hyde *to Messrs. Longman.*

3236

[*October, 1887. Saranac Lake*]. My dear Mr Scribner, I have always forgotten to make to you my great proposal. *Signed:* R. L. S. *1 p. At bottom in pencil:* Recd Nov 1st 87. *Unpublished. Stevenson suggests that Scribners get Howard Pyle to illustrate Marryat's* The Phantom Ship.

3237

[*November, 1887*]. Saranac Lake. My dear Mr Scribner, I have received yours of the 27th. *Signed:* Robert Louis Stevenson. *1 p. In pencil at bottom:* Rec Nov 4th 87. *Unpublished. It is agreed that Scribners will pay the entire royalty for* Dr. Jekyll and Mr. Hyde *to Stevenson.*

3238

[*November, 1887. Saranac Lake*]. Dear Mr Scribner, Thank you for the correspondence; in which you had certainly the best. *Signed:* Robert Louis Stevenson, *and* R. L. S. *4 pp. On black-bordered stationery. Unpublished. Stevenson writes about doing a preface to his* Memoir of Fleeming Jenkin *and about sharing the American royalty for this work with Jenkin's widow.*

3239

[*November, 1887. Saranac Lake*]. Dear Mr Scribner, Herewith Number One and I hope it is welcome as it is well-gone. *Signed:* Robert Louis Stevenson (The Insatiable Troubler). *1 p. Unpublished. Stevenson lists books, etc. which he wants to borrow and buy.*

3240

[*November, 1887. Saranac Lake*]. My dear Mr Scribner, I have just remembered that I sold the Studies without reservation; so no doubt Dodd Meade & Co did pay the £25. *Signed:* Robert Louis Stevenson. *2 pp. On black-bordered stationery. Unpublished.*

3241

[*November, 1887. Saranac Lake*]. My dear Mr Scribner, Enclosed is a fresh order. *Signed:* R. L. Stevenson. *3 pp. On black-bordered stationery. Unpublished. Stevenson writes of a* promise and a half promise to Mr McClure. *He asks Mr. Scribner to suggest a title for his series of essays for* Scribner's Magazine.

3242

[*November, 1887. Saranac Lake*]. My dear Mr Scribner, Glad to hear of the Phantom Ship. *Signed:* Robert Louis Stevenson. *5 pp., including a 2-p. list of persons to whom Stevenson asks that copies of books by him be sent. On black-bordered stationery. At top of p. 1 in pencil:* Recd Nov. 11th 87. *Unpublished. Stevenson writes of his* Memoir of Fleeming Jenkin *and of his relations with Longmans concerning* Dr. Jekyll and Mr. Hyde.

3243

[*November 20 or 21, 1887. Saranac Lake*]. My dear Mr Scribner, Heaven help me, I am under a curse just now. *Signed:* Robert Louis Stevenson. *2 pp. At top of p. 1 in pencil:* Nov 23. *Published in LFF, Vol. 2, p. 74. Stevenson asks forgiveness for having signed a bargain with S. S. McClure after having told Scribners that they should* have the power over all my work in this country.

3244

[*November, 1887. Saranac Lake*]. My dear Mr Scribner. I have sent you off today the books I had. *Signed:* R. L. Stevenson, *and* R. L. S. *3 pp. On black-bordered stationery. At top of p. 1 in pencil:* Nov 25th 1887. *Unpublished. Stevenson mentions books which he wants sent.*

3245

[*November, 1887. Saranac Lake*]. My dear Mr Scribner, In this very painful affair, I must however trouble you with a few explanations. *Signed:* Robert Louis Stevenson. *3 pp. On black-bordered stationery. At top of p. 1 in pencil:* Recd Dec 2nd 87. *Unpublished. Stevenson discusses arrangements he made with McClure for serial publication of* Catriona *which were contrary to his agreement with Scribners.*

3246

[*December, 1887. Saranac Lake*]. My dear Mr Scribner, Alas, I have to begin again upon this painful business. Only one thing in your last pleases me: you show a want of memory, which I hope may incline you to be more lenient to the same fault in me. *Signed:* Robert Louis Stevenson. *3 pp. On black-bordered stationery. At top of p. 1 in pencil:* Recd Dec 6. '87. *Unpublished. Stevenson writes further about his arrangements with McClure, involving* Catriona *and* The Black Arrow.

3247

[*December, 1887. Saranac Lake*]. My dear Mr Scribner, Please do not suppose me annoyed. *Signed:* Robert Louis Stevenson, *and* R. L. S. *2 pp. On black-bordered stationery. At top of p. 1 in pencil:* recd. Dec. 15th. *Unpublished. Stevenson writes:*

Please, for God's sake, understand this: I mean a truce to apologies; but if you have any reclamation to make make it at once, and if it be possible, it shall be made good.

3248

Dec 15 1887. Saranac Lake. Memories of the Chevalier Johnstone and Johnsons Lives of notorious pirates by swiftest conveyances Stevenson. *1 p. Telegram. Unpublished.*

3249

[*December 15, 1887. Saranac Lake*]. My dear Mr Scribner, I think I am on the way to meet your views. *Signed:* Robert Louis Stevenson. *3 pp. On black-bordered stationery. At top of p. 1:* Rec'd Dec. 19. *Unpublished. Stevenson states that he is beginning to write* The Master of Ballantrae, *and asks that certain books about eighteenth-century America be sent him.*

3250

[*December, 1887. Saranac Lake*]. My dear Mr Scribner, I have already written Mr Burlingame mostly in the matter of The Master of Ballantrae. *Signed:* Robert Louis Stevenson. *4 pp. On black-bordered stationery. At top of p. 1 in pencil:* Recd Dec 20th 87. *Unpublished. Stevenson writes of* The Master of Ballantrae *and* The Black Arrow, *and invites Mr. Scribner to come up to Saranac Lake.*

3251

[*December, 1887. Saranac Lake*]. My dear Mr Scribner, And very happy we shall be to see you. *Signed:* Robert Louis Stevenson. *2 pp. On black-bordered stationery. At top of p. 1 in pencil:* Recd. Dec. 27th '87. *Unpublished. Stevenson writes that he may hand Mr. Scribner the manuscript of part of* The Master of Ballantrae.

3252

[*December, 1887. Saranac Lake*]. My dear Mr Scribner, The books have come   But how about Dr Eggleston? small manners are what I am specially after. Yours   R. L. S. *1 p. On black-*

bordered stationery. *At top of p. 1 in pencil:* Recd Dec 28th. *Unpublished.*

3253
[*January? 1888. Saranac Lake*]. Dear Scribner, This is to say we all enjoyed your visit thoroughly. *Signed:* R. L. S. (The Boaster). *2 pp. Unpublished. Stevenson writes of doing a biography of (Francis?) Nicholson.*

3254
June 23 1888. San Francisco. Address letters yacht Casco care American consul Honolulu Stevenson. *1 p. Telegram. Unpublished.*

3255
July 14th 1892. Vailima Plantation Upolu Samoan Islands. My dear Mr. Scribner Many thanks for yours of June 17th. *Signed:* R. L. Stevenson. *3 pp. Unpublished. The letter is in the hand of Isobel Strong, signed by Stevenson. Stevenson asks that certain books be sent him.*

3256

March 12th 1885. Bonallie Tower Bournemouth. Dear Sirs, I have received from Mr Low, the terms to which he has consented on my behalf. *Signed:* Robert Louis Stevenson, *and* R. L. S. *2 pp. Unpublished. Stevenson thanks Scribners for their liberal offer for* A Child's Garden of Verses.

3257

Jan 18th 1885 [*i.e. 1886*]. Skerryvore Bournemouth. Dear Sirs, I have to acknowledge receipt of 2 Dr Jekylls. *One signature cut away. A second signature reads:* R. L. S. *3 pp. Unpublished. Stevenson writes:* About "Prince Otto" Niles has paid me for the sheets, but I much fear he means to play dog in the manger . . . I take him to be an angry man without much sense of humour. *Of* Kidnapped *R. L. S. writes:* I think it better and the public will probably like it more than Treasure Island.

3258

Feb 12th 1886. Skerryvore Bournemouth. Dear Sirs, I shall return you today or tomorrow the hundred pounds you sent me on account. *Signed:* Robert Louis Stevenson, *and* R L. S. *2 pp. Unpublished. Stevenson writes that he has delayed sending the hundred pounds because his bank account was low. With this letter he sent manuscripts of a paper by himself and a story by his wife.*

3259

March 8th 1886. Skerryvore Bournemouth. Dear Sirs, I am in receipt of your letter of 24th February. *Signed:* Robert Louis Stevenson. *2 pp. Unpublished. Stevenson writes that* Beyond a few dollars from Messrs Henry Holt & Co. and certain sums that I recently (in despair) demanded for advance sheets, I have never up to now received one red cent for any book of mine in the States. *He writes that he will copy and send the text of* Kidnapped *as soon as possible.*

3260

March 14th 1886. Skerryvore Bournemouth. Dear Sirs, I have received the Book Buyer with the beautiful portrait. *Signed: Robert Louis Stevenson. 3 pp. With addressed envelope and mounted stamps. Unpublished. Stevenson praises a wood-engraved portrait of himself by one Johnson. Of his father's lighthouse work he writes:* I might write books till 1900 and not serve humanity so well.

3261

[Spring, 1886]. Skerryvore Bournemouth. Dear Sirs, I have to acknowledge a vast variety of favours of all kinds. *Signed:* Robert Louis Stevenson. *1 p. Unpublished. Stevenson writes that Cassells plan to issue* Kidnapped *about July first.*

3262

July 16th 1886. Skerryvore. Messrs Charles Scribner's Sons Dear Sirs, "Kidnapped" Please note the following corrections which I shall be heartily obliged if you would make at your earliest convenience. *Signed:* Robert Louis Stevenson. *4 pp. Unpublished. This letter, written 2 days after publication of* Kidnapped, *contains corrections desired by Stevenson. They are noted in Vol. 1, p. 163 and elsewhere, in the Catalogue of the Beinecke Collection. Stevenson also lists the titles of the chapters of a proposed novel to be called* The Gold Fever.

3263

July 27th 1886. Skerryvore. Dear Sirs, I have to acknowledge receipt of fifty pounds . . . I should be very backward if I did not take some interest in a firm that has so much changed my prospects in the States. *Signed:* Robert Louis Stevenson. *1 p. Unpublished.*

3264

[Late 1886. Bournemouth]. Dear Sirs, I have had a long illness which has thrown all my plans to leeward. *Signed:* Robert Louis Stevenson. *2 pp. Unpublished. Stevenson writes that* The Merry Men *is in the printer's hand.*

3265

[*Postmarked:* Mr 31 87. Bournemouth]. Dear Sirs, You must try to learn to excuse my disgraceful habits of neglect. *Signed:* Robert Louis Stevenson. *4 pp. With addressed envelope and mounted stamps. Unpublished. Stevenson returns a check connected with some carelessness of his; he also sends Scribners a check for £20 received by Stevenson from Harper & Brothers in payment for their pirated edition of* The Merry Men and other Tales and Fables, Treasure Island, Dr. Jekyll and Mr. Hyde, *and* Kidnapped.

3266

May 3rd 1887. Skerryvore Bournemouth. Dear Sirs, I am in receipt of yours and of the returned draft for one hundred and fortyseven pound . . . *Signed:* Robert Louis Stevenson. *3 pp. Unpublished. Stevenson refers to Scribners'* good taste and honour, *also to* conscience money *paid by Harper & Brothers. See the correspondence between the latter and Stevenson.*

3267

[*Summer? 1887. Bournemouth?*]. Dear Sirs, I am glad to be able to reply by a M. S. *Signed:* Robert Louis Stevenson. *2 pp. Written on black-bordered stationery. Unpublished. The manuscript referred to was probably that of* Ticonderoga.

3268

[*October, 1887. Saranac Lake*]. A thousand thanks for books and papers, and the new editions. *Unsigned. 1 p. Endorsed in another hand:* rec'd Oct. 21st 1887. *Unpublished.*

R.L.S. TO SIR WALTER GRINDLAY SIMPSON, BT.

3269

[*Cir. April, 1884. Hyères*]. My dear Simpson, The Bag has not yet turned up; but the letter did and greatly pleased us. *Unsigned. Unfinished? 3 pp. Unpublished.*

R.L.S. TO FANNY SITWELL (FRANCES JANE FETHERSTONHAUGH, LATER LADY COLVIN)

3270

Sept 1st [*1873*]. Monday. 17 Heriot Row Edinburgh. I have arrived as you see, without accident. *Signed:* R. L. S. *4 pp. Partly published in* The Letters, *1911, Vol. 1, pp. 58–59, where about 32 lines of the autograph are omitted. Stevenson describes his* wretched journey *from London to Edinburgh. In connection with a walk about the dark streets of Edinburgh he writes:* I could not help fancying as I went along all sorts of foolish things — chansons — about showing all these places to you, Claire, some other night; which is not to be. *In his* Voyage to Windward, *pp. 462–463, J. C. Furnas quotes the latter passage as showing that Stevenson used Claire as a nickname for Mrs. Sitwell, and as proving false the allegation that he had a love affair with a blacksmith's daughter named Claire.*

3271

[*1873?*] Here is a word just to tell you how well I am. *Signed:* R. L. S. *4 pp. On black-bordered stationery. Stevenson describes an evening out in the rain. At the end is a poem of 12 lines, beginning:* All things on earth and sea. *The poem was first printed in* Three Short Poems by Robert Louis Stevenson, *London, 1898, pp. [17]–19. The letter and the poem are printed in* Three Letters from Robert Louis Stevenson, *Essex House Press, 1902, p. 3.*

3272

[*April, 1874 ?*] Café Palais Royal, Paris. Madonna, I am in a somewhat curious humour. *Signed:* R. L. Stevenson. *4 pp. Written diagonally across 2 pp. Partly published in* Henry A. Colgate. The Stevenson Library . . . Sold by Auction . . . February Eighth . . . The Anderson Galleries . . . *New York, 1928, p. 38, lot 180, where about 22 lines of the autograph are omitted.*

3273

[*1874?*] Swanston. On the back, the desired poem; for I believe it is one, though small. *Signed:* R. L. S. *4 pp. Stevenson writes of working on* a game about morals which is nearly half drafted.

At the end is a poem of 12 lines, beginning: Here you rest
among the vallies, maiden known to but a few. *The poem was
first printed in* Three Short Poems by Robert Louis Stevenson,
London, 1898, *pp.* [11]–13. *The letter and the poem are printed
in* Three Letters from Robert Louis Stevenson, *Essex House
Press, 1902, pp. 4–5.*

3274

[*1874 or 1875?*] Here is what I have often said in good prose,
put into bad verse. *Signed:* R. L. S. *2 pp. Contains poem (7
stanzas, 33 lines) beginning:* I read, dear friend, in your dear face.
The last 4 stanzas were first printed in Three Short Poems by
Robert Louis Stevenson, *London, 1898, pp.* [23]–25. *The letter
and the complete poem with a few additional lines are printed
in* Three Letters from Robert Louis Stevenson, *Essex House
Press, 1902, pp. 5–7.*

3275

[*August, 1875*]. Chateau Renard Loiret. Dear Madonna, I
have been walking these last days from place to place. *Signed:*
Robert Louis Stevenson. *2 pp. Published in LFF, Vol. 1, pp.
105–106, where 4 lines of the autograph are omitted. Stevenson
writes about a walking tour with Sir Walter Simpson. The letter
contains 13 lines of verse, beginning:* Far have you come, my
lady, from the town, *and 13 additional lines under title:* Nous
n'irons plus au bois, *beginning:* We'll walk the woods no more.

3276

[*August, 1877. Penzance*]. You will do well to stick to your burn.
Signed: Robert Louis Stevenson. *4 pp. Written on stationery of
17 Heriot Row. Published in LFF, Vol. 1, pp. 120–121, where
about 4 lines of the autograph are omitted. Stevenson writes
about stories on which he was at work.*

3277

[*1886?*] Skerryvore Bournemouth. Dear Mrs Speedy, I fear you labour under an error about me; I am no editor. *Signed:* Robert Louis Stevenson. *1 p. Unpublished.*

3278

Oct. 1st [*1882*]. Mont Pellier. My dear girl, I am pretty near determined to leave here tomorrow or next day. *Signed:* Louis. *4 pp. Unpublished. Stevenson writes principally about his health.*

3279

[*October, 1882. Montpellier*]. My dear, The Doctorbus just left me and pronounces me better. *Signed:* Louis. *4 pp. Pen sketches by Stevenson. Published in the* Skerryvore Edition, Letters, Vol. 2, pp. 107–108, *where 5 lines of the autograph are omitted and several words are changed. Stevenson wants his mother to come with Fanny to Paris; he does not like to have Fanny travel alone.*

3280

Oct '82. Montpellier. I am a very low horrid fellow. *Unsigned. 3 pp. Published in the* Skerryvore Edition, Letters, Vol. 2, pp. 110–111. *Contains 4 lines of verse, beginning:* Silence et repos. *Stevenson writes about his health, a visit to Dr. Cassio, etc. Mrs. R. L. S. has written a note to R. L. S.'s mother on a p. not used by R. L. S.*

3281

[*Early 1883*]. Dear wierd[*sic*] woman, You have made a slight confusion by not properly explaining the arrangement you made at Hyères. *Signed:* The Man of the House. *2 pp. Unpublished.*

3282

[*July, 1885. Bournemouth*]. Dear Fanny, I am well. I inclose two letters. *Signed:* Louis. *3 pp. With addressed envelope and mounted stamp. Unpublished. Stevenson complains about cakes made by Valentine, and describes activities of his dog, Bogue.*

3283

[*Postmarked:* Oc 20 85. Bournemouth]. Dear Pig. I inclose a most spirited and cheerful epistle from the Samuel. *Signed:*

The Parker. *1 p. With addressed envelope and mounted stamp. Unpublished.*

3284

[*1885 or 1886. Bournemouth*]. My dear fellow There's no place like home. Morning: went down to the pond and discussed with le Beaucose, about the dam, the coasts &c. *Signed:* Robert Louis Stevenson. *2 pp. Unpublished.*

3285

[*1885? or 1886? Bournemouth?*] My dear Fanny, Good evening to your honour, likewise to Sam. *Signed:* R. L. S., Louis *and* Robert Louis Stevenson. *4 pp. Photostat. Unpublished. Contains drawings by Stevenson. Contains 14 lines of verse, beginning:* I am as good as deaf When separate from F; *and 20 additional lines, beginning:* Though I should rise at morning.

3286

[*April? 1886*]. Skerryvore Bournemouth. Dear Child, I enclose some letters. I want Rodin back: you can get Henley to translate it to you. *Signed:* The Meagre Living Pen. *4 pp. Unpublished. Stevenson writes about people he has seen, and about trouble in the kitchen between Valentine and May Anne.*

3287

[*April, 1886*]. Smedley's Hydropathic Matlock Bridge Derbyshire. My dear Fanny, We arrived here in the most dreadful snowstorm of the season. *Signed:* R. L. S. *2 pp. Unpublished. Stevenson has gone with his father to Matlock for the latter's health, gives information about their trip and first impressions of Matlock.*

3288

[*Cir. April 15, 1886. Matlock*]. My dearest child, All right. I will do just as you wish. *Signed:* R. L. S. *2 pp. Dated by R.L.S.'s mother. Unpublished. Stevenson writes:* I have no plans but to keep my father in patience as long as I can, and then streak for home like a swallow.

3289

[*April, 1886. Matlock*]. My dear fellow, Please tell my mother that Hunter has seen my father and thinks him a little better. *Signed:* R. L. S. *3 pp. Dated by R.L.S.'s mother. Unpublished. Stevenson wearies of his stay in Matlock. He writes:* I am sure it does not agree with me.

3290

[*April, 1886. Matlock*]. My dearest child   I send back your little note. *Signed:* The flying Hart, *and* L. *4 pp. Unpublished. Stevenson writes of treatment to his legs, etc., of his father and a Mrs. King.*

3291

[*June, 1886? London*]. Dear Fanny, I demand and the custodian requests your presence on Monday as ever was. What train? Yours ever R L. S. *1 p. Written on* British Museum *stationery. Unpublished.*

3292

[*September 20, 1886. Bournemouth*]. My dear fellow, tomorrow you shall receive another fiver. *Signed:* R. L. S. *4 pp. Unpublished. Stevenson writes of* dam politics going on here.

3293

[*September? 1886? Bournemouth*]. Dear fellow I have arranged with Powell. *Signed:* R L. S. *2 pp. A corner of this letter is torn away. Unpublished.*

3294

[*1886. Bournemouth?*] My dear fellow, Send the thing to Jones, and answer our questions. *Signed:* R L. S. *2 pp. Published in the* South Seas Edition, Letters, *Vol. 2, p. 312, where 3 lines of the autograph are omitted.*

3295

[*1886? Bournemouth*]. Dear Dutchman, Enclosed please find an extraordinary telegram. *Signed:* Louis. *2 pp. Unpublished.*

3296

[*1886? Bournemouth*]. Dear fellow, I am just the reverse of you, and sleep better when I am with you. *Signed:* R L S. *3 pp. Unpublished.*

3297

[*March? 1887. Bournemouth*]. My dear woman, Today I burned all morning in writing the old Jenkin part. *Signed:* The Man. *2 pp. Unpublished. Stevenson mentions Lord Tennyson's liking* The Merry Men.

3298

[*April? 1887. Bournemouth*]. My dear fellow, I am very well. Let Sam get his writing thing I will send a cheque. *Signed:* Louis. *4 pp. In pencil. Published in the* South Seas Edition, Letters, Vol. 2, pp. 341–342, *where 5 lines of the autograph are omitted. Stevenson mentions that his father and mother are with him, both unwell, and that Mrs. Jenkin left this morning. He writes about playing the piano:* I never played so like a human being as today.

3299

[*April? 1887. Bournemouth*]. My dear old girl, Thanks for your kind and interesting letter and the lovely picture of the beau. *Signed:* Louis. *3 pp. Published in the* South Seas Edition, Letters, Vol. 2, pp. 342–343. *Stevenson writes about his health and the arrival of a writing table.*

3300

[*April? 1887. Bournemouth*]. My dear girl, The blood has stopped: Colvangle [*i.e. Colvin*] is here. *Signed:* R. L. S. *2 pp. Unpublished.*

3301

[*Autumn, 1887? Saranac Lake?*] Poor creature this is to let you know that we have taken the bull by the horns and ordered from New York, all out of our own heads, the following articles: coffee, bacco box marked with my name, beer, list for windows, cheese, crackers, wine, coffee-pot and coffee-mill. *Signed:* R.

L. S. 1 p. The letter including the signature is typed. To Mrs. R. L. S.? Unpublished.

3302

[October 10? and 11? 1887] Monday *[and]* Tuesday. *[Saranac Lake].* My dearest little man, I am just in bed, not quite yet nine, and the lad is playing the devil with the organ in the next appartment[*sic*], which confuses me. *Signed:* R. L. S. *4 pp. On black-bordered stationery. Unpublished.*

3303

[1887. Saranac Lake]. Dearest fellow, my ninth letter today! *Signed:* Louis. *1 p. Unpublished. Stevenson writes:* My stove is in; tomorrow the piano comes.

3304

[December, 1887. Saranac Lake]. My excellent fellow, this goes from me in a more cheerful humour. *Signed:* Louis. *1 p. Unpublished. Stevenson writes of a tale on which he and Lloyd Osbourne were at work:* The Gaol Bird, *of Lloyd's fiddle and R. L. S.'s whistle, of a letter from Burlingame.*

3305

[Winter 1887–1888. Saranac Lake]. My dearest fellow, Doubts as to your movements have withheld me from really writing. *Signed:* Louis. *1 p. Published in the* South Seas Edition, Letters, *Vol. 3, pp. 55–56. Stevenson writes about papers at which he has been at work, a romance on which Lloyd Osbourne was engaged, and about Fanny's visit with her relatives in Danville, Indiana.*

3306

[Spring, 1888. Manasquan]. My dearest Girlie, I have not written to you for some days. *Signed:* Louis. *4 pp. On black-bordered stationery. Published in the* South Seas Edition, Letters, *Vol. 3, pp. 57–58. Stevenson writes of strained relations (with Henley?)*

3307

[May, 1888. Manasquan]. My dearest fellow, This will not reach you till some time after our wedding day. *Signed:* Louis.

3 pp. Published in the South Seas Edition, Letters, *Vol. 3, pp. 60–61. Stevenson writes, shortly before his eighth wedding anniversary, about his early days and marriage with Fanny.*

3308

[1893. Vailima]. Dear fellow, What I feared somehow! *Signed: R. L. S. 1 p. Published in the* South Seas Edition, Letters, *Vol. 4, p. 192. About a sick child.*

3309

[1894?] My dear, I was furious over this, above all with Paul who did not bring the letter till after Mr Bohn had come and gone. *Signed: R. L. S. 2 pp. Unpublished.*

3310

[1894 ? Vailima]. My dear old fellow   Tomorrow we are to ask de Crespigny and Henford [?] to lunch. *Signed: Louis. 1 p. Unpublished. Stevenson writes:* The house is not right without you.

R.L.S. TO HIS MOTHER, MARGARET
ISABELLA BALFOUR STEVENSON

3311
[*October, 1863*] Saturday. [*Spring Grove, Isleworth*]. My dear Mamma I could not write you on Wedensday[*sic*] this week as I had a headache. *Signed:* R. Stevenson. *3 pp. Drawing by Stevenson. Dated by R.L.S.'s mother. Unpublished.*

3312
12th Nov 1863. [*Spring Grove, Isleworth*]. Ma chere Maman Jai recu votre lettre Aujourdhui et comme le jour prochaine est mon jour de naissance je vous ecrit ce lettre. *Signed:* R. Stevenson. *3 pp. In French and English. Published in LFF, Vol. 1, pp. 7–8. Just before the signature Stevenson writes:* My dear papa you told me to tell you whenever I was miserable. I do not feel well and I wish to get home Do take me with you.

3313
[*December 19, 1863*] Sunday. Craven Hotel [*London*]. Mamma I have left Springrove[*sic*] at last I was the last boy to leave school. *Signed:* R. Stevenson. *1 p. Dated by R.L.S.'s mother. 5 lines of this 18-line letter are published in Henry A. Colgate. The Stevenson Library . . . Sold by Auction . . . New York, 1928, p. 32, lot 166. R.L.S.'s father has written an addition to this letter.*

3314
[*Early July, 1868*] Sunday even. Leven. My dear Mamma, If I am to write the essay, I require Carlyle's "Heroes and Hero-Worship" and that shortly. *Signed:* R. L. Stevenson. *4 pp. Partly dated by R.L.S.'s mother. 7 lines of this 85-line letter are printed in Autograph Letters [etc.] . . . from the Library of the late Robert Louis Stevenson . . . Part I . . . Sold . . . New York, 1914, p. 11, lot 46.*

3315
[*July, 1868*] Sunday. Leven. My dear Mother, I do envy you all the fun you must be having. *Signed:* R L Stevenson. *4 pp. Dated by R.L.S.'s mother. Unpublished.*

3316

[*July, 1868*]. Kenzie House Anstruther. My dear "Madame,"
I got here all right: met the Stirlings and the Crawfords on the
way. *Signed:* R L. Stevenson. *4 pp. Unpublished.*

3317

[*July, 1868*] Tuesday [*and*] Wednesday. Kenzie House, [*Anstruther*]. My dear Mama, I got here safely, box portmantie and
all. *Signed:* R. L. Stevenson. *6 pp. Dated by R.L.S.'s mother.
Unpublished.*

3318

[*July, 1868*] Thursday. Kenzie House, Anstru[*ther*]. My dear
Mere, I don't remember whose turn it is. *Signed:* R L. Stevenson. *3 pp. Dated by R.L.S.'s mother. Published in the* Skerryvore *Edition, Letters, Vol. 1, pp. 18–19. Stevenson finds his
father's handwriting illegible.*

3319

[*September 3, 1868*] Friday. New Harbour Hotel, Pulteney,
Wick. My dear Mamma Today Papa left in the morning before
I was up to go south. *Signed:* R L. Stevenson. *8 pp. Dated by
R.L.S.'s mother. At top of p. 1: No I. A few lines of this letter
are printed in A. C. Goodyear . . . Autograph Collection . . .
Sold by Auction . . . New York, 1927, lot 291.*

3320

[*Sept. 5, 1868*] Monday. [*Wick*]. My dear Mamma I wish you
would put the dates in days of the week as well as in days of
the month. *Signed:* R L Stevenson. *6 pp. Dated by R.L.S.'s
mother. 26 lines of this 112-line letter are printed in* Autograph
Letters [*etc.*] *. . . from the Library of the late Robert Louis
Stevenson . . . Part I . . . Sold . . . New York, 1914, p. 12, lot 50.*

3321

[*September 11, 1868. Friday. Wick*]. My dear Mother, To go on
with my description:—Wick lies at the end or elbow of an open
triangular bay. *Signed:* R. L. Stevenson. *8 pp. Dated by R.L.S.'s
mother. Published in LFF, Vol. 1, pp. 15–17, where about 5
lines of the autograph are omitted.*

3322

[*September 12, 1868*] Saturday. [*Wick*]. My dear mother, On the reverse you will find an exact imitation of Pope. *Unsigned. 2 pp. Dated by R.L.S.'s mother. 8 lines of this 75-line letter are printed in* Autograph Letters [*etc.*] . . . from the Library of the late Robert Louis Stevenson . . . Part I . . . Sold . . . *New York, 1914, p. 12, lot 51. Stevenson records visits with the Rutherfords and Russels, and writes 28 lines of verse, titled:* A Monody on the death of Mr Pogue O'nelle In the Augustan taste, *beginning:* Ye nymphs that haunt this barren coast around.

3323

[*September 14, 1868*]. New Harbour Hotel Pulteney [*Wick*]. My dear Mother, My trip to Thurso took up so much of my time, that I have been rather remiss in my correspondence. *Signed:* R. L. Stevenson. *10 pp. Unpublished. About religious services, meals and some of the people at Wick.*

3324

[*September, 1868*] Saturday 10 A. M. [*Wick*]. My dear Mother, The last two days have been dreadfully hard. *Signed:* R. L. Stevenson *and* R. L. S. *8 pp. Illustrative diagrams on p. 7. Dated by R.L.S.'s mother. Partly published in LFF, Vol. 1, pp. 19–20, where about 39 lines of the autograph are omitted.*

3325

[*September, 1868*] Sunday [*and*] Monday. Pulteney [*Wick*]. My dear mother, Another storm: wind higher rain thicker. *Signed:* R. L. Stevenson. *16 pp. Dated by R.L.S.'s mother. Partly published in LFF, Vol. 1, pp. 20–24, where about 73 lines of the autograph are omitted. Stevenson writes of people at Wick, of a storm, a ship washed ashore and damage along the coast.*

3326

[*September 26, 1868*] Saturday. New Harbour Hotel [*Wick*]. My dear Mother, Inspice inclusam (epistolam understood). *Signed:* R. L. Stevenson. *2 pp. Dated by R.L.S.'s mother. About 7 lines of this letter are printed in* A Remarkable Collection of Autograph Letters by the late Robert Louis Stevenson . . .

Part III . . . Sold . . . *New York, 1916, p. 26, lot* 131. *Contains 4 lines of verse, beginning:* Nothing have I for to say.

3327

June 18th 1869. Friday. Lighthouse Steamer Between Cantick and Hoy. June 19th Saturday. Blumel Sound. Dear Mamma, I herewith begin my journal letter. *Signed:* R. L. Stevenson. *30 pp. Drawings by Stevenson. Written on stationery of the* Northern Lighthouses. *About 25 lines and 2 drawings of this letter are printed in Henry A. Colgate.* The Stevenson Library . . . Sold by Auction . . . *New York, 1928, pp.* [33]–34, *including facsimile of one p. Stevenson writes a detailed account of a trip with his father on a lighthouse steamer. The letter contains a drawing of* North Unst Lighthouse, the most northern dwelling house in her majesty's dominion. *Mr. Beinecke has adopted this drawing as his bookplate.*

3328

June 20th 1869. Sunday. Off Lerwick [*Shetland Islands*]. Tuesday 22nd. My dear mamma, This night both my first departed. *Signed:* R. L. Stevenson. *18 pp. Diagrams by Stevenson. Written on stationery of the* Northern Lighthouses. *Unpublished. Stevenson continues his detailed account of his trip to the Shetland Islands.*

3329

[*August? 1870. Earraid*]. My dear Mother, Young Brebner is seated opposite to me, reading Shakespeare. *Signed:* R. L Stevenson. *4 pp. Place and year entered by R.L.S.'s mother. Unpublished.*

3330

[*July 23, 1872. Tuesday. London*]. My dear Mother, I am very much ashamed that I have not sooner written. *First 4 pp. of letter. Written on stationery of* The Craven Hotel, Craven Street, Strand. *Partly dated by R.L.S.'s mother. Unpublished. Stevenson writes of attending a Roman Catholic service and of visiting museums.*

3331

August 2 [*1872*] Friday. [*Hotel Landsberg, Frankfurt*]. Today, as I and Simpson were just sitting down to dinner in the café in the Schiller Platz, I looked across the room. *Signed:* R L. Stevenson. *2 pp. Partly published in LFF, Vol. 1, p. 36, where 19 lines of the autograph are omitted. Partly about meeting a clergyman named Duncan.*

3332

Xmas Day. 1872. B[*ridge*] of A[*llan*]. My dear Mother, I have had all things considered & thanks principally to "Philip", a very passable Christmas day. *Signed:* R. L. Stevenson. *8 pp. Written on stationery of* 17 Heriot Row. *Unpublished.* "Philip" *is Thackeray's* The Adventures of Philip.

3333

Dec. 27th 1872. Friday. B[*ridge*] of Allan. My dear Mother, Today, it has rained without intermission & shows no symptom of stopping even now. *Signature cut away. 8 pp. Written on stationery of* 17 Heriot Row. *Unpublished. Stevenson is with his cousin Bob, who is painting. Stevenson describes the Jaffray girls he sees in the next house, and the crowd in the billiard room.*

3334

[*December 30*] 1872. Monday. B[*ridge*] of A[*llan*]. My dear Mother, On Saturday, Bob had to go into town for an hour or two; but he had no time to go & give you our news; which indeed is non-existent. *Signed:* R L. Stevenson, *and* R. L. S. *14 pp. Written on stationery of* 17 Heriot Row. *Unpublished. A chatty letter about the Jaffray family, John Brand, Hodgson, Thackeray, a gloomy photographer named Andrew Manson, and a ride in an open carriage.*

3335

July 29th 1873. Tuesday [*Sudbury*]. My dear Mother, I am too happy to be much of a correspondent. *Signed:* R. L. S. *4 pp. Written on stationery of* Cockfield Rectory, Sudbury, Suffolk. *Partly published in LFF, Vol. 1, pp. 48–49, where about 13 lines of the autograph are omitted.*

3336

[*October, 1873*]. 15 Chepstow Place [*London*]. My dear Mother, I have been to see Dr Andrew Clark, who has peremptorilly forbidden me to go up for the Exam. and put me on a diet. *Signed:* R. L. Stevenson. *3 pp. Unpublished. Dr. Clark also forbade him to return to Scotland at this time.*

3337

[*Late October, 1873*] Thursday. Chepstow Place [*London*]. My dear mother, the telegram ne s'explique pas beaucoup. *Signed:* R. L. Stevenson, *and* L. S. *4 pp. Written on stationery of* 17 Heriot Row. *Unpublished. Stevenson lists things he wants sent to him in view of his expected stay in Mentone.*

3338

[*November 9, 1873*] Sunday. Orange. All right and happy. Met a sister of Piozzi Smyth's between Dijon and Lyons. *Signed:* R. L. S. *Parts of 2 pp. of letter. Unpublished.*

3339

[*November 15, 1873, and following days. Mentone*]. just jot down a word or two as the beginning of a note I shall try to finish for you tomorrow. *Signed:* R. L. Stevenson. *Last 8 pp. of letter. Partly written on stationery of* 17 Heriot Row. *Dated by R.L.S.'s mother. Unpublished. Stevenson writes of neighbors and residents at his hotel in Mentone, including the Dewars, Mrs. Devenish Walsh and Mr. and Mrs. Alfred Dowson.*

3340

[*November, 1873*] Wednesday [*and*] Friday. My dear Mother, Your choice of papers is admirable. *Signed:* Robert-Louis Stevenson. *3 pp. Dated by R.L.S.'s mother. About 11 lines of this 54-line letter are printed in A. C. Goodyear. . . . Autograph Collection . . . Sold by Auction . . . New York, 1927, lot 292.*

3341

[*December 17, 1873*] Monday. Monaco. My dear Madame, I am here now with Colvin. Weather as before. Body as before. *Signed:* R L Stevenson. *3 pp. Dated by R.L.S.'s mother. Pub-*

lished in the South Seas Edition, Letters, *Vol. 1, pp.* 131–132, *where 2 lines of the autograph are omitted.*

3342
Jan 2nd 1874. Hotel Mirabeau Menton. Here I am over in the east bay of Mentone, where I am not altogether sorry to find myself. *Signed:* Robert Louis Stevenson. *6 pp. Published in* The Letters, *1911, Vol. 1, pp.* 98–99. *About Stevenson's and Colvin's move to a new hotel, cold weather, and a little girl: Marie Johnstone.*

3343
Jan 4th 1874. Sunday. Menton. I got your letter today; but I am not sure that I do remember the Bishop of Toledo. *Signed:* Robert Louis Stevenson. *8 pp. Partly published in LFF, Vol. 1, pp.* 68–69, *where the first 33 lines of the autograph are omitted. Stevenson defends the working classes in connection with some action in Parliament in which Duncan M'Laren, M. P., figures. Partly about a Mrs. R.*

3344
Jan 7th 1874. Menton. Yes. I have been compared already to the Bishop of Toledo. I shall cease further correspondence on the next allusion to this ecclesiastic. *Signed:* Robert Louis Stevenson. *8 pp. Partly published in LFF, Vol. 1, pp.* 69–70, *where about 41 lines of the autograph are omitted. Partly about Marie Johnstone (a little American girl), and Nelitchka (a little Russian girl who spoke six languages).*

3345
Jan 14th / 74. Wednesday. Menton. The name of the Russian who puts me in mind of Jesse — or rather, I should say, the Russian, not her name, — is the Princess Zasetsky. *Signed:* ever your afft son Robert Louis Stevenson. *6 pp. Published in the* Skerryvore Edition, Letters, *Vol. 1, pp.* 142–143.

3346
[January 17? 1874] Saturday *[and]* Tuesday. *[Mentone].* My dear madam, let not anyone henceforward speak against my dress. *Signed twice:* R. L. S. *8 pp. R.L.S.'s mother has dated this:*

January 19, 1874. *Unpublished. Much about Mme. Garschine and Mme. Zassetsky.*

3347

21st Jan. [*1874*] Wednesday. Menton. Yesterday, I bought a new hat. It created the strangest delight in Mme Zayeska. *Unsigned. 4 pp. Unpublished.*

3348

[*January 29, 1874*] Thursday. [*Mentone*]. Marot vol 1. arrived. Thanks. The post has been at its old games. *Signed:* Robert Louis Stevenson. *4 pp. Partly published in* The Letters, *1911, Vol. 1, p. 117, where 12 lines of the autograph are omitted. About Scottish songs admired by Stevenson's Russian friends.*

3349

[*February 4, 1874*] Wednesday. [*Mentone*]. I know a book you can send me. Robertson's History of Scotland. *Signed:* Robert Louis Stevenson. *4 pp. Dated by R.L.S.'s mother. Unpublished. Stevenson writes of his intention to go to Alassio.*

3350

[*February 16, 1874. Mentone*]. My dear Mother, I did not write by yesterday's post, because I had no pen. *Signed:* Robert Louis Stevenson. *2 pp. Dated by R.L.S.'s mother. Unpublished.*

3351

[*February 17, 1874. Mentone*]. My dear madame, I must try to write a bit today. *Signed:* Robert Louis Stevenson. *4 pp. Dated by R.L.S.'s mother. Unpublished. Mostly about the Russian ladies, Nelitchka, and Robinet.*

3352

[*February 22, 1874. Mentone*]. My dear Mother, I am glad to hear you are better again. *Signed:* Robert Louis Stevenson. *2 pp. Dated by R.L.S.'s mother. Published in* The Letters, *1911, Vol. 1, p. 121.*

3353

[*February 27, 1874. Mentone*]. My dear Mother, February has as usual been depressing me. *Signed:* Robert Louis Stevenson, *and* R. L. S. *2 pp. Dated by R.L.S.'s mother. Unpublished. Largely about Nelitchka, and a game of characters.*

3354

[*March 9, 1874*] Monday. [*Mentone*]. We have all been getting photographed and the proofs are to be seen today. *Signed:* R. L. S. *2 pp. Partly published in* The Letters, *1911, Vol. 1, p. 123, where about 26 lines of the autograph are omitted. Partly about Nelitchka.*

3355

[*March 16, 1874. Mentone*]. My dear Mrs Stevenson Those who criticise the Bshp of Tldo do so at their peril. *Signed:* Ludovicus Toledensis, *and* Robert Louis Stevenson. *4 pp. Dated by R.L.S.'s mother. Unpublished. About one Ross, about spoken and written English, and about Stevenson's normal day.*

3356

[*March 28, 1874. Mentone*]. My dear Mother, Beautiful weather, perfect weather; sun, pleasant cooling winds; health very good: only incapacity to write. *Signature cut away. 3 pp. Dated March 28, 1873, by R.L.S.'s mother; the letter, however, was evidently written at Mentone in 1874. Published in LFF, Vol. 1, p. 75, where 6 lines of the autograph are omitted. Mostly about Prince Galitzin, a newly arrived member of the Russian party at Mentone.*

3357

[*April, 1874. Paris?*] My dear Mother, [*13 lines scratched out*] I write now that I have really turned the thing over in my mind about a scheme I had half matured at Mentone. *Signed:* Robert Louis Stevenson. *2 pp. Unpublished. About the possibility of his studying law at Göttingen, and using Prince Galitzin's notes which the latter has offered him.*

3358

[*April 17, 1874. Paris*]. It is a very great pity that I cannot make out Göttingen. *Signed:* Robert Louis Stevenson. *Parts of 2 pp. of letter. Dated by R. L. S.'s mother. Unpublished.*

3359

June 16th [*1874*] Tuesday. [*Hempstead*]. Dear mother, Just home in a wet warm wind. *Signed:* R. L. Stevenson *and* R. L. S. *5 pp. Year written by R.L.S.'s mother. About 16 lines of this 64-line letter are printed in A. C. Goodyear . . .* Autograph Collection . . . Sold by Auction . . . *New York, 1927, lot* 293.

3360

[*Early summer, 1874*]. Yacht Heron Off Glenelg. My dear Mother, Here we are My health is a miracle to man. *Signed:* Robert Louis Stevenson, *and* R. L. S. *3 pp. Written on stationery bearing R.L.S.'s monogram, during a yachting trip with Sir Walter Simpson. 19 lines of this 42-line letter are published in* Autograph Letters [*etc.*] . . . from the Library of the late Robert Louis Stevenson . . . *Part I . . . Sold . . . New York, 1914, pp.* 15–16, *lot* 67.

3361

[*August 7, 1876. Inverness*]. My dear Mother, Yesterday was one good day; and today it has begun again to disgrace itself. *Signed twice:* R. L. S. *3 pp. Written on stationery of* 3 Gt Stuart Street, Edinburgh. *On p. 1 the letter is dated, as above, in pencil in a hand other than Stevenson's. Unpublished. R. L. S. writes about the weather and the scenery around Inverness.*

3362

[*September 9, 1876*]. Compiegne. My dear mother, I have at last overtaken all your letters from Aug 23rd down to September 4th. *Signature cut away. 2 pp. Dated by R.L.S.'s mother. Unpublished. Written during his* Inland Voyage, *Stevenson states:* I do not know that I would have stuck to it as I have done, if it had not been for professional purposes: for an easy book may be written and sold.

3363

[January, 1877. Paris]. My dear Mother, Major Adair seems to me in the author's happiest vein. *Signed*: R. L. Stevenson. *4 pp. Dated by R.L.S.'s mother. Unpublished. Stevenson writes about meeting a very beautiful woman and her pretty daughter at a party in the Rue Notre Dame des Champs. His mother has written on p. 1:* I wonder if these were Fanny and Belle? *It seems quite likely that they were.*

3364

[January, 1877? Paris]. My dear mother, I am sitting in a café opposite the Gare du Nord. *Signed*: R. L. S. *2 pp. Dated by R.L.S.'s mother. Unpublished.*

3365

[February 1, 1877. Paris]. My dear mother, I am sorry I have been so long in writing, and was still more sorry, when I received yours last night, to hear about poor Jesse. *Signed*: Robert Louis Stevenson. *4 pp. Dated by R.L.S.'s mother. Unpublished. Partly about buying from Hiram Reynolds Bloomer a sketch by him.*

3366

[1877. Nemours?] My dear mother, All is well. I was proud to hear that my Watts had not forgotten me. *Signed*: Robert Louis Stevenson, *and* R. L. S. *2 pp. Dated by R.L.S.'s mother. Unpublished. Stevenson writes:* I don't believe you people [*R.L.S.'s parents*] know how much I care for you . . . I have been meditating a great deal about Christianity and I never saw it to be so wise and noble and consolatory as I do now.

3367

[February 17, 1878] Sunday *[Paris]*. My dear mother, My book has run to sheet Q.; with my usual superstition I see a prophecy in that. *Signed*: R.L.S. *1 p. Dated by R.L.S.'s mother. Partly published in Henry A. Colgate.* The Stevenson Library . . . Sold by Auction . . . *New York, 1928, p. 39, lot 184, where about 10 lines of the autograph are omitted.*

3368

[*February, 1878. Paris*]. My dear mother, I am kept here a day
or so longer than I had meant. *Signed:* R. L. S. *3 pp. Dated by
R.L.S.'s mother. Unpublished.*

3369

[*February 27, 1878. Paris*]. My dear mother £30 recd; many
thanks. *Signed:* Robert Louis Stevenson. *2 pp. Dated by R.L.S.'s
mother. Unpublished. Among other things about* Will o' the
Mill, *John Collier, Colvin.*

3370

[*Spring, 1878. France*]. My dear mother, Yes, I think David
Douglas would be all right. *Signed:* Robert Louis Stevenson.
*1 p. Unpublished. Stevenson lists some names, possibly of
people to whom he wants copies of* An Inland Voyage *sent.*

3371

[*November 25? 1878*] Monday. [*London*]. My dear mother, The
walking tour broke down. My heel gave way and hurt horrid,
and it was dull, cold and not singularly pretty on the road.
Signed: R. L. S. *2 pp. Written on* Savile Club *stationery. Dated:
November 28, by R.L.S.'s mother. Unpublished. Stevenson
mentions work on a* chance thing, *viz.:* Deacon Brodie.

3372

[*December 6, 1878. London*]. My dear mother, . . . I have not
yet got the money. *Signed:* Robert Louis Stevenson, *and* R. L. S.
3 pp. Written on Savile Club *stationery. Dated by R.L.S.'s
mother. Unpublished. Stevenson makes further mention of his
and Henley's work on* Deacon Brodie.

3373

[*May, 1879. London*]. My dear mother, I have been in such a
muddle about my plans that I did not know what to write.
Signed: R. L. S. *3 pp. Dated by R.L.S.'s mother. Written on*
Savile Club *stationery. Unpublished.*

3374

[*June 19, 1879. Paris*]. My dear mother, I have filled up the surveyor's game. *Signed:* R. L. S. *2 pp. Dated by R.L.S.'s mother. Published in the* Skerryvore Edition, Letters, *Vol. 1, pp.* 351–352.

3375

[*July, 1879. London*]. My dear mother After a desperate struggle with the elements of every sort and principally money, I arrived last night in London the possessor of 4 shillings. *Signed:* R. L. S. *2 pp. Written on* Savile Club *stationery. Dated by R.L.S.'s mother. Published in the* Skerryvore Edition, Letters, *Vol. 1, p.* 353.

3376

June 30th [*and*] July 6th 1880. Silverado. My dear mother, You must indeed pardon me. This life takes up all my time and strength. *Signed:* R. L. S. *2 pp. Written in pencil. Published in facsimile in Stevenson's* Silverado Journal, San Francisco, 1954, *between pp. [92] and [93]. Stevenson writes of his improving health and plan to return soon to England.*

3377

[*July 16, 1880. California*]. Why Fanny talks of me as a genius above I know not. *Signed:* R. L. S. *1 p. Unpublished. This is an addition to a letter by Mrs. R. L. S.*

3378

[*October 22, 1880. Paris*]. L. S. chips in. After that I had to stay yet another day to try to see Caldecott. *Signed:* R. L. S. *2 pp. Dated by R.L.S.'s mother. Unpublished. This is an addition to a letter by Mrs. R. L. S.*

3379

Dec. 15th [*1880. Davos*]. My dear mother, I shall tell you about this morning. *Unsigned. 1 p. Unpublished. Stevenson writes about sledges moving on the snow covered roads. This is an addition to a letter by Mrs. R. L. S.*

3380

Feb 5th 81/ [*Davos*]. My dear mother, I have yours. I think there is no doubt, on the whole that I should stay here. *Unsigned. 3 pp. Unpublished. Dr. Ruedi says that R.L.S. might go directly to a place in the Scottish Highlands for a visit, without stopping anywhere en route. This does not seem feasible to R. L. S. Mrs. R.L.S. has written an addition to this letter.*

3381

[*March, 1881. Davos*]. My dear mother, on receipt, not of your last — the last had the money in it — we again consulted Ruedi. *Unsigned. 2 pp. Dated by R.L.S.'s mother. Unpublished. Stevenson writes about recently published articles of his, Fanny's bad health, Humphrey Sandwith, etc. Mrs. R. L. S. has written an addition to this letter.*

3382

[*March, 1881. Davos*]. This from girl's [*Fanny's*] letter has been delayed anytime by my blame: she has been quite ill. *Signed:* R. L. S. *1 p. Unsigned. Stevenson writes of Fanny's plan to see a doctor in Paris.*

3383

[*Late March, 1881. Davos*]. My dear mother, I have just received your kind letter; it finds me a widower for a week. *Signed:* R. L. S. *2 pp. Unpublished. Mrs. R. L. S. has gone to see a doctor in Paris. Stevenson writes of going to Italy in May.*

3384

[*April 4, 1881*]. Monday. [*Davos*]. My dear mother, I have a great deal of partly ill partly good news. First, poor Bertie died yesterday morning. *Signed:* Robert Louis Stevenson. *2 pp. Dated by R.L.S.'s mother. Unpublished. Fanny has returned from a trip to Paris. R.L.S. would like to meet his parents in Fontainebleau in May.*

3385

Decr 26th [*and*] 27th [*1881. Davos*]. My dear mother, Yesterday Sunday and Christmass [*sic*] we finished this eventful journey by a drive in an *open* sleigh. *Signed:* R. L. S. *4 pp.*

Written on stationery of Hôtel & Pension Buol. *Published in LFF, Vol. I, pp. 227–228, where 13 lines of the autograph are omitted. R.L.S. describes a very cold journey, and Fanny's bad health.*

3386

Jan. 3rd [*1882. Davos*]. My dear mother, Money came. There is, I do think, and so does the Doctor, an improvement [*in Mrs. R.L.S.'s health*]. *Signed:* R L. S. *1 p. Written on stationery of* Hôtel & Pension Buol. *Unpublished. Stevenson accepts his father's criticisms of the Preface to* Familiar Studies of Men and Books.

3387

[*April*] 8th. Saturday [*1882. Davos*]. My dear mother, Herewith please find belated birthday present. Fanny has another. *Signed:* R. L. Stevenson. *3 pp. Dated April 9 by R.L.S.'s mother. Partly published in LFF, Vol. 1, pp. 240–241, where 15 lines of the autograph are omitted.*

3388

[*April 17, 1882. Davos*]. My dear mother, I have just received yours. Bob was only married last summer. *Signed twice:* R. L. S. *4 pp. Unpublished. Partly about the marriage of Bob Stevenson to Louisa (Pinland?)*

3389

30th July 1882 Sunday. Kingussie. My dear mother, The Die is Cast. *Signature (in a hand other than Stevenson's?):* R. L. Stevenson. *2 pp. Unpublished. Stevenson writes about rooms he has engaged at Kingussie, and about the care of his wife's health.*

3390

21st [*October*] Saturday [*1882. Marseille?*] My dear mother, Tomorrow we hope to go in. *Unsigned. 2 pp. Unpublished. Stevenson writes of moving into a house at Campagne Defli, St. Marcel. Mrs. R. L. S. has written an addition to this letter.*

3391

11th Nov. [*1882*] Saturday. Campagne Defli [*St. Marcel*]. My dear mother, I do think I am better. *Signed:* R L. Stevenson. *2 pp. Published in the* Skerryvore Edition, Letters, *Vol. 2, pp. 112–113. Mrs. R. L. S. has written an addition to this letter.*

3392

November 13th 1882. Campagne Defli, St. Marcel, Banlieue de Marseille. My dear Mother, Your delightful letters duly arrived this morning. *Signed:* R. L. S. *3 pp. Drawing on p. 2. Published in* LFF, *Vol. 1, p. 254, where about 7 lines of the autograph are omitted.*

3393

[*November, 1882*] Tuesday. [*St. Marcel*]. My dear mother, Will you please send us £54 instanter. *Unsigned. 2 pp. Dated by R. L. S.'s mother. Unpublished. The money asked for is to make an advance payment of rent. Mrs. R. L. S. has written an addition to this letter.*

3394

Nov 19th [*1882. St. Marcel*]. My dear mother see to what we are reduced! *Signed:* R. L. S. *2 pp. Unpublished. The first sentence of this letter refers to the small scrap of paper on which it is written, containing an impression from part of a woodcut he made for* Rob and Ben; *or the Pirate and the Apothecary. Mrs. R. L. S. has written an addition to this letter.*

3395

Dec 23rd 1882. St. Marcel. My dear mother, Fanny is away into town to meet Sam. *Signed:* R. L. S. *1 p. Published in the* Skerryvore Edition, Letters, *Vol. 2, pp. 114–115.*

3396

[*January 23, 1883*]. Grand Hotel — Nice. My dear mother, I have just returned from the silliest excursion ever made. *Signed:* R L S. *2 pp. Dated by R.L.S.'s mother. Unpublished. Stevenson has just made an unnecessary railway journey of six hours because the word* not *was omitted from a telegram.*

3397

16th [*and*] 17th Feb. [*1883*]. Marseille. My dear mother, We hope to leave on Sunday, or at latest Monday for Hyères. *Signed:* John Wardrop Tawse. *2 pp. Unpublished. Stevenson writes that Fanny is on the 17th* as cross as Two Sticks.

3398

Feb 6th [*i.e. 26th ? 1883*]. Hotel des Iles d'Or Hyères. My dear mother, There is not much bettering in the rate of your correspondence. *Signed:* R. L. Stevenson. *2 pp. Unpublished. Stevenson complains of a mistral.*

3399

[*February or March, 1883. Hyères*]. My dear mother, As my father is to be away, I wish to seize occasion by the forelock. *Signed:* R. L S. *3 pp. Unpublished. Stevenson thinks he can support himself if his health holds. He does not wish to return to England. He hopes his father can find some occupation if he retires. Mrs. R. L. S. has written an addition to this letter.*

3400

[*March, 1883 ? Hyères ?*] I enclose two letters. *Signed:* R. L. S. *1 p. Unpublished. This is an addition to a letter by Mrs. R. L. S.*

3401

[*April 20, 1883. Hyères*]. My dear mother, Many thanks for the coin £50. *Signed:* R. L. S. *1 p. Dated by R.L.S.'s mother. Unpublished. Stevenson writes of better health, and states that he is* up to the waist in a story: a kind of a 1 volume novel.

3402

[*June, 1883. Hyères*]. My dear mother, please also get some cards for Sam. "Mr S. L. Osbourne" would be the legend. *Signed:* R. L. S. *1 p. Dated by R.L.S.'s mother. Unpublished. Stevenson writes that he had to get a new plate of teeth. Mrs. R.L.S. has written an addition to this letter.*

3403

June 21. 1883. [*Hyères*]. My dear mother, Sam has been worse, but is now better again. *Signed:* R. L. S. *3 pp. Written on sta-*

tionery of La Solitude. *Dated by R.L.S.'s mother. Unpublished. Stevenson writes of plans to meet his parents at Royat.*

3404

[*September 11, 1883. Hyères*]. My dear mother, I cant think why Cassells don't send me my money. *Signed:* R. L. S. *3 pp. Written on stationery of La Solitude. Unpublished. Stevenson refers to his essay on* The character of male dogs.

3405

[*November, 1883. Hyères*]. My dear mother You must not blame me too much for my silence. *Signed:* R. L. S. *3 pp. Published in LFF, Vol. 1, pp. 295–296, where about 6 lines of the autograph are omitted. Stevenson writes of work on* Prince Otto *and of rewriting parts of* The Silverado Squatters.

3406

[*December, 1883. Hyères*]. My dear mother, We have been one and another in very poor case indeed. *Signed:* Otto. *3 pp. Dated by R.L.S.'s mother. Unpublished. Stevenson writes about* Treasure Island, Prince Otto, The Silverado Squatters, *etc.*

3407

[*December, 1883. Hyères*]. My dear mother, We have been in a terrible quandary as to Sam's Christmas present. *Signed:* R L. S. *2 pp. Dated by R.L.S.'s mother. Published in the* Skerryvore Edition, Letters, *Vol. 2, p. 192.*

3408

Last Sunday of 83 [*December 30. Hyères*]. My dear mother, I give my father up. *Signed:* R. L. S. *4 pp. Published in LFF, Vol. 1, pp. 303–304, where 8 lines of the autograph are omitted. Stevenson continues to scold his father.*

3409

[*1883 ?*] My dear mother, so far Fanny, who has now bust up, and makes me very uneasy. It is her ear she suffers from. *Signed:* R. L. S. *1 p. Unpublished. Stevenson describes his wife's symptoms and asks for money. This is an addition to a letter by Mrs. R. L. S.*

3410

[*February, 1884. Nice*]. My dear mother, I see I must explain the whole affair to you. *Signed:* R. L. Stevenson. *3 pp. In pencil. Dated by R.L.S.'s mother. Unpublished. Stevenson writes of his recent acute illness. He states:* I very nearly died of course. *Mrs. R. L. S. has written an addition to this letter.*

3411

[*April 19, 1884. Hyères*]. My dear Mother, Mrs Fergusson has written a quite nice answer. *Signed:* R. L. S. *4 pp. Dated by R.L.S.'s mother. Unpublished. Stevenson writes:* My marriage has been the most successful in the world . . . She [*Fanny*] is everything to me: wife, mother, sister, daughter and dear companion.

3412

[*June, 1884. Royat*]. My dear mother, What am I to say? I only beg you not to hurry. *Signed:* Mr Muddler Mr Addlehead Mr Wandering Butterwits Mr Shiftless Inconsistency Sir Indecision Contentment. *4 pp. In pencil. Unpublished. Stevenson writes of uncertainty in his plans.*

3413

[*December 15, 1884. Bournemouth*]. My dear Mother, Perhaps the Milton is at Hyères. *Signed:* R. L. S. *2 pp. Dated by R.L.S.'s mother. Published in the* Skerryvore Edition, Letters, *Vol. 2, p. 260. Sargent's portrait of Stevenson is mentioned; also reference is made to R.L.S.'s father's appearances as President of the Royal Society of Edinburgh.*

3414

[*May, 1885. Skerryvore, Bournemouth*]. My dear mother. Charming letter — yes, Fanny looks very pretty in hat and cloak. *Signed:* R. L. S. *1 p. R.L.S.'s mother has dated this May, but R. L. S. refers to March weather. Unpublished.*

3415

[*October 8, 1885. Bournemouth*]. My dear mother, Well, I have made rather a mess of Sam's exam. *Signed:* Louis, *and* R. L. S. *2 pp. Dated by R.L.S.'s mother. Unpublished. Stevenson did*

not permit Lloyd Osbourne to take an examination, and in this
letter expresses the belief that he made a wrong decision.

3416

[*April, 1886. Matlock*]. My dear mother, I must honestly say
the place does not seem to agree with me. *Signed:* Robert Louis
Stevenson. *2 pp. Dated by R.L.S.'s mother. Published in the*
Skerryvore Edition, Letters, Vol. 2, pp. 333–334, where several
words of the autograph are omitted. Stevenson is with his father
at Matlock and in this letter complains of his father's bad humor.

3417

[*May, 1886. Bournemouth*]. My dear Mother, I was very vexed
my letter came too late. *Signed:* R L. S. *3 pp. Dated by R.L.S.'s*
mother. Unpublished.

3418

[*June 28, 1886. Bournemouth*]. My dear mother, I have been
very well till just lately when I have had a throw back and am
now in bed. *Signed:* R L. S. *2 pp. Dated by R.L.S.'s mother.*
Unpublished.

3419

Sept 14. 1886. [*Bournemouth*]. My dear mother, I do not know
where my wits have been. *Signed:* R L. S. *3 pp. Unpublished.*

3420

[*September 21, 1886. Bournemouth*]. My dear mother, Your
letter from Glasgow has just come in and interested me much.
Signed: R. L. S. *4 pp. Dated by R.L.S.'s mother. Unpublished.*
Stevenson writes of relations with servants.

3421

[*June 4, 1887. Bournemouth*]. My dearest mother, A cloud of
correspondence and another of congested torpor and stupidity
overlay me. *Signed:* R. L. S. *3 pp. Written on black-bordered*
stationery. Dated by R.L.S.'s mother. Unpublished.

3422

[*June 15, 1887. Bournemouth*]. My dear mother, I have not written for a cruel time. *Signed:* R L S. *2 pp. Written on black-bordered stationery. Dated by R.L.S.'s mother. Unpublished.*

3423

[*July 1, 1887. London*]. My dear mother, We came up yesterday from Bournemouth to Colvin's. *Signed:* R. L. S. *8 pp. Dated by R.L.S.'s mother. Unpublished. About the loss of his father Stevenson writes:* I feel it more than I can say: every day more. *He suggests that his mother come and stay with Fanny and him. He offers to send her money. He mentions plans to go to America. He devoted 2 pp. to John* ——, *who has been working for him, unsatisfactorily, at Skerryvore.*

3424

[*June, 1889. Honolulu*]. My dear mother, herewith goes a copy of my first letter from the leper settlement. *Signed:* R. L. S. *2 pp. Published in the* Skerryvore Edition, Letters, *Vol. 3, pp. 146–147. Reporting on his visit to the leper colony at Molokai.*

3425

Sept. 30th [*1889*]. "Equator Town" Apemama. Well, no morning Ta came in after all. *Unsigned. Unfinished? 4 pp. Unpublished. Stevenson complains of mosquitoes, inadequate food and glare. He mentions his hope to get to Samoa, Sydney and Scotland.*

3426

March 5, 1890. Union Club — Sydney. My dear mother I understand the family keeps you somewhat informed. *Signed:* R. L. S. *2 pp. This is a copy in the hand of R.L.S.'s mother. Published in* The Letters, *1911, Vol. 3, pp. 160–161, where words vary from those in the autograph in several places. Stevenson informs his mother of his letter to Dr. Hyde about Father Damion.*

3427

[*March 20, 1890. Sydney*]. Stop writing to Sydney: Publish this abroad. *Signed:* R. L. S. *1 p. Dated by R.L.S.'s mother. Unpublished. In this letter Stevenson still plans to come to Scotland.*

3428

[*September, 1890. Between Sydney and Samoa on the S. S. Lübeck*]. Now nearing Upolu A bad trip. this is Monday and it is still doubtful if we get in tonight. *Signed:* R. L. S. *Last 3 pp. of letter. Written on stationery of the* Norddeutscher Lloyd. *Dated by R. L. S.'s mother. Unpublished. Stevenson writes about a visit to a college in Tonga where he made a speech; and about the Rev. James Chalmers.*

3429

[*1890*]. *Signed:* R. L. S. *Parts of 2 pp. of letter. Unpublished. Stevenson writes of a possible cruise to Tahiti or Fiji, and of the imminent publication of his* Ballads.

3430

[*January, 1893. Vailima*]. My dear mother, My letter can't be found! I am recovering at last. *Signed:* R. L. S. *1 p. Unpublished. Mrs. R. L. S. has written an addition to this letter.*

3431

April 17th 1893. [*Vailima*]. My dear mother Excuse me beginning by the Amanuensis for I am very tired and if I were to begin myself shouldn't have the spirit to tell you anything. *Unsigned. 4 pp. 7 lines are in Stevenson's hand; the remainder of the letter is in the hand of Isobel Strong, including 8 lines which are her own. Unpublished. Stevenson writes of Fanny's illness, and of the household and visitors at Vailima.*

3432

June 18th 1893. Vailima. My dear mother The Epistle to the Vailimans came duly and in spite of the bad news gave us huge delight as usual. *Unsigned. 8 pp. 9 lines are in Stevenson's hand; the remainder of the letter is in the hand of Isobel Strong. Unpublished. Stevenson gives many details about people and activities at Vailima and in Apia.*

3433

July 18th 1893. Vailima. My dear Mother Kindly observe the following earrands [*sic*]. *Signed:* (R. L. S.), *with the word forged written thereunder. 4 pp. The letter is in the hand of Isobel Strong. Unpublished.*

3434

Sep. 6th 1893. Vailima Samoa. [*and later in September*] about 13° N[*orth latitude*] S S. Mariposa [*en route to Honolulu*]. My dear Mother: What is our news? Well, first of all, Graham goes home by the next mail steamer. *Signed:* R. L. S. *6 pp. The letter is in the hand of Isobel Strong (including about 3 lines of her own) except for the last 9 lines, written on the S. S. Mariposa, in Stevenson's hand. Unpublished. Stevenson writes about the construction of a back court at Vailima, supervised by Fanny, about an attractive Samoan child, a photographer named Andrews, etc.*

3435

[*October — , 1893, and*] Sunday 15th Oct. Monday. Tuesday 17th. [*Honolulu*]. My dear Mother Here I am at what used to be the Herberts place, and jolly sick. *Unsigned. 3 pp. Written on stationery of Sans Souci Seaside Resort. Unpublished. Stevenson writes of his attack of fever, and of people he has met in Honolulu.*

3436

Jan 1st [*1894. Vailima*]. My dear mother, Thank you very much for your interesting birthday letter. *Signed:* R. L. Stevenson. *4 pp. Unpublished. Stevenson writes:* I am tired out and intend to work no more for six months at least.

3437

Jany 29th [*1894. Vailima*]. My dear mother, There is now not much time between the mails. *Signed:* R. L. S. *8 pp. Unpublished. Stevenson writes of visitors at Vailima and mentions the possibility of his mother's returning to Samoa. Contains diagram of part of Vailima.*

3438

Feb 23rd 94. Vailima. My dear mother Monday the 19th we had all gone to bed pretty tired. *Unsigned. Unfinished? 8 pp. The letter is in the hand of Isobel Strong. Unpublished. It is mostly devoted to the description of a ball at Vailima.*

3439

April 24th 1894. [*Vailima*]. My dear mother, We have only a few moments to do all our letters. *Unsigned. 2 pp. Unpublished. Stevenson writes of the war, of people his mother knew in Samoa, of teaching Sunday School.*

3440

March 28: 1854. [*Edinburgh*]. dear Papa do come home to see me, my dear papa will you bring a book to mama too. *Signed:* Robert Lewis Balfour Stevenson. *1 p. At bottom:* Every word dictated by Mr Peter Sprode. *In the hand of R.L.S.'s mother. Facsimile. Unpublished.*

3441

August 7. 1856. 21 Pitt [?] Street [*Edinburgh*]. My dear Papa I hope you are quite well & how do you like your voyage. *Signed:* R. L. B. S. *4 pp. In the hand of R.L.S.'s mother, signed by Stevenson. Unpublished.*

3442

[*1863?*] My dear papa I am a great deal better but I have begun to despair of 5/−. *Signed:* R. L. B. Stevenson. *1 p. At top:* Allways[*sic*] an eye to business. *Partly published in an unidentified dealer's catalogue, where two lines of the autograph are omitted. Stevenson writes:* I am going to send doctor Paul's story of Dr Muir to the magazine (of course suppressing names).

3443

[*October, 1863*] Friday [*and*] Monday. [*Spring Grove, Isleworth*]. Pater meus I received your kind letter today with the amusing account of Coolins encounter with the dog. *Signed:* R. Stevenson. *4 pp. Drawing by Stevenson on p. 4 titled:* The Walk. *2 or 3 lines of this letter are printed in A. C. Goodyear ... Autograph Collection ... Sold by Auction ... New York, 1927, lot 290. Stevenson asks his father to send him a diary of the doings of his dog, Coolins. Stevenson sends a specimen of a Latin exercise composed by him. He writes:* I have done something! I have made a grand step! I have appeared before the eyes of the publick not only as an author but. *Here the sentence ends unfinished.*

3444

[*February, 1864. Mentone*]. My dear papa I hope that your chest will be better before this letter arrives. *Signed:* R. L. Ste-

venson. *4 pp. With mounted head of man (in water color?).*
Dated by R.L.S.'s mother. Unpublished.

3445

[*March, 1864. Mentone*]. My dear papa We have got a general "de la suite de l'empereur de Russie." *Signed:* R. Stevenson.
3 pp. Drawings by Stevenson. At top of p. 1: Scene from "The
Unsociable Grosbeak of Menton." *Dated by R.L.S.'s mother.*
P. 1 of this letter is reproduced in facsimile in Autograph Letters
[*etc.*] . . . from the Library of the late Robert Louis Stevenson
. . . Part I . . . Sold . . . *New York, 1914, facing p. 8.*

3446

[*February, 1865. Glen Villa, Torquay*]. Dear Papa I am in
daily hourly expectation of Jessy, so is Mama. *Signed:* R. Stevenson. *2 pp. The place and the year are written by R.L.S.'s*
mother. Unpublished.

3447

[*February? 1865*] Sunday. Glen Villa [*Torquay*]. Mein guter
Väter I take the opportunity of writing to you and reporting
to you my progress. *Signed:* R. Stevenson. *4 pp. Partly dated by*
R.L.S.'s mother. 7 lines of this 57-line letter are printed in Autograph Letters [*etc.*] . . . from the Library of the late Robert
Louis Stevenson . . . Part I . . . Sold . . . *New York, 1914, p. 9,*
lot 34.

3448

[*April, 1866*]. Thursday. 2 Sulyarde T[*errace, Torquay*]. Respected paternal relative, I write to make a request of the most
moderate nature. *Signed:* R Stevenson. *3 pp. On black-bordered*
stationery. Published in LFF, Vol. 1, pp. 8–9. Stevenson asks
his father for half a crown.

3449

[*1866?*]. Wednesday. Darnley Ho. Bridge of Allan. My dear
Papa, I wish you to go to Roland's; get my foil and mask and
glove; and buy me another foil, mask and glove from the Captain. *Signed:* R Stevenson. *3 pp. Unpublished. R. L. S.'s mother*
has written an addition to this letter.

3450

[*July, 1868*]. 'Kenzie House or whatever it is calld Anstruther. My dear Father, My lodgings are very nice and I don't think there are any children. *Signed:* R. L. Stevenson. *6 pp. Dated by R.L.S.'s mother. Partly published in* The Letters, *1911, Vol. 1, pp. 11–12, where about 31 lines of the autograph are omitted.*

3451

17th July [*1868*]. Office Anster [*i.e. Anstruther*]. My dear father, We had an accident here today: a truck went over and knocked in the divers' assistents[*sic*]. *Signed:* R L. Stevenson. *1 p. Unpublished.*

3452

[*September, 1868*] Thursday. [*Wick*]. My dear father, I have had a long hard days work in cold, wind and almost incessant rain. *Signed:* R. L. Stevenson. *3 pp. Dated by R.L.S.'s mother. Unpublished. About harbor construction.*

3453

[*January ? 1874*] Friday. [*Mentone*]. I don't know what to say to you, my life has become so stereotyped again. *Unsigned. Incomplete? 2 pp. Unpublished. Stevenson is glad that students made a row.*

3454

[*January 26, 1874*] Monday [*and*] Thursday. [*Mentone*]. My dear father, Recd divers . . . Bills of Exchange. *Signed:* R. L. Stevenson, *and* Robert Louis Stevenson. *6 pp. Dated: January 21, 1874, by R.L.S.'s mother. Partly published in* The Letters, *1911, Vol. 1, p. 116, where about 30 lines of the autograph are omitted.*

3455

[*February 1, 1874. Mentone*]. I am so sorry to hear of poor Mr Murrys death. *Signed:* Robert Louis Stevenson. *4 pp. Dated by R.L.S.'s mother. Published in* The Letters, *1911, Vol. 1, pp. 118–119, where 9 lines of the autograph are omitted. Stevenson is disgusted with the idea that the easy classes in Britain should pay no higher rate of income tax than those with smaller in-comes.*

3456

[*February 6, 1874*] Friday. [*Mentone*]. The wine has arrived and a dozen of it has been transferred to me. *Signed:* Robert Louis Stevenson. *4 pp. Partly published in* The Letters, *1911, Vol. 1, p. 119, where about 16 lines of the autograph are omitted. About a masquerade, a visit from Andrew Lang, and Steven-son's new cloak.*

3457

[*March 11, 1874*] Wednesday. [*Mentone*]. I am very nearly through with my money again. *Signed:* R. L. S. *2 pp. Dated by R.L.S.'s mother. Unpublished. Mostly about his expenses.*

3458

Decr 17th [*1880. Davos*]. My dear Father, Here is the scheme as well as I can foresee. *Signed:* R L. S. *3 pp. Partly published in LFF, Vol. 1, pp. 187–188, where 13 lines of the autograph are omitted.*

3459

[*December, 1880. Davos*]. My dear father, did I mention Pen-nant's Tour through the Highlands. *Signed twice:* R. L. S. *7 pp. Unpublished. This letter is largely concerned with R.L.S.'s pro-jected history of the Scottish Highlands, including books he wishes to use as source material. 1 p. contains 5 queries. It is not certain that all these pp. are a part of the same letter.*

3460

[*December, 1880. Davos*]. My dear father, the next box of books I wish to contain the books marked with a cross. *Unsigned. 2 pp. Unpublished. The letter, written in ink, is preceded by a list of books written in pencil. Stevenson writes of his plans for a book on the Highlands.*

3461

14th May [1881]. Saturday. [Paris]. My dear father, You are exactly right as to my state of mind, and I at once recognised it. Want of thankfulness. Signed: R. L. S. 2 pp. Unpublished.

3462

[October, 1881. Davos]. My dear father, It occurred to me last night in bed that I could write The Murder of Red Colin: A Story of the Forfeited Estates. Signed: R L. S. 1 p. Unpublished. Mrs. R. L. S. has written an addition to this letter addressed to R. L. S.'s mother.

3463

Decr 9th [1881. Davos]. My dear father, You have misunderstood me as to the books. Signed: R L S. 3 pp. A few lines of this letter are published in The Rosenbach Company. A Catalogue of Original Manuscripts [etc.] ... New York, 1933, p. 39, lot 315. Stevenson is pleased by offers made by two London publishers for items he is to write. Really I ought to begin to make money now.

3464

17th October 1882. [Marseille]. My dear father, At last your letters arrive thick, Hyères having consented to yield up its spoils. Signed: R. L. Stevenson. 4 pp. Written on stationery of Terminus Hotel, Marseille. Partly published in LFF, Vol. 1, p. 253, where 20 lines of the autograph are omitted. Mrs. R. L. S. has written an addition to this letter.

3465

Jan 11. 1883. Grand Hotel Nice. My dear father, No. Cassandra was not Cassandra, as you imagine. I have just come from being weighed and I am down to 7 stone 11¼, far lower than I have ever been in my recollection. Signed: R. L. S. 5 pp. Unpublished. Stevenson expresses dissatisfaction with himself, and uncertainty about his future. Cassandra is Thomas Stevenson's nickname for Mrs. R. L. S.

3466

August 1883. Saturday. Royat. My dear father, On receipt of a very cheering double letter from my mother and you, I yesterday telegraphed to save time. *Signed:* R. L. Stevenson. *3 pp. Written on stationery of* La Solitude, Hyères-les-Palmiers, Var. *About 8 lines of this 39-line letter are printed in* Autograph Letters [*etc.*] . . . from the Library of the late Robert Louis Stevenson . . . Part I . . . Sold . . . New York, 1914, p. 22, lot 110.

3467

12th Oct. 1883. [*Hyères*]. My dear father, I have just lunched; the day is exquisite. *Signed:* Robert Louis Stevenson. *4 pp. Written on stationery of* La Solitude. *Published in LFF, Vol. 1, pp. 291–292, where 4 lines of the autograph are omitted.*

3468

[*October, 1883. Hyères*]. My dear father, Many thanks for yours and my mother's letter which came together this morning. *Signature and part of letter cut away. 4 pp. Written on stationery of* La Solitude. *Dated by R.L.S.'s mother. Unpublished. Stevenson writes about laying down wine in his cellar, and about writing* The Travelling Companion.

3469

[*January, 1884. Pension Rose Torelli, Nice*]. My dear father, I write you a first line to say that I am better. *Signed:* Whilst crippled Andy. *2 pp. Written, in pencil, on stationery of* La Solitude. *Dated by R.L.S.'s mother. Unpublished. Stevenson describes a recent sharp illness. Mrs. R. L. S. has written an addition to this letter.*

3470

[*March or April, 1884. Hyères*]. My dear father, My eyes are on the mend though I can still as you see only write with a very high action. *Signed:* R. L. S. *4 pp. Written on stationery of* La Solitude. *Dated by R.L.S.'s mother. Unpublished.*

3471

[*April 19, 1884. Hyères*]. My dear father, Yesterday I very powerfully stated the Heresia Stevensoniana. *Signed:* Doctor

Stevenson. *6 pp. Dated by R.L.S.'s mother. Published in* LFF, *Vol. 1, pp.* 315–316, *where 4 lines of the autograph are omitted. Stevenson writes about* Thrawn Janet, The Merry Men, *and* Scott's *novels.*

3472

April 20th 84. [*Hyères*]. My dear father, I have been much out of sorts for some days, but today I begin to mend. *Signed:* R. L. S. *4 pp. Unpublished.*

3473

[*October 29, 1884. Bournemouth*]. My dear father, We have been twice cheated out of a house. *Signed:* R L S. *3 pp. Dated by R.L.S.'s mother. Partly published in* A Remarkable Collection of Autograph Letters by the late Robert Louis Stevenson . . . Part III . . . Sold . . . New York, 1916, p. 39, *lot 226, where about 14 lines of the autograph are omitted. Stevenson writes about renting a house at Bournemouth, viz. Bonallie Tower, Branksome Park.*

3474

[*November 5, 1884*]. Bonallie Towers Branksome Park Bournemouth (The three B's). My dear father, Allow me to say, in a strictly Pickwickian sense, that you are a silly fellow. *Signed:* Robert Louis Stevenson. *3 pp. Dated by R.L.S.'s mother. Published in* LFF, *Vol. 1, p. 336. Stevenson expresses differences with his father concerning* Admiral Guinea.

3475

[*November, 1884. Bonallie Tower, Bournemouth*]. My dear father I have no hesitation in recommending you to let your name go up. *Signed twice:* R. L. S. *4 pp. Dated by R.L.S.'s mother. Published in* LFF, *Vol. 1, pp.* 334–335, *where about 8 lines of the autograph are omitted. Stevenson writes about the proposal of his father for the office of President of the Royal Society of Edinburgh.*

3476

March 20th 1885. B[*onallie*] T[*ower*] B[*ranksome*] P[*ark*] B[*ournemouth*]. My dear father, It is certainly very annoying, but after all a great deal of water runs under the bridge. *Signed:* R L. S. *3 pp. About 17 lines of this 46-line letter are printed in A. C. Goodyear. . . . Autograph Collection . . . Sold by Auction . . . New York, 1927, lot 299. Stevenson writes about his father's having been chosen President of the Royal Society of Edinburgh, and about work on* Kidnapped.

3477

Oct. 24: 1885. Skerryvore Bournemouth. My dear father, A lower epistle I certainly never received but I consoled myself by the fact that I have received "o' them" before now, and that the sun came out again after the cloud. *Signed:* Robert Louis Stevenson. *2 pp. Unpublished. R. L. S. and his father are both in low spirits.*

3478

Jan 18th 1886. [*Bournemouth*]. My dear father, I am up to the neck in work and keeping very well in health. *Signed:* R. L. S. *2 pp. Unpublished. Stevenson writes that he has resumed work on* David Balfour *and has adopted two proposals regarding it made by his father.*

3479

21th [*sic*] Jan. 1886. Skerryvore. My dear father. Yesterday we were both ahead, and today I am up but the Vandergrifter (that heraldic animal) [*his wife*] still couchant. *Signed:* R. L. S. *3 pp. Unpublished. Of* David Balfour *Stevenson writes:* I don't think it will be so interesting to read, but it is curious and picturesque.

3480

[*May 23. 1886. Bournemouth*]. My dearest father, The Cassandra woman being fled I have been alone with Sam. *Signed:* R L. S. *2 pp. Dated by R.L.S.'s mother. Unpublished.*

3481

[*June 6, 1886. Bournemouth*]. My dearest father, Your letter to Fanny has come in. *Signed:* R. L. S. *2 pp. Dated by R.L.S.'s mother. Unpublished.*

3482

[*October, 1863*] Wedensday[*sic*]. [*Spring Grove, Isleworth*].
My dear Parients [*sic*] I have received your three kind letters.
Signed: R. Stevenson. *4 pp. Drawing by Stevenson. 13 lines of
this 42-line letter are printed in* Autograph Letters[*etc.*] . . .
from the Library of the late Robert Louis Stevenson . . . Part
I . . . Sold . . . *New York, 1914, p. 7, lot 17.*

3483

[*July, 1868*] Tuesday. Kenzie House Anstruther. I am utterly
sick of this grey, grim, sea-beaten hole. *Signed:* R L Stevenson,
and R. L. S. *6 pp. Dated by R.L.S.'s mother. Unpublished.*

3484

Oct 29th 1873. Wednesday. 15 Chepstow Place [*London*]. My
dear Father & Mother, I am afraid this letter will surprise you
a little but I have to let you know what Dr Clarks opinion is.
Signed: R. L. Stevenson. *4 pp. Written on stationery of 17
Heriot Row, Edinburgh. Unpublished. Stevenson informs his
parents that Dr. Clark ordered him to go to the Riviera.*

3485

[*November or December, 1873*] Saturday. [*Mentone*]. Which,
it's very stupid of you, not to tell me the other side . . . That
Clarke was quite right in stopping my wine, I know. *2 pp. from
the middle of letter. The first of the extant pp. is numbered: 2.
Unpublished.*

3486

Decr 11 · 73. Tuesday [*and*] Wednesday. [*Mentone*]. Let us
have a shy at pleasantry The parson here — no, in the other
bay, is called Marant Brock. *Signed:* Robert Louis Stevenson.
*6 pp. Unpublished. December 11 came on a Thursday in 1873.
Mostly about the guests at his hotel.*

3487

Dec 22nd [*1873*] Monday [*and*] Wednesday [*and*] Xmas day.
Monte Carlo. Glad to hear at last how you are. I am still very

well . . . I have not been so well yet, I think. *Signed twice: Robert Louis Stevenson. 16 pp. Unpublished. Description of a trip to Monte Carlo made with Colvin.*

3488
28th [*December, 1873*] Sunday. [*Mentone*]. The braces are in London at the dead letter office. *Signed:* Robert Louis Stevenson. *4 pp. The month and year are entered by R.L.S.'s mother. Unpublished.*

3489
10th Jan 1874. Saturday. Menton. Yes I think I did get an umbrella. *Signed:* Robert Louis Stevenson. *4 pp. Partly published in LFF, Vol. 1, pp. 70–71, where about 32 lines of the autograph are omitted.*

3490
11th Jan 1874. Sunday. Menton. In many ways, this hotel is more amusing than the Pavillon. *First 4 pp. of letter. Partly published in* The Letters, 1911, Vol. 1, *pp. 103–104, where about 25 lines of the first 4 pp. of the autograph are omitted.*

3491
[*January 18, 1874*] Sunday. [*Mentone*]. in bed — that means before I have got up — don't be alarmed — I do not rise till eleven. *2 pp. from the middle of letter. Dated by R.L.S.'s mother. Unpublished. About Nelitchka, a dish of eggs, and improved health.*

3492
Jan. 19th 1874. Monday. Menton. O so Monsieur has managed to write a good letter at last. *Signed:* Robert Louis Stevenson. *8 pp. Partly published in* The Letters, 1911, Vol. 1, *pp. 111–112, where about 32 lines of the autograph are omitted. This letter contains 8 numbered answers to questions.*

3493
[*January 26, 1874. Mentone*]. . . . . It's no joke about my clothes. Mme Garschine was inveighing against the English want of taste in costume . . . she told me that . . . I dressed (for an

Englishman) very well. *Signed:* R L. S. *Last 2 pp. of letter. The first of the extant pp. is numbered: 4. Dated by R.L.S.'s mother. Unpublished.*

3494

[*January 27, 1874*] Tuesday. [*Mentone*]. . . . I suppose even Lindsay is too big to come out here. *Signed:* Robert Louis Stevenson. *Last p. of letter, numbered: 3. Dated by R.L.S.'s mother. Unpublished.*

3495

[*January, 1874*] Saturday. Menton. Do not attempt to understand the posts. *Signed:* R. L. S. *4 pp. Unpublished. About slow postal service, Russian tea, the Russian ladies and Nelitchka.*

3496

[*February 3, 1874. Mentone*]. . . . On the whole I suspect my walk is not more than to the Napiers and back. *Signed:* Robert Louis Stevenson. *Last p. of letter, numbered: 3. Dated by R.L.S.'s mother. Unpublished.*

3497

[*February 11, 1874. Mentone*]. . . . You would be equally savage — no, more so — if I chose to tell you what they said. *Signed:* Robert Louis Stevenson. *Last 2 pp. of letter. The first of the extant pp. is numbered: 2. Dated by R.L.S.'s mother. Unpublished.*

3498

[*March, 1874*] Wednesday. [*Mentone*]. I have been a long time without writing Forgive me. *Signed:* R. L. Stevenson. *8 pp. Dated: March 14, by R.L.S.'s mother. Unpublished. About photographs, Mme. Zassetsky, and Nelitchka.*

3499

[*February, 1878*] Thursday night. Hotel Meurice, Paris. My dear father and mother, your letters recd with thanks. My book is being printed. *Signed:* R. L. S., *and* Robert Louis Stevenson. *3 pp. Dated by R.L.S.'s mother. Unpublished.*

3500

[*1878?*] My dear father and mother, I wish to do no more today than tell you how much you are in my thoughts, and how much I love you. *Signed:* Robert Louis Stevenson. *2 pp. R.L.S.'s mother has written on the letter:* This must have been written in 1878 when we were vexed by his staying so much away from home. *Published in Maggs Bros.* Autograph Letters and Historical Documents, *London, 1954, Catalogue No. 823, p. 60. P. 1 of this letter is reproduced in facsimile facing p. 45 of the catalogue.*

3501

[*May, 1879. London*]. My dear father and mother, I think I know what I am going to do . . . I shall go to the Merediths. *Signed:* R. L. S. *3 pp. Written on* Arts Club *stationery. Dated: May 19, by R.L.S.'s mother. Unpublished.*

3502

[*June, 1880*]. Calistoga Napa Co Cal. My dear father and mother, It is a great while since I have written and then only a note. *Signed:* R. L. S. *2 pp., written in pencil. R.L.S.'s mother has written at top of p. 1:* Received July 14. 1880. *Unpublished. Stevenson writes of diphtheria suffered by his wife and step son, and of his homesickness and his plan to return soon to Scotland.*

3503

[*October 11, 1880. London*]. My dear gents, Get the Examiner for October 2nd It will amuse you. *Signed:* R. L. S. *3 pp. Dated by R.L.S.'s mother. Written on* Savile Club *stationery. Unpublished.*

3504

[*October 28, 1880. Troyes*]. My dear people, I have been very much out of health and spirits. *Signed:* R. L. S. *3 pp. Dated by R.L.S.'s mother. Unpublished. Stevenson is disgusted with the high prices he had to pay at the Grosvenor Hotel in London. Mrs. R. L. S. has written an addition to this letter.*

3505

November 5th [*1880*]. Hotel Belvedere Davos. Switz. My far too good people, Your two letters and fifty quid are all duly received. *Signed: R. L. S. 3 pp. Unpublished. Mrs. R. L. S. has written an addition to this letter.*

3506

November 10th 1880. Wednesday. [*Davos*]. My dear people, We have had a lot of bother about the price of this place, and have been trying to find a house. *Unsigned. 4 pp. Unpublished.*

3507

Nov 18th or 17th 1880. [*Davos*]. My dear people, We are at last snowed in, but not yet deeply. *Signed: R. L. S. 4 pp. Unpublished. Stevenson complains about the high prices at his hotel.*

3508

Nov 28th [*1880*]. Sunday. [*Davos*]. My dear people, The books have come. *Signed: R L. S. 2 pp. Unpublished. Stevenson is vexed that some of the books he wanted have not arrived. He asks for additional type for Lloyd Osbourne. He writes:* I have no style and cannot write, I daresay you will be glad of this but it galls me to the bone.

3509

[*December 8, 1880. Davos*]. My dear people I am getting on like an angel and feeling better. *Signed: R. L. S. 2 pp., partly in pencil. Dated by R.L.S.'s mother. Unpublished. Describes Lloyd Osbourne's printing activities.*

3510

[*January 15, 1881. Davos*]. I gave this to Fanny to write, feeling so wretched; she seems not to have got to an end. *Unsigned. Dated by R.L.S.'s mother. 1 p. Unpublished. This is an addition to a letter by Mrs. R.L.S.*

3511

[*January 27, 1881. Davos*]. Dear gents, j'ai un cold. Ruedi says better tomorrow. *Signed: R. L. S. 1 p. Dated by R.L.S.'s mother.*

Unpublished. Dr. Ruedi feels that Stevenson should remain in Davos until April, 1882. This is an addition to a letter by Mrs. R.L.S.

3512

1st April 1881. [*Davos*]. My dearest people, Bertie [*F. A. Sitwell*] is dying — I hope fast — but he is now dying. I do so wish Fanny were here. *Signed:* R. L. S. *4 pp. Unpublished. Stevenson worries about high costs at Davos, and would like to go to France. He writes that he would like to publish* The Amateur Emigrant.

3513

[*May 1, 1881*] Sunday [*Hotel du Pavillon Henry IV, St. Germain-en-Laye*]. My dear people, a week in Paris reduced me to the limpness and lack of appetite peculiar to a kid-glove. *Signed:* R. L. S. *2 pp. Dated by R.L.S.'s mother. Published in LFF, Vol. 1, pp. 201–202, where 2 words of the autograph are omitted.*

3514

[*May 5, 1881. Hotel St. Romain, Rue St. Roch, Paris*]. My dear people, He is dictating, though it is she who writes. *Unsigned. 5 pp. The letter is in the hand of Mrs. R.L.S. Dated April 5 by R.L.S.'s mother; this is an error for May 5. Unpublished. Stevenson complains about the insolence and incompetence of certain Paris bankers and St. Germain hotel keepers. Mrs. R.L.S has written an addition to this letter.*

3515

[*February 16, 1882. Davos*]. Here the being [?] went out for a time. It was a slight congestion of the brain she had, no one knows why; it did not last many minutes. *Signature cut away. 1 p. Written on stationery of* Hôtel & Pension Buol. *Dated by R.L.S.'s mother. Unpublished. This is an addition to a letter by Mrs. R. L. S.*

3516

[*February, 1882*] Wednesday. [*Davos*]. My dear people, I believe Fanny is getting better again. *Signed:* R. L. S. *2 pp. Written on stationery of* Hôtel & Pension Buol. *Dated by R.L.S.'s mother. Unpublished. Stevenson writes of an offer to become* one of the props of a new magazine.

3517
[*Early 1882. Davos*]. My dear people What imbecile kept sending revises to Japp? *Unsigned. 1 p. Written on stationery of* Hôtel & Pension Buol. *Unpublished.*

3518
Oct. [9] 1882. Monday. Terminus Hotel, Marseille. My dear people, I have been nearly beside myself. *Signed:* R. L. Stevenson. *2 pp. The day of the month is written by R.L.S.'s mother. Unpublished.*

3519
[*October 21, 1882*]. Campagne Defli, St. Marcel, Banlieue de Marseille. My dear people, I have been two days in bed and two on the sofa with a hemorhage. *Signed:* R. L. S. *2 pp. Dated by R.L.S.'s mother. Unpublished.*

3520
[*January 17, 1883. Nice*]. My dear father & mother, Thanks for your joint letter. *Signed:* R. L. Stevenson. *2 pp. Written on stationery of the* Grand Hôtel, Nice. *Dated by R.L.S.'s mother. Unpublished. Stevenson is sad at the thought he will probably not be able to rent a satisfactory country house.*

3521
[*January 24, 1883*]. Grand Hotel, Nice. My dear people, My father's delightful letter just came in. *Signed:* R L S. *4 pp. Unpublished. Fanny is unhappy at the notion R.L.S.'s parents think she is bad for him.* What she is to me, no language can describe, and she can never learn. *Stevenson asks his parents to write Fanny a comforting letter.*

3522
[*February 1, 1883*]. Hotel du Petit Louvre Cannebiére Marseille. My dear people, How is my mother? — nothing, I observe, was said about her in the last. *Signed:* R. L. S. *1 p. Partly published in Edith B. Tranter.* First Editions and Autograph Manu-

scripts of American and English Authors . . . Auction Sale . . . *New York, 1952, p. 83, where about 8 lines of the autograph are omitted. Stevenson writes:* I have calculated that my six books have brought me in upwards of six hundred pounds. *Contains 3 lines of verse, beginning:* In eighteen hundred and eighty three.

3523

[*February 2, 1883*]. Hotel du Petit Louvre Cannebière Marseille. My dear people, I have just got a charming letter from my father. *Signed:* R. L. S. *2 pp. Dated by R.L.S.'s mother. Unpublished. Stevenson writes of a prospective visit from his parents.*

3524

15 Feb. [*1883*]. Hotel du Petit Louvre Cannebière Marseille. My dear people Hooray! hooray! hooray! Got rid of the house; grrrrrrreat success! . . . We hope soon to move to Hyères. *Signed:* Bradlaugh M'Kinnon. *1 p. Unpublished. Stevenson mentions an attack of illness Fanny has had.*

3525

[*February 24, 1883*]. P. R. Hyères Var. My dear people. This is a beautiful and charming spot. *Signed:* R. L. S. *1 p. Dated by R.L.S.'s mother. Unpublished. Mrs. R.L.S. has written an addition to this letter.*

3526

May 5th [*1883*]. Chalet Solitude [*Hyères*]. My dearest people, I have had a great piece of news. *Signed:* Treasure Eilan. *2 pp. Published in LFF, Vol. 1, p. 266. Stevenson is delighted that he has been offered £100 for* Treasure Island.

3527

May 8th 1883. la Solitude Hyeres. My dear people, I was disgusted to hear my father was not so well. *Signed:* R L. S. *2 pp. Published in LFF, Vol. 1, p. 267, where 4 lines of the autograph are omitted. Stevenson writes:* O if the health will hold, I should easily support myself.

3528

Nov 15th 1883. [*Hyères*]. My dear people, I inclose two testimonials, shall I call them? *Signed:* R. L. S. *2 pp. Unpublished. Stevenson writes about his literary work and articles about him.*

3529

[*December 25, 1883. Hyères*]. My dear father & mother, this it is supposed will reach you about Christmas. *Signed:* R. L. S. *3 pp. Dated by R.L.S.'s mother. Published in* LFF, *Vol. 1, pp. 302–303, where about 2 lines of the autograph are omitted. Stevenson lectures his father about ingratitude and lack of resignation.*

3530

Jan 1st [*1884. Hyères*]. My dear people, A good new year to you. *Signed:* Jno. Bunyan. *4 pp. Written on stationery of La Solitude. Published in* LFF, *Vol. 1, pp. 304–305, where 4 lines of the autograph are omitted. Stevenson writes about his finances and some horticultural allegory.*

3531

[*January or February, 1884? Nice?*] Get Smeoroch up! How did she come to take to Dick: How did she know Dick would be in town. Mind gone R. L. S. *1 p. Unpublished. Smeoroch was a Skye terrier owned by the Stevenson family in Edinburgh. This is an addition to a letter by Mrs. R.L.S.*

3532

[*March, 1884. Hyères*]. My dear people, I have forgotten what is your hotel in London. *Signed:* R. L. Stevenson Politiker. *4 pp. Dated by R.L.S.'s mother. Unpublished. Stevenson has a low opinion of the* Daily News *and the* Chronicle, *and of Gladstone.*

3533

[*April 12, 1884. Hyères*]. My dear people I have now read nothing, book, letter, paper, for about a month, and I think reading a mighty small privation. A man can do without anything except tobacco and his wife, and even these for a while. *Signed:* ever your afft. cousin[*sic*] Robert Louis Stevenson.

3 pp. Written on stationery of La Solitude. *Dated by R.L.S.'s mother. Unpublished. Mrs. R.L.S. has written an addition to this letter, commenting on Stevenson's signing himself:* cousin.

3534

[*April, 1884. Hyères*]. My dear people, Altogether still in a dilapidated state mentally, I will manage this time, by hook or crook, to communicate something. *Signed: R. L. S. 7 pp. Written on stationery of* La Solitude. *Dated by R.L.S.'s mother. Unpublished. Stevenson writes about getting* A Child's Garden of Verses *into the hands of the printer.*

3535

[*May, 1884. Hyères*]. My dear people, I think you had better send £100 in circular notes. *Signed: R L. S. 3 pp. In pencil. Written on stationery of* La Solitude. *Dated by R.L.S.'s mother. Unpublished. Stevenson writes that his health is improving, and asks for some books. Mrs. R. L. S. has written an addition to this letter.*

3536

[*June, 1884. Royat*]. My dear people, Considerable success but great cold at Royat. *Signed: R L S. 4 pp. In pencil. Dated by R.L.S.'s mother. Unpublished.*

3537

[*June, 1884. Hotel Chabassière, Royat*]. My dear people, The weather has been demoniac. *Signed: R. L. S. 7 pp. Dated by R.L.S.'s mother. Partly published in LFF, Vol. 1, p. 320, where about 31 lines of the autograph are omitted. Stevenson recalls childhood miseries, and asks for a large-type Bible.*

3538

[*June 27, 1884. Royat*]. My dear people, if we have been bad correspondents, you must make some allowance for us. *Signed: R. L. S. 4 pp. Dated by R.L.S.'s mother. Unpublished. Stevenson writes of the illness of four in his household, and of plans to come to England.*

3539

[*December 9, 1884. Bonallie Tower, Bournemouth*]. My dear people. The dreadful tragedy of the Pall Mall has come to a happy but ludicrous ending. *Signed: R. L. S. 4 pp. Dated by R.L.S.'s mother. Published in LFF, Vol. 1, pp. 343–344, where 2 lines of the autograph are omitted.*

3540

[*1885? Bournemouth?*] My dear People, Fairly well; but once more dry rotten. *The house is enchanting.* I am yours explodedly R. L. S. *1 p. Unpublished. The house referred to may be Skerryvore at Bournemouth.*

3541

[*May, 1885. Bournemouth*]. My dear people There came here a lean, Brown, bloodshot woman, claiming to be Fanny. *Signed twice: R. L. S. 2 pp. Dated by R.L.S.'s mother. Unpublished.*

3542

Feb 3rd 1886. [*Bournemouth*]. Dear People, Fanny (who is far from well) would do well to go to Bath. *Signed: R. L. S. 1 p. Unpublished.*

3543

[*April, 1886. Bournemouth*]. My dear people We are all on the mend and mean soon to be quite well. *Signed: R L. S. 3 pp. Written in pencil. Dated by R.L.S.'s mother. Published in Autograph Letters . . . from the Library of the late Robert Louis Stevenson . . . Part I . . . Sold . . . New York, 1914, p. 25, lot 125, where 3 lines of the autograph are omitted.*

3544

[*July 7, 1886. Bournemouth*]. My dear people, It is probably my fault and not yours that I did not understand. *Signed twice: R. L. S. 4 pp. Dated by R.L.S.'s mother. Published in LFF, Vol. 2, pp. 38–39, where about 3 lines of the autograph are omitted.*

3545

[*July 15, 1886. Bournemouth*]. My dear people, We have at last come to some sort of clearness. *Signed: Robert L. S. 2 pp.*

Dated by R.L.S.'s mother. Unpublished. Stevenson writes that he and Fanny may come to Scotland.

3546

[*July 19, 1886. Bournemouth*]. My dear people, This is a scratch to say that my cold is better. *Signed:* R. L. S. *1 p. Unpublished. Stevenson writes about the death of his uncle, David Stevenson.*

3547

[*End of July, 1886. Bournemouth*]. My dear People, Thanks for the money duly received. *Signed:* Barton McGuckin, S. S. C., M. R. I. A. &c. *2 pp. Dated by R.L.S.'s mother. Unpublished.*

3548

[*August, 1886. Bournemouth*]. My dear people, We have decidedly given up Scotland; I fear it was madness from the first. *Signed:* R. L. Stevenson. *2 pp. Dated by R.L.S.'s mother. Unpublished. Stevenson is pleased with checks he has received in connection with* Treasure Island *and* Kidnapped.

3549

[*August 27, 1886. Bournemouth*]. My dear people, I am home and have in a manner got to work. *Signed:* R. L. S. *2 pp. Dated by R.L.S.'s mother. Unpublished.*

R.L.S. TO HIS COUSIN, ROBERT ALAN
MOWBRAY STEVENSON

3550

17th April 1868. Friday. [*Edinburgh?*] My dear Bob, I entirely
agree with your strictures on the form of play. *Signed:* R. L.
Stevenson, *and* R. L. S. *2 pp. Published in Christie, Manson &*
Woods. Catalogue of Important Unpublished Autograph Letters of Robert Louis Stevenson . . . Sold by Auction . . . *London,*
1922, p. 4, where about 7 lines of the autograph are omitted.
Stevenson writes about work on his play, Monmouth, *in the*
writing of which he had expected his cousin Bob to collaborate
with him.

3551

September 1868. Friday. [*Wick*]. My dear Bob, When I wrote
you my last letter I was under the influence of a morbid frame
of mind which attacks me often. *Signed:* R. L. Stevenson, *and*
R. L. S. *4 pp. Partly published in Christie, Manson & Woods.*
Catalogue of Important Unpublished Autograph Letters of
Robert Louis Stevenson . . . Sold by Auction . . . *London, 1922,*
pp. 5–6, where about 61 lines of this 126-line letter are omitted.
Stevenson writes about Horace, Pope and the Book of Job.
Contains 5 lines of verse, beginning: Tis thus and thus that I
shall sing; *also the dedication of Stevenson's play,* Monmouth,
to R. A. M. S. in 18 lines of verse, beginning: Worthier had
been this offering of thee.

3552

Oct 2. 1868. Thursday [*i.e. Friday?*] 17 Heriot Row [*Edin-*
burgh]. My dear Bob, Your very friendly and interesting letter
has at once pleased and disappointed me more than I can tell.
Signed: R. L. Stevenson, *and* R. L. S. *4 pp. Partly published in*
Christie, Manson & Woods. Catalogue of Important Unpublished Autograph Letters of Robert Louis Stevenson . . . Sold
by Auction . . . *London, 1922, pp. 6–7, where about 71 lines of*
this 125-line letter are omitted. P. 1 of this letter is reproduced
in facsimile in Harry Glemby. Early English Literature . . .
Sold by Auction . . . *New York, 1926, p. [151]. Stevenson com-*
pares Keats and Swinburne, and writes of his own entry into

the profession of letters, and of his contemplated teaching in a Sunday school.

3553

Nov 17th [*and*] Dec 10th 1868. Edinburgh. My dear Bob, I have been for a fortnight past confined to bed and the house. *Signed twice:* R. L. Stevenson. *8 pp. Map by Stevenson. About 45 lines of this 246-line letter are published in Christie, Manson & Woods.* Catalogue of Important Unpublished Autograph Letters of Robert Louis Stevenson . . . Sold by Auction . . . *London, 1922, pp. 7–8. The last p. of this letter is reproduced in facsimile in John Quinn.* The Library . . . Part Five . . . Sold . . . *New York, 1924, p. 906. Stevenson writes of his love of nature and of his correspondence with R. A. M. S.* My daily life is one repression from beginning to end, and my letters to you are the safety valve. *4 pp. of the letter are devoted to a description of a night journey in a mail coach between Wick and Golspie. The letter contatins 2 lines of verse titled* Autumn, *beginning:* In country sides, the long, wet, sunken lanes. *R.L.S.'s mother has written an addition to this letter.*

3554

Jan. 7th 1870. Friday. 17 Heriot Row [*Edinburgh*]. My dear Bob, I can't sufficiently apologize for my tardy answer. *Signed:* R L Stevenson, *and* R. L. S. *4 pp. 27 lines of this 56-line letter are published in Christie, Manson & Woods.* Catalogue of Important Unpublished Autograph Letters of Robert Louis Stevenson . . . Sold by Auction . . . *London, 1922, p. 8. Stevenson writes of an encounter with a drunken man who spouted Shakespeare, and ends with 2 lines of verse, beginning:* Of such gray seeming with so red a heart.

3555

March 29th 1870. Tuesday. 17 Heriot Row [*Edinburgh*]. My dear Bob, During almost the whole of this winter, I have been free from my usual attacks of morbid melancholy. *2 pp. Signed:* R. L. Stevenson. *Published in Christie, Manson & Woods.* Catalogue of Important Unpublished Autograph Letters of Robert Louis Stevenson . . . Sold by Auction . . . *London, 1922, p. 9, where about 16 lines of the autograph are omitted. Stevenson*

1081

writes of attacks of melancholy and his wandering in Greyfriars Churchyard, and of work on Monmouth *and* Deacon Thin (*i.e.* The Builder's Doom).

3556

16th June. 1870. Thursday. Swanston Cottage. My dear Bob, I was very glad, excessively glad, to hear of your success. *Signed:* R L. Stevenson. *7 pp. On black-bordered stationery. Partly published in Christie, Manson & Woods.* Catalogue of Important Unpublished Autograph Letters of Robert Louis Stevenson . . . Sold by Auction . . . *London, 1922, pp. 9–10, where about 57 lines of this 102-line letter are omitted. Stevenson writes that he has been* very much hit with a certain damsel who shall be nameless. *He* detected a nasty over-friendliness toward me on the part of her relations, *so when she was taken away by her parents,* it was perhaps as well she left when she did.

3557

October 1872. Tuesday [*and*] Wednesday Morning. [*Edinburgh*]. My dear Bob, A damned lot of waves and counterwaves have been beating upon me of late. *Signed:* R. L. Stevenson. *4 pp. Unpublished. Stevenson expresses misgivings about his wishes, religion, activities, etc.* I want an object, a mission, a belief, a hope to be my wife; and, please God, have it I shall.

3558

[*December, 1873*]. Monaco [*and*] Jan 4th [*1874*] Sunday. [*Mentone*]. My dear Bob, I am at Monaco with Colvin, sitting outside in the sun. *Signed:* Robert Louis Stevenson. *5 pp. Unpublished. Stevenson writes of music and painting, also mentions Sir Charles Dilke and Robinet.*

3559

[*September, 1874*]. Llandudno. I want to hear about you, mon vieux, and I dont know your address. *Signed:* Robert Louis Stevenson. *6 pp. Written on stationery bearing R.L.S.'s monogram. Partly published in Christie, Manson & Woods.* Catalogue of Important Unpublished Autograph Letters of Robert Louis Stevenson . . . Sold by Auction . . . *London, 1922, pp. 10–11, where about 55 lines of this 107-line letter are omitted. Stevenson writes about a Carracci picture, gives a recipe for securing sound sleep, and expresses a wish to* buy a caravan *and go* yachting on dry land.

3560

[*Late autumn, 1874*]. 17 Heriot Row [*Edinburgh*]. My dear Bob, the notion I had of coming over for a couple of days was relinquished. *Signed:* Robert Louis Stevenson. *8 pp. Written on stationery bearing the monogram of R. L. S. Unpublished. Stevenson writes about Japanese art, the Elgin Marbles, and some of the writings at which he was at work.*

3561

[*August 6, 1879. Glasgow*]. My dear Bob. I am under way. *Signed:* R. L. S. *2 pp. Published in* Christie, Manson & Woods. Catalogue of Important Unpublished Autograph Letters of Robert Louis Stevenson . . . Sold by Auction . . . *London, 1922, p. 11, where about 5 lines of the autograph are omitted. Written on the eve of Stevenson's departure for America.*

3562

[*Spring, 1881? Davos?*] Mon cher Bob, You are a good gent to write. I vote for you all over the shop. *Signed:* R. L. S. *3 pp. Unpublished. Stevenson mentions being hounded by his conscience in a matter connected with his wife and others relating to Henley.*

3563

[*April, 1882. Davos*]. My dear Bob Yours received. I have received a communication by same mail from my mother. *Signed three times:* R L. Stevenson le roi de Béotie. *4 pp. Published in the* Skerryvore Edition, Letters, *Vol. 2, pp. 92–94, where about 4 lines of the autograph are omitted. Stevenson writes about the* New Arabian Nights, *Lloyd Osbourne, Stevenson's wood engraving, and plans to live in France.*

3564

[*May or June, 1882? Edinburgh*]. My dear Bob — Certainly not. Your pictures look all right. *Signed:* R L. S. *2 pp. Written on black-bordered stationery of* 17 Heriot Row. *Unpublished. Stevenson writes of painting by Corot and by R. A. M. S.*

3565
[*July, 1886. Bournemouth*]. Sir, your foolish letter was unduly received. *Signed:* Pimperly Stipple, *and* Threnodiae Auctor. *2 pp. Contains portrait and line of music by Stevenson. Published in LFF, Vol. 2, pp. 36–38, where about 20 lines of the autograph are omitted. Stevenson writes about music.*

3566
[*1886. Bournemouth*]. My dear Bob, I am not so noble a pickler as I used to be. *Signed:* Le Pickleur. *4 pp. Stevenson writes about music and piano playing (pickling). The letter contains 10 lines of verse, beginning:* He pickled low, he pickled loud. *The first 6 of these lines are printed in Edith B. Tranter.* First Editions and Autograph Manuscripts of American and English Authors . . . Public Auction Sale . . . *New York, 1952, p. 92, lot* 444.

3567
[*September, 1894. Vailima*]. Dear Bob, You are in error about the Picts. *Signed:* R. L. S. *16 pp. Photostat. Published in LFF, Vol. 2, pp. 353–359, where about 18 lines of the autograph are omitted. Stevenson writes about the ethnology of Scotland, his own genealogy, about the difficulties of collaboration, Christianity and sex, etc.*

3568
[*N.d.*] My dear B You remember what you said to me as we walked down to the studio . . . You on your side have tried to raise trouble about nothing. *Unsigned. In pencil. Written on verso of manuscript of Henley's poem,* The Captain's Bride. *Unpublished.*

3569

[*May, 1880*]. c/o Mrs Aslonine 11th Av & 18th St East Oakland. My dear Stoddard, I am guilty in thy sight and in the sight of God. *Signed:* Robert Louis Stevenson. *2 pp. Published in LFF, Vol. 1, pp. 173–174. Stevenson discusses some of Stoddard's writing, and advises him not to be disgusted with it.*

3570

[*May? 1880. San Francisco*]. My dear Stoddard, You will seriously oblige me and my dear gusset . . . by coming here to lunch and talk with me today. *Signed:* Robert Louis Stevenson. *1 p. In pencil. Published in Charles Warren Stoddard.* Exits and Entrances, *Boston, 1903, p. 26.*

3571

[*December, 1880*]. Hotel Belvedere Davos Platz Switzerland. Dear Charles Warren Stoddard Many thanks to you for your letter and the photograph. *Signed:* R. L. Stevenson. *3 pp. Published in LFF, Vol. 1, pp. 191–192, where 3 lines of the autograph are omitted. With this letter Stevenson sent manuscript verses in his hand:* To C. W. Stoddard. Ne sutor ultra crepidam . . ., *2 pp., described elsewhere.*

3572

Feby 26th 1894. Vailima Samoa. Madam, Your questions are very wide ones and I hesitate to answer them. *Signed:* Robert Louis Stevenson. *1 p. Unpublished. Stevenson declines to define a novel, or to state which is the best novel or who is the best novelist. He refers to* Kidnapped *and* Catriona *as his* favourites — those in which I seem to have done more nearly what I tried to do.

3573

Nov 2nd 1892. Vailima. My dear Austin — First and foremost I think you will be sorry to hear that our poor friend Arak has gone back to the German Firm. *Signed:* O Tusitala. *4 pp. Contains drawing by Isobel Strong. The letter is in the hand of Isobel Strong, signed by Stevenson. Published in the* South Seas Edition, Letters, *Vol. 4, pp.* 128–130, *where about 35 lines of the autograph are omitted and the wording is slightly changed. Stevenson writes about Arak, a* black boy, *and about a horse mounted by a heavy captain.*

3574

Nov. 15th 1892. Vailima. My dear Austin — The new house is begun. *Unsigned. 4 pp. The letter is in the hand of Isobel Strong. Published in the* South Seas Edition, Letters, *Vol. 4, pp.* 130–133, *where one line of the autograph is omitted and the wording is slightly changed. Stevenson writes of construction of the house at Vailima, of cart-loads of lumber drawn by cattle and the natives who drove the cattle.*

3575

June 18th 1893. [*Vailima*]. Respected Hoskins This is to inform you that the Jersey cow had an elegant little cow-calf Sunday last. *Signed:* Uncle Louis. *3 pp. Diagrams. The letter is partly in the hand of Isobel Strong, partly in Stevenson's, signed by him. Published in the* South Seas Edition, Letters, *Vol. 4, pp.* 196–199, *where 2 lines of the autograph are omitted and the wording is slightly changed. Stevenson writes about an obstreperous ill-natured cow, her calf and a bull.*

3576

[*June ? 1893. Vailima*]. My dear Hoskyns, I am kept away in a cupboard because everybody has the Influenza. *Signed:* Uncle Louis, *and* R. L. S. *2 pp. Diagram. Published in the* South Seas Edition, Letters, *Vol. 4, pp.* 201–204, *where 2 lines of the autograph are omitted and the wording is slightly changed. Stevenson writes of deep-sea creatures and the feeding of his horses.*

3577

[*June ? 1893*]. Vailima. My dear Austin — Now when the over-seer is away I think it my duty to report to him anything serious that goes on on the plantation. *Unsigned. 4 pp. The letter is in the hand of Isobel Strong. Published in the* South Seas Edition, Letters, *Vol. 4, pp. 204–207, where 8 lines of the autograph are omitted and the wording is slightly changed. Stevenson writes about a Samoan girl with a sore foot, about the* devil *which caused it, and a native woman who acted as a ventriloquist in connection with it.*

R.L.S. TO MRS. ISOBEL OSBOURNE STRONG, LATER MRS. FIELD

3577A
[*Summer, 1880? Scotland?*]. You receive herewith the best letter in the world from Sam. *Unsigned. 2 pp. Unpublished. This is an addition to a letter by Mrs. R. L. S.*

[*September ? 1880. Edinburgh*]. *See no. 3232. Letter to Nellie van de Grift Sanchez and Isobel Strong.*

3578
[*November, 1880*]. Hotel Belvedere Davos Platz Switzerland. No, my che-ildren, not Kamschatka this trip; only the top of the Alps or thereby. *Signed:* Your dear papa R. L. S. *4 pp. Published in* The Letters, *1911, Vol. 2, pp. 8–9, where 14 lines of the autograph are omitted. Stevenson writes about German customs officers.*

3579
Sept. 18. 1894. [*Vailima*]. Dear and Far Morocco, Please find within another account. *Signed:* The Prisoner of Zenda. *2 pp. With envelope addressed as follows:* For the shapely hands of Teuila-Morocco. Sept. 18. 1894. R L. S. *On a separate leaf accompanying this letter are 20 lines of verse, beginning:* My dear and fair, my kind and pretty, *2 pp. The letter is unpublished. The poem is published in Stevenson's* Teuila, *1899.*

3580

November 11th [*1888*]. Tautira. One November night, in the village of Tautira, we sat at the high table in the hall of assembly. *Signed:* Robert Louis Stevenson, *and* R. L. S. *2 pp. Published in* LFF, *Vol. 2, pp. 124–125. Most of this consists of a draft of a proposed dedication to Symonds of Stevenson's book on South Sea travel.*

3581

[*1888 or 1889*]. Dear Mr Tati, Here I send my final versions with some notes, which please cast your eye over critically. *Signed:* Robert Louis Stevenson, Sed nunc Teriitera, *and* R. L. S. *2 pp. Unpublished. Stevenson discusses translations of Tahitian poems into English.*

3582

[*1885, 1886 or 1887. Bournemouth*]. Dear Lady Taylor All's
well that ends well. *Signed:* Robert Louis Stevenson. *2 pp.
Partly published in Sotheby & Co.* Catalogue of Valuable Printed Books . . . Sold by Auction . . . July 6, 1953 . . . *London, 1953,
p. 35, where about 16 lines of the autograph are omitted. Stevenson writes rather obscurely about pheasants.*

R.L.S. TO HIS WIFE'S NEPHEW, FRED THOMAS

3583

[*Postmarked:* Oct 31 1887. Saranac Lake]. Dear Fred, I send off to you today: Beethoven's violin & pianoforte sonatas. *Signed:* Robert Louis Stevenson, *and* R. L. S. *2 pp. With addressed envelope and mounted stamp. Unpublished. Stevenson writes to his wife's nephew of Danville, Indiana, about music by Beethoven, Bach, Handel and others, which he expects the young man to play.*

3584

[*1892 ? Vailima*]. Dear Sir John, You keep up against me a newspaper war. *Unsigned. 2 pp. Apparently a draft retained by Stevenson. Unpublished. Stevenson writes that he thinks Thurston out of touch with Samoan affairs and misinformed about R. L. S.*

3585

[April 9 and 12, 1892. Samoa]. Unsigned. 4 pp. Draft of portions of a letter printed in The Times, *London, June 4, 1892, p. 18. About Samoan politics.*

3586

Dec 5th 1868. Sat. 17 Heriot Row [*Edinburgh*]. My dear Henrietta, We're going to have some people at dinner on Saturday next. *Signed:* R L. Stevenson. *2 pp. Written on stationery bearing the motto:* Coelum non Solum. *With addressed envelope. Unpublished. Stevenson invites his cousin to a dinner.*

3587

[*1871? Edinburgh*]. My dear Henrietta, I have got into the shadiest possible mess. *Signed:* R. L. Stevenson. *4 pp. Written on black-bordered stationery bearing the motto:* Coelum non Solum. *Facsimile. Unpublished. Stevenson has lost an invitation which he neglected to answer.*

3588

[*Postmarked:* No 8 71. Edinburgh]. My dear Henrietta, I shall have much pleasure in dining with you on Friday next. *Signed:* Louis Stevenson, R. L. S. *and* Charles Grandison. *Written on black-bordered stationery bearing the motto:* Coelum non Solum. *With addressed envelope and mounted stamp. Facsimiles. Unpublished.*

R.L.S. AND W. E. HENLEY TO
HERBERT BEERBOHM TREE

3589

[*July 6?* *1885*]. 18 Camden Gardens   Shepherds Bush [*London*] W. My Dear Tree, We have come to the following conclusions about the "Macaire . . . [*foregoing sentence crossed out*] It is now some five months since "Macaire" was put in your hands; and we think it high time some definite arrangement should be reached. *Signed:* W. E. H R. L. S. *3 pp. The letter, including the two signatures, is in Henley's hand. Unpublished.*

3590

3/8/85. [*Bournemouth?*] My dear Tree We have to thank you for your letter, apart from any question of terms, we have no desire to see 'Macaire' played as a *lever de rideau. Signed:* W. E. Henley Robert Louis Stevenson. *1 p. The letter, including both signatures, is in Stevenson's hand. Unpublished.*

R.L.S. TO HIS WIFE'S BROTHER, JACOB
VAN DE GRIFT

3591

[*July, 1880*]. P. O. San Francisco. My dear Sir. Your letter came a day or two ago; and perhaps I should have written sooner. *Signed:* Robert Louis Stevenson. *2 pp. In pencil. With addressed envelope and mounted stamp. The postmark has been cut from the envelope. Unpublished. Stevenson writes of the poor health of his wife and himself, of his father and mother whom he expects soon to see again, of plans to return to California.*

R.L.S. TO HIS MOTHER-IN-LAW, MRS. ESTHER KEEN VAN DE GRIFT

3592

Jan 31st. [*1888*]. Saranac Adirondacks N. Y. My dear Mrs Van de Grift, I am about the worst person going to give you news of Fanny. *Signed:* Robert Louis Stevenson. *3 pp. On black-bordered stationery. With addressed envelope. Unpublished. Stevenson writes to his mother-in-law about his wife's visits to New York, Philadelphia and elsewhere, and her recent bad health from which she is recovering.*

3593

[*Postmarked:* Apr 12 1888. Saranac Lake]. My dear Mrs. Van de Grift, I write to let you have my first news of Fanny from San Francisco. *Signed:* Robert Louis Stevenson. *4 pp. With addressed envelope and mounted stamp. Unpublished. Stevenson quotes from a letter he has received from his wife describing her illness on her trip west, the life of her daughter, Isobel, and the latter's son, Austin Strong.*

R.L.S. TO MRS. ROSAMUND (BALL) MARRIOTT WATSON

3594

June 30th 1893. Vailima, Samoa. Dear Mrs Marriott-Watson, You have put me to some embarrassment by your book which I got yesterday. *Signed:* Robert Louis Stevenson. *1 p. Unpublished. Stevenson criticizes his correspondent's books and literary style.*

3595

[June or July, 1881. Kinnaird Cottage, Pitlochry, Perthshire].
My dear Virgil Williams, it would be difficult to tell you in
what spirit I read your words, so kindly written. *Signed:* R. L.
Stevenson. *2 pp. Unpublished. Stevenson expresses gratitude for
Mr. and Mrs. Williams's kindness to him in San Francisco when
he was* sick, sad and poor. *Mrs. R.L.S. has written an addition
to this letter, addressed to Mrs. Williams.*

R.L.S. TO DORA NORTON WILLIAMS
(MRS. VIRGIL WILLIAMS)

3596
[*October, 1880. Edinburgh*]. So much for Fanny. From me merely a salutation to you and the great latin poet. *Signed:* R L S. *1 p. Unpublished. Stevenson writes of plans to go to Davos for the winter. This is an addition to a letter by Mrs. R. L. S.*

3597
[*Winter, 1880–1881. Davos*]. Dear Mrs Williams, I begin by thanking you for the thing about Nicaragua. *Signed:* Robert Louis Stevenson. *2 pp. Facsimile. Published in Katharine Durham Osbourne. Robert Louis Stevenson in California, 1911, suppressed issue, pp. 108–109, where about 2 lines of the autograph are omitted. The letter is principally devoted to reminiscences of San Francisco.*

3598
[*April? 1887. Bournemouth*]. My dear Mrs Williams, That I should have been so long in acknowledging Virgils present of the photographs is the more strange because I was knocked on the head with wonder. *Unsigned. 7 pp. Unpublished. R. L. S. writes about photographs made by two Californians, Messrs. Louden and Gibbs. Mrs. R. L. S. has written an addition to this letter.*

3599

[*July, 1884. Royat*]. My dear Sir, Many thanks for your inter-esting letter, which followed me to . . . Royat. *Signed twice:* Robert Louis Stevenson. *3 pp. Written on stationery of* La Soli-tude. *Partly published in Edith B. Tranter.* First Editions and Autograph Manuscripts of American and English Authors . . . Auction Sale . . . *New York, 1952, p. 85, where about 23 lines of the autograph are omitted. Stevenson writes about the writer's art, Thoreau, Edinburgh, etc.*

3600

[*1887? Bournemouth?*] Dear Madam, As your note is so pleas-antly expressed, I have the pleasure to break through my rule . . . and to send you, Dear Madam, my autograph Robert Louis Stevenson. *1 p. On black-bordered stationery. Unpublished.*

3601

[*Within period 1890–1894. Samoa*]. Sir, I am very sorry to ap-pear, even for a moment, in what seems opposition to the mis-sionaries . . . A certain number of ladies in Apia . . . have adopted a profession of which the least we can say is that it is not modest. [*The first of these sentences is crossed out in this draft*]. *Signed:* Robert Louis Stevenson. *1 p. Draft. At top of p.:* Contagious Diseases. *Stevenson recommends compulsory medi-cal examinations of prostitutes.*

3602

[*Within period 1890–1894. Samoa*]. Sir, Mr. Hills finds it hard to believe that any man can differ from him on the subject of our discussion. *Unsigned. 7 pp. Draft of one or two letters, incom-plete. Unpublished. R. L. S. is engaged in a controversy with a Mr. Hills in the matter of diseased prostitutes in Apia. Ste-venson recommends compulsory medical examinations of pros-titutes and the confinement of diseased ones in a hospital.*

3603

[*January 27, 1893. Vailima*]. Your enchanting letter just arrived; and O! to think of you and dear Jack Buckland carreering about

Sydney! *Signed:* R L S. *Last 2 pp. of letter. Dated by R.L.S.'s mother. Unpublished.*

3604

[*1893? or 1894? Samoa*]. The state of Samoa has again become grave and disquieting. *Incomplete and unsigned. 2 pp. Draft, typewritten (by Lloyd Osbourne?). Unpublished. Stevenson writes of hostility between Malietoa, Mataafa and Tamasese.*

3605

[*1894. Samoa*]. The dead-lock continues. The warriors are still out in the bush. *Unsigned. 10 pp. Partly in the hand of R.L.S. and partly in that of Isobel Strong. Draft of a letter, partly in duplicate. Unpublished. About the release of Samoan chiefs who had been held as prisoners, uncertainty as to who the real rulers of Samoa were, the danger of famine and bankruptcy, etc.*

3606

[*N.d.*] Good morning to your pig tail, mam! Please pig tail, will you let me have last month's total early in the morning and oblige Tom Broling. *1 p. Unpublished.*

PART THIRTEEN

LETTERS BY
MRS. ROBERT LOUIS STEVENSON

MRS. R.L.S. TO CHARLES BAXTER

3607

[*After October, 1882. Marseille or Nice*]. My dear friends, I have lost a child myself, and I have no word of consolation to offer. *Signed:* Fanny V de G. Stevenson. *To Mr. and Mrs. Charles Baxter. Written on parts of 2 pp. following a note of sympathy by R. L. S. to Baxter for the loss of the latter's child. Unpublished.*

3608

[*June, 1883. Hyères*]. My dear Mr Baxter, Many thanks for settling the question of my identity so far as it can be settled. *Signed:* F. V de G. Stevenson. *3 pp. Written on stationery of* La Solitude. *Unpublished.*

3609

[*December, 1883? Hyères*]. My dear Mr Baxter, A word, Leave your blue ribbon at home. *Signed:* F V de G. Stevenson. *1 p. Unpublished. This is an addition to a letter by R. L. S.*

3610

[*Postmarked:* 15 Dec 83. Hyères]. My dear Mr. Baxter, I hope to receive by return mail the date of your departure from Edinburgh en route for Hyeres. *Signed:* F. V de G. Stevenson. *4 pp. Written on stationery of* La Solitude. *With addressed envelope and mounted stamp. Unpublished.*

3611

[*January, 1884. Pension Rose, Nice*]. Our dear couple, When upon your departure, you left the pair of us snivelling. *Signed:* F. V de G Stevenson. *4 pp. Mostly in the hand of Mrs. Stevenson, a few lines in R.L.S.'s hand. A portion of the letter was dictated by Stevenson, but his wife is the author of most of it. Written on stationery of* La Solitude. *To Baxter and Henley. Unpublished.*

3612

[*January. 1884. Pension Rose, Nice*]. Louis is much worse, the doctor says in great danger, almost no hope. *Signed:* F V de G — *1 p. Unpublished.*

3613

[*January, 1884. Nice*]. My dear Mr Baxter. Louis has passed a much better night, but little pain and no wandering in his mind. *Signed:* F V de G Stevenson. *4 pp. Written on stationery of* La Solitude. *Unpublished.*

3614

Ja 23 84. Nice. Wonderfully better. *1 p. Telegram. Unpublished. About R. L. S.'s health.*

3615

Ja 24 84. Nice. Critical but better. *1 p. Telegram. Unpublished.*

3616

[*January, 1884. Nice*]. My dear Mr Baxter, Louis thinks I have not written to you, so I am to write a letter this afternoon. *Signed:* F. V de G. Stevenson. *3 pp. Written on stationery of* La Solitude. *At top of p. 1 in pencil:* received . . . Jan 27–84. *Unpublished.*

3617

[*Postmarked:* 26 Janv 84. Nice]. My dear Mr Baxter, I cannot understand whether S[*impson*] is coming or not. *Signed:* F. *Postal card. Unpublished.*

3618

Ja 26 84. Nice. Has Simpson started if not send money to Bob quickly answer. *1 p. Telegram. Unpublished.*

3619

Fe 2 84. Nice. Parents not necessary much better. *1 p. Telegram. Unpublished.*

3620

[*February, 1884. Nice*]. My dear Friend, I send the enclosed, I believe it should be sent to the firm, but I do not understand business matters. *Signed:* F. V de G Stevenson. *1 p. At top in pencil:* received 4 Feb 84. *Unpublished.*

3621

[*February 4, 1884. Nice*]. My dear Mr Baxter Why is all this sudden excitement going on with Louis' parents? *Signed:* F. V de G Stevenson. *7 pp. Dated by Baxter. Unpublished. Dr. Drummond, who saw Stevenson at the beginning of his illness at Nice, was supplanted by Dr. Wakefield. Stevenson's parents evidently sent one or more inquiring telegrams to Dr. Drummond, who was* angry and indignant *although he gave Mrs. R. L. S. advice privately.*

3622

[*February? 1884. Pension Rose, Nice*]. My dear Mr Baxter, Louis says please negociate this bill. He also says to write hereafter to Hyères. *Signed:* F. V de G. Stevenson. *3 pp. Written on stationery of* La Solitude. *Unpublished.*

3623

[*Postmarked:* 25 Fev 84. Hyères]. My Dear Mr Baxter, Louis wishes me to ask you to send to Bob twenty pounds immediately. *Signed:* F. V de G. Stevenson. *4 pp. With addressed envelope and mounted stamp. Unpublished.*

3624

[*Postmarked:* 3 Mars 84. Hyères]. My dear Mr Baxter, Will you please send forty pounds to Louis? *Signed:* F V de G Stevenson. *2 pp. Written on stationery of* La Solitude. *With addressed envelope and mounted stamp. Unpublished. R.L.S. has written an addition to this letter.*

3625

[*Postmarked:* 29 Mars 84. Hyères]. My dear Mr Baxter, It is a shameful time since I have written to you. *Signed:* F V de G.

1109

Stevenson. *1 p. With addressed envelope and mounted stamp. Unpublished.*

3626

[*April, 1884. Hyères*]. My dear Mr Baxter, Louis is stronger & the weather good, so we leave, nothing happening to the contrary tomorrow. *Signed:* F V de G Stevenson. *1 p. Written on stationery of* La Solitude. *At top:* recd. 16 April 1884. *Unpublished.*

3627

[*September, 1885*]. Skerryvore, Bournemouth. My dear Mr Baxter, A good deal of feeling has been occasioned by the disappearance of an individual known by several aliases, but passing in ·London under the name of William Ernest Henley. *Signed:* F. V. de G. Stevenson. *2 pp. Unpublished.*

3628

[*Autumn, 1885*]. Skerryvore. Dear Mr Baxter, Louis asks that you send what money you have of his. Day before yesterday he had another bad hemorrhage. *Signed:* F. V de G. S. *2 pp. Unpublished.*

3629

Dec 8th [*1885?*]. Skerryvore. Dear Mr Baxter, I return you Mr. Young's letter as you ask. *Signed:* F. V. de G. Stevenson. *4 pp. Unpublished.*

3630

[*November, 1886. London*]. My dear Mr Baxter, Enclosed you will find the paper properly signed by Louis. *Signed:* F. V. de G. Stevenson. *2 pp. Written on stationery of the* British Museum. *Unpublished.*

3631

[*June 25, 1888*]. San Francisco. Dear Mr Baxter, Tomorrow we leave, and I have just a moment to drop you a line before we start. *Signed:* Fanny V. de G. Stevenson. *4 pp. Dated by Baxter. Unpublished.*

3632

March [8] 1889. Honolulu. My dear friend, This is only to show that my heart is in the right place. *Signed:* F. V. de G. S. *1 p. Unpublished. This is an addition to a letter by R.L.S.*

3633

[*August, 1890. Sydney*]. My dear friend, or may I say as Louis does, My dear Charles? I add a few wandering words to my husband's letter. *Signed:* Fanny V de G. Stevenson. *4 pp. Unpublished.*

3634

[*October 14, 1891. Vailima*]. My dear Charles, I am in despair about the two large boxes sent to Mr. Gleeson White at Christchurch. *Signed:* F. V. de G. Stevenson. *6 pp. Unpublished.*

3635

May 21st [*1893. Vailima*]. My dear Charles, Any form of words that I could use seem to me no more than a mockery. *Signed:* Fanny V. de G. Stevenson. *2 pp. Mrs. Stevenson refers apparently to the death of Baxter's wife. Unpublished.*

MRS. R.L.S. TO EDWARD LIVERMORE
BURLINGAME

3636

[*Autumn, 1887*]. Saranac Lake Adirondack Mntns. Dear Mr Burlingame, I trust you were surprised at my apparent want of courtesy in not answering your very kind letter. *Signed: F. V. de G. Stevenson. 4 pp. On black-bordered stationery. Unpublished. Mrs. R.L.S. writes of life at Saranac Lake, and hopes Mr. and Mrs. Burlingame will come to visit them.*

3637

[*January, 1887*]. Skerryvore . . . Bournemouth. Mr Stevenson being too ill to write himself, asks me to say that he sends the last of the proofs. *Signed:* F. V de G. Stevenson. *2 pp. Unpublished. The proofs are of* The Merry Men and other Tales and Fables.

3638

[*November, 1884. Bournemouth*]. My dear Mr Colvin, I am grieved that you cannot come to us. *Signed: F. 3 pp. Partly published in E. V. Lucas.* The Colvins and their Friends, *pp. 159–160, where about 10 lines of the autograph are omitted. Mrs. R.L.S. is angry because Stevenson's mother has given him a cold.*

3639

[*November, 1884. Bournemouth*]. My dear Mr. Colvin. Many thanks for the telegram. *Signed: F V de G. Stevenson. 2 pp. Unpublished. Mrs. R.L.S. writes that Stevenson* seems steadily tending toward being worse, *and wonders which doctor to call in.*

3640

[*June, 1885. Bournemouth*]. Best of Custodians, And as well beloved as though yet professor, we have been wondering and wondering what had become of you. *Signed: Fanny V de G. Stevenson. 3 pp. Partly published in E. V. Lucas.* The Colvins and their Friends, *p. 161, where about 17 lines of the autograph are omitted.*

3641

[*Summer, 1885. Bournemouth*]. Dearest and best of Custodians. Just a word to let you know that we still live. *Signed: Fanny. 4 pp. Published in* Scribner's Magazine, *Vol. LXXV, No. 3, New York, March, 1924, p. 322, where about 9 lines of the autograph are omitted. Mrs. R.L.S. writes that* Louis is much better bodily, but mentally more or less an idiot. *Of Henry James she writes:* He seems very gentle and comfortable.

3642

[*Summer, 1885. Bournemouth*]. Best of Custodians, Our conduct, as usual, has been horrid. *Signed: Fanny. 4 pp. Published in* Scribner's Magazine, *Vol. LXXV, No. 3, New York, March, 1924, pp. 322–323. Mrs. R.L.S. mentions* a good deal of wearing company for some time. *She writes:* After ten weeks of

Henry James the evenings seem very empty, though the room is always full of people. *She writes of the Taylors and the Shelleys.*

3643

[*Early September, 1885*]. New London Hotel Exeter. My dear Mr Colvin. I have sent a note to Henley, yesterday, to explain the long silence. *Signed:* Fanny. *4 pp. Published in* Scribner's Magazine, *Vol. LXXV, No. 3, New York, March, 1924, p. 321, where about 16 lines of the autograph are omitted. Mrs. R.L.S. writes of Stevenson's severe illness in Exeter following a visit to Thomas Hardy. As to Mrs. Hardy Mrs. R.L.S. writes:* What very strange marriages literary men seem to make.

3644

[*September, 1885. Bournemouth*]. Dearest Monument. We arrived home, as my telegram informed you. *Signed:* F. V. de G S. *4 pp. Unpublished. Mrs. R.L.S. writes of the shortcomings of a new servant, of the arrival of Stevenson's parents,* furious to find Bournemouth bleak grey and cold. *She writes that* It is very unfair to that poor old man [*R.L.S.'s father*] to keep him in a climate that is very bad for him.

3645

[*September, 1885. Bournemouth*]. My dear Mr Colvin, I cannot conceive what has happened to my letters. *Signed:* F. *2 pp. 6 lines of this 38-line letter are published in E. V. Lucas.* The Colvins and their Friends, *p. 165. Mrs. R.L.S. has received no letter from Colvin or Henley in answer to her recent ones, and blames the post office.*

3646

[*Autumn, 1885. Bournemouth*]. Dear Friend. I am filled with compunction at the sight of the chest of drawers. I am now convinced that I hunted you to death about it. *Signed:* F. V. de G. S. *4 pp. 4 lines of this 52-line letter are published in E. V. Lucas.* The Colvins and their Friends, *p. 165. Mrs. R.L.S. writes of Lloyd Osbourne and his failure to receive a letter of credit (in the West Indies?)*

3647

[*Autumn, 1885. Bournemouth*]. Dear and shamefully neglected Custodian. You have had by this a hasty scrawl from me, but I owe you more. *Signed:* Fanny. *4 pp. Unpublished. Mrs. R.L.S. writes about Stevenson and his parents.* Louis is very well, coming down every day at about three and staying up until after dinner quite late.

3648

[*Autumn, 1885. Bournemouth*]. Dear Custodian. Again Louis is better, and possessed by a story that he will try to work out. *Signed:* F. *3 pp. Unpublished. Mrs. R.L.S. would like to have her husband see Colvin's doctor. She writes of her own bad health.*

3649

[*Autumn, 1885. Bournemouth*]. Ever dear Custodian. I was grieved not to see you when I was in London. *Signed:* F. V. de G. S. *2 pp. 13 lines of this 36-line letter are published in E. V. Lucas.* The Colvins and their Friends, *pp. 172–173. As Stevenson's parents are about to make a visit to Skerryvore, Mrs. R.L.S. suggests that Colvin may wish to delay his visit. She feels that Henley is at the mercy of a* miserable quack *doctor (Mennell?). She refers to* Dr. Jekyll and Mr. Hyde, *the manuscript of which has just been sent to Longmans, as* a very good weird thing.

3650

[*October, 1885*]. Skerryvore Westbourne Bournemouth. Dear Custodian, I had meant to write to you at once, but the dear old father has been very bad, and yesterday was sent off home, which I think he will never leave again. *Signed:* Fanny. *4 pp. 10 lines of this 59-line letter are published in E. V. Lucas.* The Colvins and their Friends, *p. 164. Mrs. R.L.S. writes of Stevenson's concern with his father's business affairs, of Sargent's portrait of Stevenson, of a plan to go to Aix-les-Bains, and of a play described by her to William Archer who* begs to have it written.

1116

3651

[December, 1885. Bournemouth]. Dearest and most ill treated of Custodians, I feel that I, too, am in a manner of speaking, a custodian. *Signed:* Fanny V de G Stevenson. *4 pp. Partly published in* Scribner's Magazine, *Vol. LXXV, No. 3, New York, March, 1924, p. 323, where about 14 lines of the autograph are omitted. Mrs. R.L.S. writes of a slight set-back in Stevenson's health, of photographs of him of which one looks like an angel and another like a devil.*

3652

[December, 1885. Bournemouth]. Dearest Custodian I begin by saying that Louis is better, the parents are in Torquay. *Signed:* F. V. de G. S. *4 pp. Published in* Scribner's Magazine, *Vol. LXXV, No. 3, New York, March, 1924, pp. 323–324, where about 11 lines of the autograph are omitted. Mrs. R.L.S. writes of her recovering from overdoses of salicylate, of her warning to an Irish servant, and of her cat Ginger and Thomas Stevenson's dog Smeoroch.*

3653

[January? 1886]. Pleasant Custodian. need I say *come? Signed:* F. V. de G. Stevenson. *2 pp. Unpublished. Mrs. R.L.S. describes Stevenson's liver trouble, and mentions his father's wish to take him to Torquay.*

3654

[January? 1886. Bournemouth]. Faithless, but still dear Custodian. *Restore that painting!* Instantly restore that picture so basely purloined from . . . Sargent! *Signed:* F. *2 pp. Published in* E. V. Lucas. The Colvins and their Friends, *p. 170. Mrs. R.L.S. writes that she believes Stevenson's parents will be gone before Colvin arrives.*

3655

[March? 1886]. Dearest Custodian Please lose no time in seeing Mr Balfour *(Dr. George Balfour?) Signed:* F. *4 pp. Unpublished. Mrs. R.L.S. writes of difficulties between Stevenson's father and the David Stevensons, and of possible honors for the former.*

3656

[*Spring, 1886*] Sunday Night. Skerryvore. Best of Custodians, Just a line to say that we have arrived home without accident. *Signed:* Fanny. *3 pp. 12 lines of this 32-line letter are published in E. V. Lucas. The Colvins and their Friends, p. 171. Mrs. R.L.S. writes:* Louis fancies that he feels some stirring of the intellect. I hope he does, for it was growing alarming.

3657

[*Spring, 1886. Bournemouth*]. Dearest Custodian, Many thanks for your letter and what is called "prompt action." *Signed:* F. V de G. S. *7 pp. Unpublished. Mrs. R.L.S. has a letter from Colvin on a subject which she wishes to keep secret for a time. Dr. Scott is willing to sign a certificate that Stevenson's father is able to manage his business.*

3658

[*Early July, 1886*]. Skerryvore. Dearest of Custodians, I received your note this morning. Already Louis is better. *Signed:* F. V de G Stevenson. *4 pp. 24 lines of this 52-line letter are published in E. V. Lucas. The Colvins and their Friends, pp. 168–169. Mrs. R.L.S. writes that Stevenson favors a trip by sea to Bordeaux and thence to the Pyrenees.*

3659

[*September? 1886. London*]. Best of Custodians, Pray excuse this dismal paper. *Signed:* F. *4 pp. Written on stationery of the* Buckingham Palace Hotel, London. *Unpublished. Mrs. R.L.S. writes of the* arch idiot Mennell, *who, she believes, made incorrect diagnoses of the illnesses of Stevenson's cousin Bob, Henley, and others.*

3660

[*November, 1886. Bournemouth*]. Dear Custodian, We arrived very comfortably indeed, and the journey seemed to do Louis good. *Signed:* F. V de G. S. *3 pp. Published in* Scribner's Magazine, *Vol. LXXV, No. 3, New York, March, 1924, p. 324, where 3 words of the autograph are omitted. Mrs. R.L.S. feels that much piano playing is not good for her husband.*

3661

[*November? 1886. Bournemouth*]. Dearest Custodian All goes on well though slowly. *Signed:* F. V. de G. Stevenson. *2 pp. Published in E. V. Lucas.* The Colvins and their Friends, *p. 173, where about 9 lines of the autograph are omitted. Mrs. R.L.S. writes about a disturbing letter from Charles G. Robertson, and about acting as a* buffer *between Stevenson and his parents.*

3662

[*November or December, 1886*]. Skerryvore. Best of Custodians, I got your note after I had already sent one off to you. *Signed:* F. V de G. S. *3 pp. Unpublished. Mrs. R.L.S. writes that Stevenson's parents are about to leave, and asks Colvin to make a visit to Skerryvore. She mentions poems* (Underwoods?)

3663

[*Early, 1887*]. Skerryvore Bournemouth. Will a kind Custodian forgive me for this long continued ill behaviour? *Signed:* Fanny. *2 pp. Unpublished. Mrs. R.L.S. writes that Stevenson's parents are in Torquay and that his father* wants to go to Edinburgh and break heads.

3664

May 1st [*1887*]. Skerryvore. Best of Custodians, I send the enclosed. We have been looking over old papers, and the sorrowful thing turned up. *Signed:* Fanny. *4 pp. Unpublished. Mrs. R.L.S. writes that her former husband, Sam Osbourne, has deserted his present wife and disappeared. This news is upsetting to Mrs. R.L.S. and particularly to her son. Stevenson gave money which Lloyd Osbourne sent to a lawyer in San Francisco for the use of the deserted wife.*

3665

[*June, 1887*]. Skerryvore Bournemouth. Dear Custodian, I was just about writing to say that we would be with you on the day you mention when a letter came from Aunt Alan at the same time with a telegram from Bob who is coming here today. *Signed:* F V. de G. Stevenson. *4 pp. On black-bordered stationery. 28 lines of this 66-line letter are published in E. V. Lucas.* The Colvins and their Friends, *p. 171. Mrs. R.L.S. men-*

tions a visit from Dr. Ruedi and a prospective visit from Charles S. Fairchild. She writes of a worm (?) that looks like an ivy twig.

3666

[*June, 1887*]. Skerryvore Bournemouth. Could a guardian angel give me some information . . .? *Signed:* Fanny V. de G. Stevenson. *4 pp. On black-bordered stationery. Partly published in E. V. Lucas.* The Colvins and their Friends, *pp.* 176–177, *where about 17 lines of the autograph are omitted. Mrs. R.L.S. asks Colvin how to address the Queen and Princess of Hawaii, whom she expects to see in London. She writes that Stevenson* is wild to start for America at once, which seems madness to me.

3667

[*June, 1887*]. Skerryvore Bournemouth. Dear friend, I am thankful to say that Louis is much better again. *Signed:* F. V de G. S. *1 p. On black-bordered stationery. Unpublished. Mrs. R.L.S. writes that she and her family may turn up soon in London.*

3668

[*Early summer, 1887*]. Skerryvore Westbourne Bournemouth. Dear friend. I shall try to answer your letter, so far as I can, at least. *Signed:* F. V. de G. Stevenson. *5 pp. On black-bordered stationery. Published in* Scribner's Magazine, Vol. LXXV, No. 3, New York, March, 1924, pp. 325–326, where about 26 lines of the autograph are omitted. Mrs. R.L.S. writes that the lawyer who drew up the will of Stevenson's father had *mismanaged* things, and that it looked at first as though *the Church of Scot-land might walk off with the whole* estate. Stevenson's mother, however, *gets the life rent of everything and two thousand pounds. When and if the family returns from a winter in Colorado, Stevenson's mother is to live at Skerryvore, and the house at 17 Heriot Row, Edinburgh, will be sold.*

3669

Aug 18th [*1888*]. Taiohae Hiva oa Marquesas Isles. Dear and never forgotten Custodian: Oh that you and a few—a very few friends were with us in these enchanted Isles. *Signed:* F. V de G. Stevenson. *6 pp. Published in* Scribner's Magazine, *Vol.*

LXXV, No. 4, New York, April, 1924, pp. 408–410. Mrs. R.L.S. writes of natives, including cannibals, she has met in the Marquesas Islands.

3670

Dec 4th [*1888*]. Tautira, Tahiti. Dear, long neglected, though never forgotten Custodian, I write you from fairy land. *First 8 pp. of letter. No signature in this portion. Published in* The Letters, *1911, Vol. 3, pp. 80–89, where 25 lines of the portion of the autograph here preserved are omitted. Mrs. R. L. S. writes of a month spent with Ori, a sub chief at Tautira, while the* Casco *was being repaired, of the exchange of names and a great feast.*

3671

May 21st [*1889*]. Honolulu. Best of friends, It was a joy inexpressible to get word from you at last. *Signed:* Fanny V de G. Stevenson. *2 pp. Published in* The Letters, *1911, Vol. 3, pp. 121–124, where about 16 lines of the autograph are omitted. Mrs. R.L.S. is much annoyed by the fact that Stevenson wants to make his book on the South Seas a scientific dissertation. She is angry with Burlingame for persuading Stevenson to sign a contract to deliver the manuscript of* The Master of Ballantrae *by a certain date.*

3672

June 18th 1889. [*Honolulu*]. My dear ones, This is about the last chance for a word of goodby. *Signed:* Fanny V. de G. Stevenson. *8 pp. Published in* Scribner's Magazine, *New York, April, 1924, pp. 410–412, where a few lines of the autograph are omitted. The letter is to Sidney Colvin and Mrs. Sitwell. Mrs. R.L.S. writes about Ah Foo, a Chinese cook; and about her son-in-law, Joe Strong, with whom the Stevensons nearly had a break on account of Strong's bad conduct.*

3673

Jan 20th [*1890*]. Apia. Dear Custodian, I hardly dare use that word with the knowledge in my heart that we intend to remove our bodily selves from out your custody. *Unsigned. 9 pp. Published in* E. V. Lucas. The Colvins and their Friends, *pp. 222–*

231, *where about 33 lines of the autograph are omitted. Mrs. R.L.S. writes of a stormy trip in the schooner* Equator, *the incompetent crew, the killing of sharks, the singing of songs, the failing health of Joe Strong, the 400-acre plantation in Samoa which they plan to buy, Ah Foo a Chinese cook, Siteone a wild Samoan, and others.*

3674

[*January, 1890. Apia*]. My dear friend, The cutter is going out very soon to meet the mail steamer. *Signed:* Fanny. *8 pp. Published in* Scribner's Magazine, *Vol. LXXV, No. 4, New York, April, 1924, pp. 415–417. Mrs. R.L.S. writes about native servants, Stevenson's break with Henley, and his plan to make his book on the South Seas scientific.*

3675

April 12th 1890. Sydney. Best of Friends. I fear it will be a disappointment that we are not to be in England as soon as we expected. *Signed:* Fanny V. de G. Stevenson. *4 pp. Published in* Scribner's Magazine, *Vol. LXXV, No. 4, New York, April, 1924, pp. 417–418, where a few words of the autograph are omitted. Mrs. R.L.S. informs Colvin that instead of returning to England as planned, they will return to Samoa in the* Janet Nicholl *on account of Stevenson's bad health.*

3676

[*August, 1890. Sydney*]. Louis gave out here and I add a few words. *Signed:* Fanny. *7 pp. Partly published in E. V. Lucas.* The Colvins and their Friends, *pp. 220–222, where 78 lines of Mrs. Stevenson's autograph are omitted. She writes much about R.L.S.'s health and his need for a warm moist climate. She states that the news of Colvin's death* would kill Louis on the spot. *She contemplates life in Samoa without enthusiasm, and of the Samoans she writes:* I do not like them. I do not trust them. *This is an addition to a letter by R.L.S.*

3677

[*December, 1892. Vailima*]. Dear Friend I add just a word. *Signed:* F. *11 pp. Unpublished. Mrs. R.L.S. writes about the British consul, T. B. Cusack-Smith, and his jealousy of Steven-*

*son and Haggard. She writes of Graham Balfour who has left
for England. She states that she is opposed to including Stevenson's story,* The Waif Woman, *in* Island Nights' Entertainments.

3678
[July? 1895. San Francisco]. It sounds very bald, but you can see
what what [sic] Louis could have made of it. *Signed:* Fanny.
*Last 2 pp. of letter. Unpublished. Mrs. R.L.S. writes about a
portrait she made of Stevenson, about Isobel Strong's services
to him as amanuensis, about Charles Baxter's granting permission to print certain small items by R.L.S. without her permission.*

3679
July 17th [1895]. 7 Montgomery Avenue San Francisco. My
dear friend, Graham Balfour has started for England. *Signed:*
Fanny V. de G. Stevenson. *4 pp. Written on black-bordered sta-
tionery. Unpublished. Mrs. R.L.S. complains further of Charles
Baxter's unauthorized disposition of writings by Stevenson.*

3680
Aug 15th [1895. San Francisco]. My dear friend, I have just
received your letter of July 31st. *Signed:* Fanny. *4 pp. Written
on black-bordered stationery. Unpublished. Mrs. R.L.S. complains further about Charles Baxter's activities.*

3681
August 19th [1895. San Francisco]. My dear friend, I sent off
a letter to you just before yours came enclosing one from Henry
James. *Signed:* Fanny. *4 pp. Written on black-bordered station-
ery. Unpublished. Mrs. R.L.S. mentions Baxter's refusal to see
Burlingame in New York, and writes of a portrait she made of
Stevenson.*

3682
Oct 1st 1895. 7 Montgomery Avenue [San Francisco]. My dear
friend, I am only sending a note to say that I doubt very much
whether Charles [Baxter] has any legal right to dispose of MS.S.
without my consent. *Signed:* Fanny V. de G. Stevenson. *2 pp.
Written on black-bordered stationery. Unpublished. Mrs. R.L.S.*

mentions one Strang, an artist; and Mr. Lloyd, a San Francisco lawyer who looked after Fanny Stevenson and her children while her first husband was away, and who renewed his services to her after the death of R.L.S.

3683
Oct 3d 1895. 7 Montgomery Avenue San Francisco Cal. My dear friend, I sent you a hasty note yesterday. *Signed:* Fanny. *6 pp. Written on black-bordered stationery. Unpublished. Mrs. R.L.S. states that Charles Baxter* legally cancelled his trusteeship of Louis' estate in favour of Lloyd and me. *She asks Colvin's help in getting* The Hanging Judge *produced.*

3684
October 30th [*1895. San Francisco*]. My dear friend, I send the play [The Hanging Judge] by today's mail. *Signed:* Fanny. *4 pp. Written on black-bordered stationery. Unpublished. Mrs. R.L.S. writes of* The Hanging Judge; *of Lloyd Osbourne's* health, which has suddenly broken down under, I really do believe— the strain that Charles [*Baxter*] has put upon him; *and of plans to go to Honolulu.*

3685
November 4th [*1895. San Francisco*]. My dear friend, Lloyd is slowly getting better. *Signed:* Fanny. *2 pp. Written on black-bordered stationery. Unpublished. Mrs. R.L.S. writes further about possible production of* The Hanging Judge, *possible publication of the* Fables, *and her dislike of Strang's portrait of Stevenson.*

3686
November 9th [*1895. San Francisco*]. My dear friend. We are off, now, in a very few days; Lloyd still remains very weak and nervous. *Signed:* Fanny. *3 pp. Unpublished. Mrs. R.L.S. is pleased with publication of* Vailima Letters, *but does not wish to have the* Fables *published. She writes further about possible production of* The Hanging Judge.

3687

[*January?* *1896*]. Hotel San [*sic*] Souci Waikiki Honolulu. My dear friend, This is just a stupid note to let you and the Monument know how we are getting on. *Signed:* Fanny. *4 pp. Written on black-bordered stationery. Published in E. V. Lucas. The Colvins and their Friends, pp. 261–263, where 11 lines of the autograph are omitted. The letter is to Sidney Colvin and Mrs. Sitwell. Mrs. R.L.S. writes of meeting the Hawaiian queen. She disagrees with Stevenson's mother as to what words are to be cut on his tomb.*

3688

February 19th [*1896*]. Honolulu. My dear friend, I wrote to Mrs Sitwell about Lloyd's marriage. *Signed:* Fanny V. de G. Stevenson. *4 pp. On black-bordered stationery. Unpublished. Mrs. R.L.S. writes about Lloyd Osbourne's prospective marriage to Katharine Durham, and about letters written by Stevenson to Mrs. Dora Williams and Miss Adelaide Boodle.*

3689

February 22nd [*1896. Honolulu*]. My dear friend, I had already written you a note when I got your letter. *Signed:* Fanny. *4 pp. On black-bordered stationery. Mrs. R.L.S. writes of a visit to Mr. Doxie, a bookseller, to whom she expressed her displeasure at his selling reproductions of an item by R.L.S. (Desiderata) which had been handed to William Doxie by Charles Baxter.*

3690

March 20th [*1896*]. Honolulu. My dear friend, Your letter has filled me with the desire to go to England that I might be near you during the work on the Life. *Signed:* Fanny. *4 pp. On black-bordered stationery. Partly published in E. V. Lucas. The Colvins and their Friends, p. 263, where 39 lines of the autograph are omitted. Mrs. R.L.S. mentions her son's convalescence and forthcoming marriage. She complains of lack of money. About the biography of R.L.S. which Colvin expected to write she states:* I should say go ahead as frankly as possible, and then, if necessary, we can tone down. I should like to be honest, but at the same time not to hurt anyone's feelings.

3691

[*Before April 24, 1896. Honolulu*]. P. S. There is a man coming to London with Samoan dancers. *Unsigned. Last 2 pp. of letter. Unpublished. Mrs. R.L.S. writes of one Marquardt, a chief of police in Apia, to whom she plans to give letters of introduction to friends in England.*

3692

April 24th [*1896*]. Honolulu. My dear friend, I am up to the eyes in answering congratulatory letters [*about her son's marriage*]. *Signed:* Fanny. *3 pp. On black-bordered stationery. Partly published in E. V. Lucas. The Colvins and their Friends, pp. 263–264, where 48 lines of the autograph are omitted. Regarding her prospective trip to England, Mrs. R.L.S. fears the English climate and the demands that would be made of her as Stevenson's widow. As to the biography of Stevenson she writes:* You are the only one fit for the work.

3693

October 6th [*1896*]. Vailima. My dear Friend, My first news is that Lloyd has got his appointment as vice consul general. *Signed:* Fanny. *6 pp. On black-bordered stationery. Unpublished. Mrs. R.L.S. writes further about the prospective* Life of Stevenson, *and about her son and daughter-in-law.*

3694

June 26th 1898. [London]. My dear friend Between you and me there must be—there can be—no quarrel. *Signed:* Fanny V de G. Stevenson. *3 pp. Mrs. Stevenson writes that it will be more fitting for Colvin to write the life of R.L.S. than for her and her son to undertake it.*

3695
Feb 26th [*1895*]. Vailima. My dearest Cogia Hassan, I have not forgotten—I never can forget—the days when we were all so happy together! *Signed:* Fanny. *3 pp. With addressed envelope. Unpublished. Written two months after Stevenson's death.*

MRS. R.L.S. TO W. COURTHOPE FORMAN

3696

27 April 1900. 2751 Broadway, San Francisco. Dear Sir, My unconscionable delay in answering your letter has been unavoidable. *Signed:* Fanny V. de G. Stevenson. *4 pp. including a supplementary leaf on which Mrs. R.L.S. has made a plan of Vailima. With addressed envelope and mounted stamp. Unpublished. Mrs. R.L.S. identifies members of the Stevenson household in a photograph.*

3697

[*Early September, 1885*]. New London Hotel, Exeter. Dear Mrs Hardy, As you see, we have gotten no further than Exeter. *Signed:* F. V. de G. Stevenson. *2 pp. Unpublished. Stevenson's health having broken down, Mrs. R.L.S. asks Mrs. Hardy's advice about securing lodgings in Dorchester.*

3698

[*Early September, 1885*]. New London Hotel, Exeter. Dear Mrs Hardy, Many thanks for your note. *Signed:* F. V. de G. Stevenson. *2 pp. Unpublished. Mrs. R.L.S. writes that she thinks it best to get her ill husband to their home in Bournemouth as soon as possible.*

3699

[*September, 1885*]. New London Hotel, Exeter. Dear Mrs Hardy, Mr Stevenson has come to a sudden determination to return home immediately. *Signed:* Fanny V de G. Stevenson. *3 pp. Unpublished. Mrs. R.L.S. writes that they will attempt to visit the Hardys in Dartmoor in 1886.*

3700

[*Winter, 1885–1886*]. Skerryvore, Bournemouth. Dear Mrs Hardy, I have often thought of writing to you. *Signed:* F. V de G. Stevenson. *3 pp. Unpublished. Mrs. R.L.S. writes of her husband's health, and suggests that the Hardys visit them at Skerryvore.*

3701

[*1881 or 1882. Davos*]. . . . nor any one at all until he [*R.L.S.*] is better. Dont ask for answers from him yet awhile. *Signed:* Fanny V de G. Stevenson. *Last 2 pp. of letter. Unpublished.*

[*January, 1884. Pension Rose, Nice*]. *See no. 3611. Letter to Charles Baxter and W. E. Henley.*

3702

[*May 2 and 3, 1884*] Friday night [*and*] Saturday Morning. [*Hyères*]. My dear Mr Henley, I want you to give me some perfectly quiet sane advice. *Signed:* F. V de G Stevenson. *4 pp. Dated by Henley. Unpublished. Mrs. R.L.S. writes of her husband's severe hemorrhages, of Coggie Ferrier's help, and asks Henley's advice about having Dr. Mennell come (from England?) to examine Stevenson.*

3703

[*May 3, 1884. Saturday night. Hyères*]. dear Mr Henley, Telegram received. Louis is very low and seems growing weaker and paler. *Signed:* F V de G Stevenson. *4 pp. Unpublished. Of her husband's very severe illness Mrs. R.L.S. writes:* His courage is wonderful. I never saw anything like it.

3704

[*1884 ? Montpellier*]. My dear Mr Henley, The prescription came, was instantly made up. *First 2 pp. of letter. Unpublished. Mrs. R.L.S. describes the effects on her husband of a new medicine.*

3705

[*June, 1884. Royat*]. My dear Mr Henley, It is no want of interest in you and your doings . . . that has prevented [*me*] from writing this long time. *Signed:* F V de G. *6 pp. of letter. Unpublished. Mrs. R.L.S. mentions a forthcoming presentation of Deacon Brodie (on July 2, 1884?) and urges Henley to keep up his interest in writing plays.*

3706

[*July? 1884. Royat?*] Dear People, When, and how, and who, and what are you? Not a word do we hear. Louis is better again. *Signed: F. V de G S. 2 pp. To Mr. and Mrs. Henley. Unpublished. Mrs. R.L.S. mentions visits from Mr. and Mrs. Grant Allen.*

3707

[*Autumn? 1884. Bournemouth?*] My dear Mr. Henley, When you come, which I hope will be soon, you must not expect Louis to do any work. *Signed: F. 3 pp. Unpublished. Mrs. R.L.S. writes of Stevenson's discouragement about his health and his expectation of finishing no more than his projected life of Wellington.*

3708

[*Autumn, 1884. Bournemouth*]. of his books with sentimental young ladies. *Signed: Fanny V de G. S. Last p. of letter. Unpublished. Mrs. R.L.S. asks:* Did Louis tell you how I lay wide awake, one entire night, and found that I could repeat every word of the "Admiral" [Guinea] from the beginning to the end? *She suggests certain revisions in the play.*

3709

[*Autumn, 1884. Bournemouth*]. My dear Playwright, I have been looking at the Admiral. *Signed: F. 4 pp. Unpublished. Mrs. R.L.S. suggests revisions in* Admiral Guinea.

3710

[*Autumn? 1884. Bournemouth*]. My dear Mr Henley, We are thinking of accompanying the Bobs and the Lemons to a hotel near Poole, next week. *Signed: F. V de G. 4 pp. Unpublished. Mrs. R.L.S. states that Stevenson had no particular desire to meet Lord Rosebery, a meeting evidently desired by Henley, and in this connection writes:* You know we love you in spite of your many faults, so try and bear with our few. *She writes also of Sir Percy and Lady Shelley.*

3711

[*Early 1885. Bournemouth*]. My dear Mr Henley, I have just had Dobell for a consultation. *Signed:* F. V de G. Stevenson. *2 pp. Unpublished. Mrs. R.L.S. writes that Stevenson is to go away to some quiet spot where he does not know any one, and stay a month.*

3712

[*1885. London*]. My dear Henley, Your last note gave Louis great pleasure. *Signed:* F. V. de G. Stevenson. *3 pp. Unpublished. Mrs. R.L.S. writes of protecting her ill husband from visitors including his father.*

3713

[*August, 1885*]. New London Hotel, Exeter. My dear Mr Henley, It is now a week since we left home, and we are no farther away than Exeter. *Signed:* F. V de G. Stevenson. *4 pp. Unpublished. Mrs. R.L.S. describes an attack of hemorrhages which kept Stevenson in Exeter several weeks after visiting Thomas Hardy in Dorchester. She was helped in nursing Stevenson by Lady Shelley who hurried up from Torquay.*

3714

[*188–. Bournemouth*]. My dear Mr Henley I was quite insane when I wrote to you last, but you seem no better yourself. *Signed:* F. V. de G. Stevenson. *4 pp. Unpublished. Mrs. R.L.S. asks Henley not to come with Colvin to visit Stevenson because the latter* can only see one at a time. *She mentions a pleasant visit from Katharine de Mattos.*

3715

[*After November 13, 1885. Bournemouth*]. My dear friend, Louis' birthday was one worth having. *Signed:* F V de G Stevenson. *2 pp. Unpublished. Mrs. R.L.S. writes of Stevenson's improved health, a visit from his cousin Bob and a ghost at Skerryvore.*

3716

[*1886? Bournemouth?*] My dear friend, Can you not send the chatelaine here for a change of air? *Signed:* F. V de G. Stevenson. *3 pp. Unpublished. Mrs. R.L.S. asks Henley to send his wife for a visit.*

3717
[*October? 1886. London?*] My dear Mr Henley, I didn't write to you before because I knew you would hear through Mr Baxter. *Signed:* F. V. de G. S. *4 pp. Written on* British Museum *stationery. Unpublished. Mrs. R.L.S. writes of her husband's health, of two doctors who examined him, of the* Gosse *affair, of the silent reception of Henry James's latest novel.*

3718
[*1887? Bournemouth?*] My dear Mr Henley, I must add a word. *Signed:* Fanny V de G Stevenson. *2 pp. Unpublished. Mrs. R.L.S. praises Henley's play* (Mephisto?). *This is an addition to a letter by R.L.S.*

3719
[*June or July, 1887*]. Skerryvore Bournemouth. My dear Buffalo William, I have been meaning to write to you for some time. *Signed:* F. V. de G. S——. *3 pp. On black-bordered stationery. Unpublished. Mrs. R.L.S. writes of a* noble scheme to go to Santa Fe . . . *for the Winter. William Frederick (Buffalo Bill) Cody brought his Wild West show to England for the first time in 1887. Mrs. R.L.S. and Henley may have attended a performance.*

3720
October 1st [*1887*]. Saranac [*Lake*]. Dear Henley, Everything seems to point toward the necessity of writing you a note tonight. *Signed:* Fanny V de G. Stevenson. *5 pp. On black-bordered stationery. Unpublished. Mrs. R.L.S. writes of the house rented at Saranac Lake, of the surrounding country, of what they have to eat, etc.*

3721

[*February? 1884*]. Pension Rose . . . No 100. Rue de France Nice. My dear Mr Ireland, I feel greatly mortified that no word has reached you from Mr Stevenson since he received your book. *Signed:* F. V de G. Stevenson. *Unpublished.*

MRS. R.L.S. TO HER SON, LLOYD OSBOURNE

3722

29th Sept 1890. Vailima. My dearest boy, I know you want a few closer details than Louis has given you. *First 5 lines of a letter. Unpublished. This is an addition to a letter by R.L.S.*

MRS. R.L.S. TO SIR ARTHUR WING PINERO

3723

March 30th 1911. [*Santa Barbara*]. Dear Sir Arthur, May I take the liberty of introducing my grand-son, Austin Strong? *Signed:* Fanny V. de G. Stevenson. *1 p. Written on stationery of* Stonehedge R. D. Route No. 1 Santa Barbara. *Unpublished. Pinero had lectured and written about Stevenson in 1903.*

3724

June 11th, 81. [*Kinnaird Cottage, Pitlochry, Perthshire*]. My dear Mr. Robertson, Both your book and your letter have been a long while upon the road. *Signed:* F. V. de G Stevenson. *2 pp. Unpublished. R.L.S. has written an addition to this letter.*

3725

Oct: 29: 1885. Skerryvore, Bournemouth. My "views" are that this little incident . . . will be the cause of bringing about more intimate and friendly relations. *Signed:* F. V. de G. Stevenson. *2 pp. With addressed envelope and mounted stamp. Unpublished. This is an addition to a letter by R.L.S.*

3726

[*Postmarked:* No 1 85]. Skerryvore, Bournemouth. Dear Mr Robertson. A note has come from Longman which makes it impossible for Louis to propose the taking back of "Jeckyl" [*sic*]. *Signed:* F. V. de G. Stevenson. *4 pp. With addressed envelope and mounted stamp. Unpublished.*

3727

[*Postmarked:* De 11 85. Bournemouth]. Dear Mr Robertson, Louis, who continues very ill, wishes me to thank you for the cheque. *Signed:* F V de G. Stevenson. *2 pp. With addressed envelope and mounted stamp. Unpublished. Mrs. R.L.S. mentions* Dr. Jekyll and Mr. Hyde *and* Olalla.

3728

Dec 3d [*1886*]. Skerryvore [*Bournemouth*]. Dear Mr Robertson, I trust you have received the map, which has, I fear, caused you considerable annoyance. *Signed:* F. V. de G. Stevenson. *7 pp. Unpublished. Mrs. R.L.S. writes of her husband's precarious health and of her attending to his correspondence. After writing that her husband has received no letter from a Mr. Wheelhouse, she states in a postscript that a letter did come from him.*

3729

[*Postmarked:* De 4 86. Bournemouth]. Dear Mr Robertson. With this I send the end of Louis' story. *Signed:* F. V. de G. Stevenson. *1 p. With addressed envelope and mounted stamp. Unpublished.*

MRS. R.L.S. TO NELLIE VAN DE GRIFT SANCHEZ

3730

[*September? 1880. Edinburgh*]. Louis is called away by a visitor, so I go on with his letter. *Signed:* The Emigrant [?] *3 pp. Written on stationery of* 17 Heriot Row. *Unpublished. To Nellie van de Grift Sanchez and Isobel Strong. Mrs. R. L. S. writes of clothes belonging to R.L.S.'s mother and to herself, also of the possibility of going to Algiers. This is an addition to a letter by R. L. S.*

3731
Ja 22 84. Nice. Consultation more satisfactory Beater. [*i.e.
Better?*]. *1 p. Telegram. About R. L. S.'s health.*

MRS. R.L.S. TO FANNY SITWELL (FRANCES JANE FETHERSTONHAUGH, LATER LADY COLVIN)

3732

[*October, 1884. Bournemouth*]. My dear Friend, I am tired, and almost c . . . , if you can conceive it. *Signed:* Fanny V de G. Stevenson. *4 pp. Unpublished. Mrs. R.L.S. writes of the removal of a tapeworm from her husband's body, of Henley's objections to alterations in one of the plays* (Admiral Guinea?)

3733

[*November, 1884. Bournemouth*]. My dearest Friend, If you *could* come and stay with me a few days I cannot tell you what a comfort it would be to me. *Signed:* Fanny. *1 p. Partly published in E. V. Lucas.* The Colvins and their Friends, *p. 159, where 9 lines of the autograph are omitted.*

3734

[*February, 1885. Bournemouth*]. My dearest friend, Many thanks for your kind and pleasant letter. *Signed:* Fanny. *4 pp. Partly published in* Scribner's Magazine, *Vol. LXXV, No. 3, New York, March, 1924, pp. 320–321, where 27 lines of the autograph are omitted. Mrs. R.L.S. writes that she plans to go to Hyères to settle affairs there, and would like to find someone to stay with R.L.S. in her absence.*

3735

[*March, 1885. Bournemouth*]. Dear Friend, I am just home, Find Louis with an attack of pleurisy. *Signed:* F. V. de G. S. *3 pp. Unpublished. Mostly about R.L.S.'s health.*

3736

[*Summer, 1885. Bournemouth*]. Best of friends The chairs look very well. *Signed:* Fanny. *4 pp. In pencil. Partly published in E. V. Lucas.* The Colvins and their Friends, *p. 161, where about 62 lines of the autograph are omitted. Mrs. R.L.S. writes of furniture for Skerryvore and of her husband's bad health.*

3737

[*January 1, 1886. Bournemouth*]. Dear Friend, Louis had assured me that he told you all about Sam. *Signed:* F. V. de G. S. *4 pp. 3 lines of this 36-line letter are printed in E. V. Lucas.* The Colvins and their Friends, *p. 173. Mrs. R.L.S. writes that her son Lloyd is having a glorious time in Venezuela, that Stevenson's health is good and that the Jenkin book moves on apace.*

3738

[*April, 1886*]. Sunday Night. Skerryvore. My dear friend. You will doubtless be surprised to find that I am at home without a word to you. *Signed:* F. V de G. S. *4 pp. 6 lines of this 48-line letter are published in E. V. Lucas.* The Colvins and their Friends, *p. 170. Mrs. R.L.S. writes that Stevenson and his father have been doing each other no good at Matlock, and that Stevenson is coming home.*

3739

[*May, 1887*]. Edinburgh. Dearest Friend, We have arrived to find our dear old man passing away painlessly. *Signed:* F. V. de G. Stevenson. *3 pp. Published in* Scribner's Magazine, *Vol. LXXV, No. 3, New York, March, 1924, p. 325, where about 3 lines of the autograph are omitted. Mrs. R.L.S. writes of the death of Stevenson's father.*

June 18th 1889. [*Honolulu*]. *See no. 3672. Letter to Sidney Colvin and Mrs. Sitwell.*

3740

[*September, 1892. Vailima*]. Dear Friend, I want to ask a favour and I dont deserve it one bit. *Signed:* F. V de G. Stevenson. *10 pp. 70 lines of this 149-line letter are published in* Scribner's Magazine, *Vol. LXXV, No. 4, New York, April, 1924, pp. 418–419. Mrs. R.L.S. asks Mrs. Sitwell to get her a black lace mantle lined with surah silk. She mentions Lafaele's request for permission to poison a family; and Arak's request for her blessing on his plan to hunt black boys in the bush with a gun, promising to kill them far away from Vailima. She writes of Graham Balfour and Lady Jersey.*

3741

[*December, 1894. Vailima*]. My dear friend, Forgive a very short letter. I am not fit to write, but I must. *Signed:* Fanny. *4 pp. 28 lines of this 56-line letter are published in E. V. Lucas.* The Colvins and their Friends, *pp. 256–257. Mrs. R.L.S. mentions her premonition of her husband's death. She asks that an advertisement be printed asking that letters written by Stevenson be sent in for her to edit. She forbids the publishing of* Moral Emblems *in the Edinburgh Edition of Stevenson's writings. She writes that Stevenson wanted to be buried in Samoa, but that he did not expect* to lie in German soil. *She urges that an English protectorate for Samoa be obtained.*

3742

[*Postmarked:* Sep 16 95]. 7 Montgomery Avenue S. F. My dear friend, I have seen your brother; a really delightful brother. *Signed:* Fanny. *4 pp. On black-bordered stationery. With addressed envelope and mounted stamp. Partly published in E. V. Lucas.* The Colvins and their Friends, *pp. 260–261, where 17 lines of the autograph are omitted. Mrs. R.L.S. writes of Mrs. Sitwell's brother, Cuthbert Fetherstonhaugh of Australia. She mentions her* impotent grief and anger *at Charles Baxter.*

[*January? 1896*]. Honolulu. *See no. 3687. Letter to Sidney Colvin and Mrs. Sitwell.*

3743

[*1884? Hyères*]. Dear Louis, I am getting anxious not to get a word from you yet. *Signed:* Fanny. *4 pp. Written on stationery of* La Solitude. *Unpublished. Mrs. R.L.S. writes of the dogs Bogue and Wogg.*

3744

[*April? 1888. San Francisco*]. My dearest Louis I am back again in San Francisco, but will see Nelly once more as she passes through. *Signed:* Fanny. *8 pp. Unpublished. Mrs. R.L.S. writes of Simoneau who had a cure for lung ailments, of a girl named Pauly (?), of inquiries about a yacht, of the quarrel with Henley.*

MRS. R.L.S. TO HER MOTHER-IN-LAW, MARGARET ISABELLA BALFOUR STEVENSON

3745

[*July 16, 1880. California*]. My dear Mrs Stevenson I am afraid you will think it strange that I have not written before, but I really have not been able. *Signed:* Fanny V. de G. Stevenson. *4 pp. Dated by R.L.S.'s mother. Unpublished. Possibly Fanny's first letter to R.L.S.'s mother. R. L. S. has written an addition to this letter.*

3746

[*October 22, 1880. Paris*]. My dear Mrs Stevenson, I am so cross with rain and mud and wet feet. *Unsigned. 2 pp. Dated by R.L.S.'s mother. Unpublished. R. L. S. has written an addition to this letter.*

3747

[*Autumn, 1880. Davos*]. ordering it from them. The weather has been, so they say, very bad for Davos. *Signed:* Fanny. *Last 4 pp. of letter. Unpublished. Mrs. R.L.S. gives her early impressions of Davos, writes about the dog Wogg and a blind dog.* I shall try to write regularly and often.

3748

[*Autumn, 1880?*] Saturday. [*Davos?*] My dear Mrs Stevenson, I have been so tired and worn out with so much to do that I broke down for a little. *First 4 pp. of letter. Unpublished. Mrs. R.L.S. writes of doctors for R.L.S., of the dog Wogg and a cat.*

3749

Dec. 15th [*1880. Davos*]. To put the bottom [?] in this letter, an accident has happened to my veil. *Signed:* Fanny. *1 p. Unpublished. This is an addition to a letter by R. L. S.*

3750

Feb 5th 81/ [*Davos*]. I am afraid you are right about the questions. *Signed:* Fanny. *6 pp. Unpublished. Mrs. R.L.S. describes the dull life and people at Davos. She writes that* Louis is learning to be very sedate and quiet, and does not give way to excitability about small things so much. *This is an addition to a letter by R.L.S.*

3751

[*March, 1881. Davos*]. I take up the letter where Louis has left it. *Unsigned. 2 pp. Unpublished. Fanny writes about the Davos climate, etc. This is an addition to a letter by R.L.S.*

3752

[*1881? Davos*]. cannot help but think it must be Louis "Edinburgh" in some form, would you be kind enough to find out? *Signed:* Fanny. *Last 4 pp. of letter. Written on stationery with printed heading:* Davos Printing Office. Managed by Samuel Lloyd Osbourne & Co. The Chalet. *Unpublished. Mrs. R.L.S. writes about J. A. Symonds, Dr. Ruedi, and about dogs and cats.*

3753

[*October, 1881. Davos*]. My dear Mrs Stevenson, I have had such a horrid cold that I havent been able to write before. *Signed:* Fanny. *4 pp. Written on stationery with printed heading:* Davos Printing Office. Managed by Samuel Lloyd Osbourne & Co. The Chalet. *Dated by R.L.S.'s mother. Unpublished. Mrs. R.L.S. writes about buying groceries, and engaging a new German maid. To this letter Stevenson has added the words:* telegram received inclosed six copies of magnum opus. (*i.e.* Not I, and other Poems?)

3754

[*October, 1881. Davos*]. My dear Mrs Stevenson, Many thanks for the cook book: I was so glad to get it. *Signed:* Fanny, *and* F. *4 pp. Unpublished. Fanny writes about curry and other foods. This is an addition to a letter by R.L.S. to his father.*

3755

[*December 3, 1881. Davos*]. My dear Mrs Stevenson, At last I believe I may say that I am better. *Signed:* Fanny. *4 pp. Written on stationery of* Hôtel & Pension Buol. *Dated by R.L.S.'s mother. Unpublished. Mrs. R.L.S. describes her illness. She writes:* I take it as a compliment that I am thought [*by R.L.S.*] like him [*R.L.S.'s father*].

3756

[*February 16, 1882. Davos*]. My dear People The Buol's want a 9 gallon cask of good whiskey, and seem willing to pay a fair price. *Unsigned. 7 pp. Written on stationery of* Hôtel & Pension Buol. *Dated by R.L.S.'s mother. Unpublished. Mrs. R.L.S. writes about Wogg's sore ear, about a scrap book of items relating to R.L.S. kept by his mother, about the weather at Davos and lung germs. R.L.S. has written an addition to this letter.*

3757

[*February 18, 1882. Davos*]. Dear Mrs Stevenson This is only a note to ask if you will kindly send Louis an elastic arrangement. *Signed:* Fanny. *4 pp. Dated by R.L.S.'s mother. Unpublished. Mrs. R.L.S. asks for an elastic support for her husband's knee. She writes of guests lost in the mountains and of Wogg.*

3758

[*October, 1882. Lyon*]. My dear Mrs Stevenson, Here I am at Lyons, just too exhausted to say a word. *Signed:* Fanny. *1 p. Written on stationery of* Hôtel de l'Univers, Lyon. *Unpublished.*

3759

21st [*October*] Saturday [*1882. Marseille?*] Please take this description of me with a grain of salt. *Unsigned. 2 pp. Unpublished. This is an addition to a letter by R. L. S.*

3760

[*October, 1882*]. My dear Mrs S. Why don't you open my letters? I told you to. *Signed:* Fanny. *Written on a p. left blank by R. L. S. in a folder containing a letter from him to his wife. Unpublished.*

3761

11th Nov. [*1882*] Saturday. Campagne Defli [*St. Marcel*]. A word from me, I am sure you cannot think, or believe, how well I am. *Unpublished. 2 pp. This is an addition to a letter by R. L. S. P. 2 of Mrs. R. L. S.'s letter ends with an unfinished sentence; the remainder of this letter, if any, is missing.*

3762

[*November, 1882*] Tuesday. [*St. Marcel*]. I think I have already told you that Louis gets nothing for the "Arabian Nights" now. *Unfinished. Unsigned. 3 pp. Unpublished. This is an addition to a letter by R.L.S.*

3763

Nov 19th [*1882. St. Marcel*]. Just a word to say that Louis really seems better. *Signed:* Fanny. *Unpublished. This is an addition to a letter by R.L.S.*

3764

[*November? 1882. St. Marcel*]. How did you like the new Longman? I hope you read "Lexington" by Howells; it is most charming. *Signed:* Fanny. *Last 2 pp. of letter. Unpublished.*

3765

[*February or March, 1883. Hyères*]. I do not think, my dear Mrs Stevenson that Louis has made anything very clear. *Signed:* Fanny, *in the hand of R. L. S. 2 pp. Unpublished. They plan to send Lloyd Osbourne to school at Toulon. This is an addition to a letter by R. L. S.*

3766

[*March, 1883 ? Hyères ?*] . . . Once she wore a set [*of diamonds*] exactly like yours. *Unsigned. Last 4 pp. of letter. Unpublished. R.L.S. has written a few words at the end of this.*

3767

[*March, 1883? Hyères*]. with a pleurisy she knows she brought it upon herself, and quite deserved it. *Signed:* Fanny. *Last 2 pp. of letter. Unpublished. Mrs. R.L.S. writes of examining the new home at Hyères, and of duty on silverware.*

3768

[*March, 1883. Hyères*]. My dear Mrs Stevenson, Would you believe that I am writing from the midst of a snow storm? *First 4 pp. of letter. Unpublished. Mrs. R.L.S. writes of La Solitude, and of people they have met at Hyères.*

3769

[*Spring? 1883. Hyères*]. abroad; and where do you suppose it comes from? *Signed:* Fanny. *Last 6 pp. of letter. Unpublished. Mrs. R.L.S. writes of the garden at La Solitude, of Stevenson's working habits and his improved health.*

3770

[*Spring? 1883. Hyères*]. Summer is that one need have almost no clothes, as there are nobody here but peasants. *Signed:* Fanny. *Last 3 pp. of letter. Unpublished. Mrs. R.L.S. writes about gardening.*

3771

[*June, 1883. Hyères*]. I should be much obliged if you would ask the Cooks people. *Unsigned. 1 p. of letter. Unpublished. This is an addition to a letter by R.L.S.*

3772

[*June ? 1883. Hyères*]. My dear Mrs Stevenson, I sincerely sympathize with you in your loneliness. *First 4 pp. of letter. Unpublished.*

3773

[*July? 1883. Marseille*]. My dear Mrs Stevenson, You will be surprised, I know at the post mark on this letter, for we are now in Marseilles. *Signed:* Fanny. *4 pp. Unpublished. Mrs. R.L.S. writes of her husband's health; she thinks he has* Roman fever. *He is having dental work done in Marseille. Mrs. R.L.S. is unwilling to urge Stevenson to carry on a correspondence with his cousin Chloe and her mother. She writes:* His letters to you and his father are hardly more than intimations that he is alive.

3774

[*July, 1883. Hyères*]. My dear Mrs Stevenson, I am rather bewildered with all the things I want to remember. *Signed:* Fanny S. *12 pp. Written on stationery of* La Solitude. *Unpublished. Mrs. R.L.S. writes of the illness of R.L.S. and Lloyd Osbourne* (drain poison); *of a lace tie and gloves, a picture she painted, etc. She mentions publication of* The Black Arrow *in* Young Folks.

1149

3775

[*1883?*]. My dear Mrs Stevenson, The boy has just come to our great delight. *Unsigned. 2 pp. Unpublished. Fanny sends thanks for gifts of prayer books, dresses and paints. R.L.S. has written an addition to this letter.*

3776

[*September, 1883. Hyères*]. My dear Mrs Stevenson, I dont know what Bob meant by my being ill. *Signed:* Fanny. *7 pp. Written on stationery of* La Solitude. *Dated by R.L.S.'s mother. Unpublished. Mrs. R.L.S. writes of the health of R.L.S., Lloyd Osbourne and herself, of Lloyd's departure for England, of Stevenson's mourning over the death of Ferrier.*

3777

[*Autumn, 1883. Hyères*]. My dear Mrs Stevenson, Dont listen to Louis when he says there is anything the matter with me. *Signed:* Fanny. *8 pp. Written on stationery of* La Solitude. *Unpublished. Mrs. R.L.S. writes of purchasing wood and wine, of the scarcity of food in Hyères, about Wogg, about the pleasure of a chemist of Hyères at receiving a contract to write weekly articles for a newspaper. R.L.S. has written 4 lines at the end of this letter asking for paper and envelopes.*

3778

[*October, 1883. Hyères*]. My dear Mrs Stevenson, Here I am all alone, Louis being gone to Nice to see Dr. Williams. *Unsigned. Incomplete? 8 pp. Written on stationery of* La Solitude. *Dated by R.L.S.'s mother. Unpublished. Mrs. R.L.S. writes about an offer from* Lippincott's Magazine *to pay Stevenson's expenses in a Mediterranean cruise and for articles he would write about Mediterranean islands, about Lloyd Osbourne and residents at Hyères.*

3779.

[*October 21, 1883. Hyères*]. My dear Mrs Stevenson, I cannot find your letter to look over it for questions to be answered. *Unsigned. 8 pp. Partly written on stationery of* La Solitude. *Unpublished. Mrs. R.L.S. writes about clothes, paintings made by her, Wogg (about whom Stevenson was writing a poem), an expected visit from Charles Baxter, and about 66 original drawings made for* The Black Arrow *printed in* Young Folks *and presented to Stevenson. Mrs. R.L.S. writes:* I think it is not often that a Stevenson steers the safe middle course. They keep such a head of steam on.

3780
[*November, 1883. Hyères*]. My dear Mrs Stevenson, Whoever told you there is no such thing as Prussian brown told a falsehood. *Signed:* Fanny. *8 pp. Unpublished. Mrs. R.L.S. writes about her painting, Lloyd Osbourne's visit to Edinburgh, Isobel Strong, medicine for Wogg, donkey rides, and Burroughs the* American R. L. S.

3781
[*November, 1883. Hyères*]. My dear Mrs Stevenson, I hasten to say at once that I am much better. *Signed:* Fanny. *5 pp. Dated by R.L.S.'s mother. Unpublished. Mrs. R.L.S. writes about paintings she has made of persons and scenes.*

3782
[*November or December, 1883. Hyères*]. My dear Mrs Stevenson Would you kindly send me a "Buttericks pattern" book. *Signed:* F. *2 pp. Written on stationery of* La Solitude. *Unpublished. Of* Treasure Island *Mrs. R.L.S. writes:* It seems to be making a sensation.

3783
[*December? 1883. Hyères*]. My dear Mrs Stevenson, I have just written to you, and I do not know that I have anything to say. *Unsigned. 4 pp. Written on stationery of* La Solitude. *Unpublished. Mrs. R.L.S. writes of the health of R.L.S. and his father.*

3784
[*December, 1883. Hyères*]. My dear Mrs Stevenson I dont know what has happened to the whole world. *First 4 pp. of letter. Written on stationery of* La Solitude. *Dated by R.L.S.'s mother. Unpublished. Mrs. R.L.S. states that her husband has*

Roman fever, *and writes of an English circus that has come to Hyères.*

3785

[December, 1883. Hyères]. I have just received yours with a date, Dec 14 and add another postscript to this patchwork letter. *Signed: F. Last 6 pp. of letter. Unpublished. Mrs. Stevenson writes of her husband's recurrent fever. She states that the periodical version of* The Silverado Squatters *is full of errors.*

3786

[December, 1883. Hyères]. In fact all my sisters and my cousins and my aunts seem bent upon the same noble determination. *Signed:* Fanny. *Last 4 pp. of letter. Unpublished. Mrs. R.L.S. writes of Lloyd Osbourne's forthcoming examinations and says that she will miss him at Christmas; of Charles Baxter's expected visit; of a visit by a Mr. Black of Edinburgh.*

3787

[January, 1884. Nice]. My dear Mrs Stevenson, If I write like a mad creature do not be surprised for I have had a period of awful wretchedness. *Unsigned. 4 pp. Written on stationery of* La Solitude. *Dated by R.L.S.'s mother. Unpublished. Mrs. R.L.S. writes of Stevenson's illness in Nice, of her being told by a doctor whom she found with great difficulty that Stevenson was dying, and of her relief at being told later by another doctor (Dr. Drummond) that Stevenson's condition was not too bad.*

3788

[January, 1884. Pension Rose Torelli, Rue de France 100, Nice]. My dear Mrs Stevenson Louis is not quite so near the high water mark as he was yesterday. *Signed:* Fanny. *3 pp. Written on stationery of* La Solitude. *Dated by R.L.S.'s mother. Unpublished. Mrs. R.L.S. asks Stevenson's parents to send money, which they need before leaving Nice.*

3789

[*January, 1884. Nice*]. My dear Mrs Stevenson, Just a note to tell you that Louis is getting on well. *Signed: F. 4 pp. Written on stationery of* La Solitude. *Dated by R.L.S.'s mother. Unpublished. Mrs. R.L.S. writes that Dr. Wakefield has been in daily attendance on Stevenson for nearly two weeks and that Dr. Drummond will accordingly answer no question about the case.*

3790

[*January or February, 1884? Nice?*] They were very angry that Louis should presume to be ill in the night and have a doctor. *Signed:* Fanny. *Last p. of letter. Unpublished. R.L.S. has added a few words to this letter.*

3791

[*February 11, 1884. Nice*]. My dear Mrs Stevenson, I am too tired to write much. *Signed:* Fanny. *2 pp. All but 3 lines in pencil. Dated by R.L.S.'s mother. Unpublished. Mrs. R.L.S. writes that Stevenson is so fastidious about his food that I am* driven to my wits end to find things for him.

3792

[*February, 1884. Nice*]. P. S. I am too tired to write. I have been taking the nurse's place for the last three nights. *Signed:* Fanny. *2 pp. Dated by R.L.S.'s mother. Unpublished. This is an addition to a letter by R.L.S.*

3793

[*February, 1884. Nice*]. My dear Mrs Stevenson, I have just got Sam's letter. Please ask him to wait a little for his answer. *Signed:* Fanny. *6 pp. Dated by R.L.S.'s mother. Unpublished. Mrs. R.L.S. writes:* I wish Sir Walter [*Simpson*] were here to help me; otherwise I think I shall suddenly kill this nurse. *She writes that Dr. Wakefield is now working under Dr. Drummond's orders. At the end she writes:* A cheerful religious letter from Louis' father would do him more good than all the medicine.

3794

[*February, 1884. Nice*]. My dear Mrs Stevenson, This is just a note to say that Louis is much stronger . . . tomorrow, if nothing happens, we leave Nice. *Signed:* Fanny. *1 p. Written on stationery of* La Solitude. *Dated by R.L.S.'s mother. Unpublished.*

3795

[*March 27, 1884. Hyères*]. My dear Mrs Stevenson, I cannot write much, for I have been writing to Louis dictation and my eyes have given out. *Signed:* Fanny. *4 pp. Written on stationery of* La Solitude. *Dated by R.L.S.'s mother. Unpublished. Mrs. R.L.S. writes that Louis eye got alarmingly worse, and that her own eyes were far from well.*

3796

[*April, 1884. Hyères*]. My dear Mrs Stevenson, We were much amused by Sam's letter. What a comic boy he is. *Signed:* Fanny. *2 pp. Dated by R.L.S.'s mother. Unpublished. Mrs. R.L.S. writes that she does not wish to sell certain paintings that she has made but wishes to give them to R.L.S.'s mother. She writes of Coggie Ferrier and the dog Bogue.*

3797

[*Spring, 1884. Hyères*]. terrible fear that they might be taken home. *Signed:* Fanny. *Last 4 pp. of letter. Written on stationery of* La Solitude. *Unpublished. Mrs. R.L.S. writes of Lloyd Osbourne's hope to be apprenticed to R.L.S.'s father. She writes of her combats with Stevenson in the finishing of* Prince Otto.

3798

[*Spring, 1884. Hyères*]. My dear Mrs Stevenson, Why did you not tell us of the birthday in time? *Unsigned. 3 pp. Written on stationery of* La Solitude. *Dated by R.L.S.'s mother. Unpublished. Mrs. R.L.S. writes of Dr. Drummond and Dr. Wakefield, and of pictures.*

3799

[*Spring, 1884. Hyères*]. My dear Mrs Stevenson I had to choke my letter off very suddenly, the last one. *Signed:* Fanny.

8 pp. Written on stationery of La Solitude. *Dated by R.L.S.'s mother. Unpublished. Mrs. R.L.S. writes of R. A. M. Stevenson, who said that R.L.S., R.L.S.'s father and he had all had* some special guidance that kept us from marrying the wrong women. *Mrs. R.L.S. writes of her husband's health and her buying special things for him to eat; of reviews and letters about his books; of the dog Bogue.*

3800

[*May, 1884. Hyères*]. My dear Mrs Stevenson Why dont we hear from you? *Signed:* Fanny. *4 pp. Written on stationery of* La Solitude. *Dated by R.L.S.'s mother. Unpublished.*

3801

[*May 18, 1884. Hyères*]. My dear Mrs Stevenson, I think you might as well tell Louis' father that he has had another very serious illness caused by the rupture of an artery. *Signed:* Fanny. *4 pp. Written on stationery of* La Solitude. *Dated by R.L.S.'s mother. Unpublished. The letter is about Stevenson's health and what is done to take care of it. Mrs. R.L.S. fears any upset that might come to Stevenson's father because of what that might do to Louis.*

3802

[*May 25, 1884. Hyères*]. My dear Mrs Stevenson, We have a regular London day, blowing, and our equivalent of an East wind. *Signed:* Fanny. *4 pp. Dated by R.L.S.'s mother. Unpublished. Mrs. R.L.S. writes of her husband's improved health and of their plans to go to Royat.*

3803

[*November 11, 1884. Bournemouth*]. My dear Mrs Stevenson, This is to tell you that Louis really seems better this morning. *Signed:* Fanny. *4 pp. Dated by R.L.S.'s mother. Unpublished. Mrs. R. L. S. writes of a doctor who wants to operate for Stevenson's cough, and of an order for a Christmas ghost story which was passed on by R.L.S. to his wife.*

1155

3804

[*September 13, 1885. Bournemouth*]. My dear Mrs Stevenson, Louis has got home *beautifully. Signed:* Fanny. *2 pp. Dated by R.L.S.'s mother. Unpublished. Mrs. R.L.S. writes that she would not exchange Skerryvore for the Queen's palace.*

3805

[*Summer, 1890*] Saturday morning. [*On board the* Janet Nicholl, *Pacific Ocean*]. We are very near Savage Island, now. *Signed:* F. *2 pp. Unpublished. Mrs. R.L.S. writes of a storm encountered on this trip.*

3806

[*January, 1893. Vailima*]. I know you wont understand this note of Louis, so I give a word of explanation. *Unsigned. 2 pp. Unpublished. Stevenson has suffered from a hemorrhage and the natives have been sick with influenza. This is an addition to a letter by R.L.S.*

3807

[*September, 1895. San Francisco*]. My dear Aunt Maggie, I have no earthly thing to write about. *Signed:* Fanny. *4 pp. On black-bordered stationery. Unpublished. Mrs. R.L.S. writes of herself and her children, of R.L.S.'s wish to write a biography of James Chalmers, of a man named Churchill who wanted to collaborate with Mrs. R.L.S. in writing a novel of the South Seas.*

3808

October 30th [*1895. San Francisco*]. My dear Aunt Maggie This is a hasty note to tell you that in a fortnight we shall be starting for Honolulu. *Signed:* Fanny. *2 pp. Written on black-bordered stationery. Unpublished. Mrs. R.L.S. describes her son's alarming symptoms.*

3809

November 4th [*1895. San Francisco*]. My dear Aunt Maggie, I am too tired to write much, or clearly. *Signed:* Fanny. *2 pp. Written on black-bordered stationery. Unpublished. Mrs. R.L.S. writes of Lloyd Osbourne's illness, of their imminent departure for Honolulu, of her disgust at the idea of publishing Steven-son's Fables.*

3810
Dec 15th, 95. [*Honolulu*]. My dear Aunt Maggie, Please excuse this scrap of paper. *Signed:* Fanny. *2 pp. Unpublished. Mrs. R.L.S. writes about her son's symptoms, and about poems taken away by Mr. Clarke.*

3811
Jan 8th 1896. San [*sic*] Souci [*Honolulu*]. My dear Aunt Maggie, I cannot conceive why you did not get the letter I wrote to you. *Signed:* Fanny. *4 pp. Written on black-bordered stationery. Unpublished. Of her late husband Mrs. R.L.S. writes:* I do not think there is one moment that I am not thinking of him. *She writes of her son's convalescence.*

3812
March 5th [*1896. Honolulu*]. My dear Aunt Maggie, I am only writing because a steamer is going out, though I have nothing to say. *Signed:* Fanny. *3 pp. Written on black-bordered sta-tionery. Unpublished. Mrs. R.L.S. writes of her son's setback in health; she mentions his forthcoming marriage and the forth-coming marriage of Graham Balfour.*

MRS. R.L.S. TO HER FATHER-IN-LAW, THOMAS STEVENSON

3813

17th October 1882. [*Marseille*]. Please tell Mrs Stevenson that the parcel she has received from the cleaners is most likely . . . a petticoat. *Unsigned. 1 p. Unpublished. This is an addition to a letter by R.L.S.*

3814

[*January, 1884. Nice*]. My dear Mr Stevenson. Louis is not quite so well today as he was yesterday. *Signed:* Fanny. *4 pp. Dated by R.L.S.'s mother. Unpublished. Mrs. R.L.S. writes that she has sent for R. A. M. Stevenson, and lists some of the heavy expenses to which she has been put.*

3815

[*January, 1884. Nice*]. P. S. Louis has made up his mind not to have the lighthouse book sent by Miss Ferrier. *Signed:* Fanny. *3 pp. Written on stationery of* La Solitude. *Dated by R.L.S.'s mother. Unpublished. This is about R.L.S.'s health, his doctors, nurse, etc. This is an addition to a letter by R.L.S.*

3816

[*October 28, 1880. Troyes*]. It was foolish to go to so dear a hotel. *Signed:* Fanny. *2 pp. Unpublished. This is an addition to a letter by R.L.S.*

3817

November 5th [*1880*]. Hotel Belvedere Davos. Switz. The doctor has been here, and has examined Louis carefully. *Unfinished (?) and unsigned. 1 p. Unpublished. This is an addition to a letter by R.L.S.*

3818

[*January 15, 1881. Davos*]. My dear people, I am glad to tell you that I have just heard that the doctor has said that he considers Louis and Mrs D. . . . his two best advertisements of Davos. *Unfinished and unsigned. 2 pp. Dated by R.L.S.'s mother. Unpublished. Principally about the arrival of Mrs. Fanny Sitwell, with her son who is suffering from tuberculosis. R.L.S. has written an addition to this letter.*

3819

[*January 27, 1881. Davos*]. My dear People, I will tell you once more to make sure, that the money came all right. *Unsigned. 1 p. Unpublished. Largely about the illnesses of Lloyd Osbourne and Mrs. Sitwell's son. This is an addition to a letter by R.L.S.*

3820

[*March 3, 1881. Davos*]. My dear People, I am too lazy to go downstairs for a clean bit of paper. *First 4 pp. of letter. Dated by R.L.S.'s mother. Unpublished. Mrs. R.L.S. writes that the doctor is* stiffer *than ever* about Stevenson's remaining in Switzerland. She mentions Bertie Sitwell.*

3821

[May 5, 1881. Hotel St. Romain, Rue St. Roch, Paris]. So much for Louis. *Signed:* Fanny. *4 pp. Dated April 5 by R.L.S.'s mother; this is an error for May 5. Unpublished. Fanny thinks that R.L.S. was mistreated in a hotel in St. Germain because he wore a colored flannel shirt. This is an addition to a letter by R.L.S.*

3822

[February 24, 1883]. P. R. Hyères Var. I blotted Louis' letter. I am better but not quite up to write. *Signed:* Fanny. *2 pp. Unpublished. This is an addition to a letter by R.L.S.*

3823

[March 25, 1884. Hyères]. My dear People, I am not very good at letter writing, since I have been doing blind man's eyes. *Signed:* Fanny. *4 pp. Written on stationery of* La Solitude. *Dated by R.L.S.'s mother. Unpublished. Mrs. R.L.S. writes that her husband has suffered from eye strain. She writes of Lloyd Osbourne, who was thought by some to be R.L.S.'s father; and of the servant Valentine Roch.*

3824

[March 29, 1884. Hyères]. My dear People, I just add a word to say that Louis' eyes are really almost well. *Signed:* Fanny. *4 pp. Written on stationery of* La Solitude. *Dated by R.L.S.'s mother. Unpublished. Mrs. R.L.S. states that she likes to write to her husband's dictation* partly, I must confess, to interfere if I think there is occasion to.

3825

[April 12, 1884. Hyères]. Louis is not mad as you may think by his signing himself "your cousin." *Signed:* Fanny. *1 p. Written on stationery of* La Solitude. *Dated by R.L.S.'s mother. Unpublished. This is an addition to a letter by R.L.S.*

3826

[April, 1884. Hyères]. My dear People, It is raining heavily, and I have taken a liver pill, so I feel rather crushed. *Signed:* Fanny. *4 pp. Dated by R.L.S.'s mother. Unpublished. Mrs.*

R.L.S. writes further about the ophthalmia from which she and her husband suffered, of photographs of herself, of Coggie Ferrier's visit.

3827

[*May, 1884. Hyères*]. We are not *out* of money. *Signed: F. 2 pp. Written on stationery of La Solitude. Dated by R.L.S.'s mother. Unpublished. This is an addition to a letter by R.L.S.*

3828

[*April 24, 1886*]. Skerryvore [*Bournemouth*]. My dear people all, We arrived with no worse happening than an addition to my cold. *Signed: F. 2 pp. Dated by R.L.S.'s mother. Unpublished. Mrs. R.L.S. mentions a news vendor in Southampton crying:* Doctor Jekyll! Doctor Jekyll!

MRS. R.L.S. TO CHARLES WARREN STODDARD

3829

[*1904?*] 2323 Hyde Street San Francisco [*Written at Vanu-manitagi Ranch, Santa Cruz Mountains, California*]. My dear Charley, Though I am at my ranch in the Santa Cruz Mountains . . . the above is my letter receiving address. *Signed:* Fanny V. de G. Stevenson. *3 pp. To Charles Warren Stoddard? Unpublished. Mrs. R.L.S. writes of her introductions to Stevenson's writings for the Biographical Edition, at which she was then working.*

MRS. R.L.S. TO MRS. STORER (?)

3830

April 20th [*1897*]. Vailima Samoa. My dear Mrs Storer [?] I
had meant to write to you by the last mail, as I felt that I owed
you an answer to Mr. Burt's letter. *Signed:* Fanny V de G. Stevenson. *4 pp. On black-bordered stationery. Mrs. R.L.S. writes
of her late husband, of injuries done to her and others by Mr.
Blacklock, former United States vice consul at Samoa, and of
her son Lloyd Osbourne who has succeeded to this position.*

MRS. R.L.S. TO HER DAUGHTER, MRS. ISOBEL OSBOURNE STRONG, LATER MRS. FIELD

3831

[*Summer, 1880? Scotland?*] are taking so much and will never be able to give anything. They are so sweet to Sam too. *Unsigned. Last 3 pp. of letter. In pencil. Unpublished. Mrs. R.L.S. writes of the kindness of Stevenson's parents to Lloyd Osbourne. R.L.S. has written an addition to this letter.*

[*September? 1880. Edinburgh*]. *See no. 3730. Letter to Nellie van de Grift Sanchez and Isobel Strong.*

3832

[*19—*]. Fairfield Chiddingfold Surrey England. My dear Teuila, The above is my address until further advices. *1st p. of letter. Photograph. Unpublished. Mrs. R.L.S. assures her daughter that she bequeaths to her all her* furniture, silver, pictures, clothing, furs and jewelry.

MRS. R.L.S. TO HER NEPHEWS, FRED, WALTER AND FRANK THOMAS

3833

[*April, 1882. Landquart, Switzerland*]. My dear boys, I received your very delightful letters just before I left Davos. *Signed:* Your Aunt Fanny. *8 pp. Unpublished. Mrs. R.L.S. writes of a dirty chimney sweep who fell asleep on R.L.S.'s bed, of carriages and carts, flowers, scenery, Wogg (the dog), Lloyd Osbourne's studies, gifts and the lead soldiers game played with R.L.S. The latter has written 3 lines at the end, signed:* Atlas!

MRS. R.L.S. TO DORA NORTON WILLIAMS
(MRS. VIRGIL WILLIAMS)

3834

Aug 25 [*1875. Antwerp*]. My dear Mrs Williams, It was, after all, just as I said it would be. We dropped right out without time to even let our friends know. *Signed:* Mrs Fanny M Osbourne. *8 pp. Unpublished. Mrs. Osbourne writes of her experiences in travelling from Indiana to Belgium with her children, which involved driving through flooded districts in Indiana.*

3835

[*December, 1875. Paris*]. My dear Mrs Williams, I dreamed of you and your husband last night. *Signed:* Fanny M O. *8 pp. Unpublished. Mrs. Osbourne writes of her and her daughter, Isobel's, work in M. Julian's art school, of their living arrangements, of a Mrs. Marshall. She mentions her sick child, Hervey.*

3836

[*May or June, 1880. Springs Hotel, Silverado*]. My dear Mrs Williams, Excuse my writing with pencil. *Signed:* F. S. *3 pp. In pencil. Unpublished. An account of her and R.L.S.'s life in Silverado shortly after their marriage.*

3837

[*September, 1880. Ben Wyvis Hotel, Strathpeffer*]. My dear Mrs Williams, Either no one received all my postal cards and letters, or else you have all forgotten me. *Signed:* F. M. S. *4 pp. Unpublished. Mrs. R.L.S. gives first impressions of Scotland and of Stevenson's parents.*

3838

[*October, 1880. Edinburgh*]. My dear Mrs Williams, I have nothing in particular to write about, except that Louis and I think you the best and kindest and truest friend in the world. *Unsigned. 4 pp. Unpublished. Fanny writes about the wardrobes of Stevenson and his mother. R.L.S. has written an addition to this letter.*

3839

[*December, 1880. Hotel Belvedere, Davos*]. My dear Mrs Williams I have tried three pens so far, and find that I am on the wrong side of the paper. *Signed:* Fanny V de G. Stevenson. *8 pp. Unpublished. Mrs. R.L.S. gives advice to Mrs. Williams, who has apparently had difficulties with her husband.*

3840

[*May, 1881. Paris*]. My dear Mrs Williams, I am afraid such a tidy person as you are will be disgusted to receive a letter written upon scraps. *Signed:* Fanny V de G Stevenson. *4 pp. Written on stationery of* Hotel Saint Romain. *Unpublished. Mrs. R.L.S. writes of an exhibition of paintings in which* the badness of the [*French*] pictures is inconceivable.

3841

[*June or July, 1881. Kinnaird Cottage, Pitlochry, Perthshire*]. My dear Mrs Williams, I am finishing Louis' sheet through an unwonted fit of economy. *Signed:* Fanny V d G. Stevenson. *9 pp. Unpublished. Fanny writes about life in Scotland and plans for a second winter in Davos. This is an addition to a letter by R.L.S. addressed to Mr. Williams.*

3842

[*September, 1881. Braemar*]. My dear Mrs Williams, I have been wanting and intending to write to you for a long time. *Signed:* Fanny V de G Stevenson. *4 pp. Unpublished. Mrs. R.L.S. writes of Stevenson's bad health, of a respirator he uses, of her hope that he will not get the professorship at the University of Edinburgh, of his* Merry Men *and work on* Treasure Island.

3843

[*November, 1881. Davos*]. My dear Mrs Williams. All the paper in the house has Sam's business card (though in this he has spelled his own name wrong) at the heading. *Signed:* F. V de G Stevenson. *8 pp. Written on stationery of* Davos Printing Office. Managed by Samuel Lloyd Osbouren [*sic*] & Co. The Chalet. *Unpublished. Mrs. R.L.S. writes about a sick dog, an unruly servant, and about Isobel and Joe Strong and other people in San Francisco.*

3844

[*November or December, 1881*]. The Chalet [*Davos*]. My dear Mrs Williams. I do not know whether I owe you a letter or not. *Signed:* Fanny V de G Stevenson. *6 pp. Written on stationery of* Hôtel & Pension Buol. *Unpublished. Mrs. R.L.S. writes of her and her husband's ill health, of their dog, and of the ingratitude of her daughter, Isobel. On p. 1 Stevenson has written:* My love to both   R. L. S.

3845

[*August? 1882. Scotland*]. My dear Mrs Williams, I have not forgotten you, as you may think. *Signed:* Fanny V de G Stevenson. *6 pp. Unpublished. Mrs. R.L.S. writes of her own bad health and her husband's examination by doctors in London; about her son, Lloyd; and the* coarse flavor *of the letters she receives from her daughter, Isobel.*

3846

[*September, 1882. Kingussie*]. My dear Mrs Williams, It is the most extraordinary thing that you do not get our letters. *Signed:* Fanny V de G Stevenson. *10 pp. Unpublished. Mrs. R.L.S. writes about a lost manuscript sent by Mrs. Williams which was later found, about* New Arabian Nights, Judge Timothy Rearden *of San Francisco, and about her children: Isobel and Lloyd.*

3847

[*October, 1882*]. Campagne Defli St Marcel Marseille. My dear Mrs. Williams, I suppose—no, I *dont* suppose that our address will surprise you. *Signed:* Fanny, *and* F. *8 pp. Written on stationery of* Terminus Hotel, Marseille. *Unpublished. Mrs. R.L.S. writes of her delight in the newly taken house at Campagne Defli, about Isobel's apparent annoyance that the Stevensons have not sent money to her, about Lloyd, etc. On p. 1 Stevenson has written the new address, and:* love to the Roman Bard and to yourself, if I may be allowed. R.L.S.

3848

[*May or June, 1883*]. La Solitude Hyères les Palmiers, Var France. My dears [*sic*] and kind friend, What shall I say to you for this long neglect? *Signed:* Fanny V de G. Stevenson *6 pp. Unpublished. Mrs. R.L.S. writes of her great satisfaction in living at* La Solitude; *of her son, Lloyd; of an unruly servant, etc.*

3849

[*Cir. July 1, 1883. Hyères*]. My dear Mrs Williams, I think I wrote to you about Louis, how he had an artery break in his lungs. *Signed:* F. V de G. Stevenson. *3 pp. Written on stationery of* La Solitude. *Unpublished. Mrs. R.L.S. writes of Stevenson's recent serious illness, of plans to go to Royat, of Joe Strong's serious illness. On p. 1 Stevenson has written:* Do, please, try and find out if Joe Strong is really very ill.

3850

[*September or October, 1883. Marseille*]. My dear Mrs Williams, You are the very best person in the whole world. *Signed:* F. V de G. Stevenson. *8 pp. Unpublished. Mrs. R.L.S. writes of a possible visit from Mr. and Mrs. Williams; of a visit from Colvin who was without funds on account of some technicality; of Lloyd Osbourne's education, bicycle, nearsightedness; publication arrangements for* The Silverado Squatters, *etc.*

3851

[*Spring? 1884. Hyères*]. My dear Mrs Williams, Aside from every other consideration it is a pleasure to get your letters because they are so long and interesting. *Signed:* F. V de G Stevenson. *6 pp. Written on stationery of* La Solitude. *Unpublished. Mrs. R.L.S. writes of dreams, of Stoddard, Gosse, Symonds, Lizzie Strong, Mrs. Campion, Judge Rearden and others.*

3852

[*Late spring, 1884. Hyères*]. My dear Mrs Williams, It is a shame for me to try to write to you tonight, for I am . . . in very low spirits. *Signed:* Fanny V de G Stevenson. *4 pp. Written on stationery of* La Solitude. *Unpublished. Mrs. R.L.S. writes much about her son, Lloyd, and his recent visit with his father. She refers to R.L.S.'s forthcoming* Child's Garden of Verses.

3853

[*December, 1884?*] Bonallie Tower. Bournemouth. My dear Mrs Williams, I am ashamed to begin a letter to you. *Signed: F. V de G. Stevenson. 6 pp. Unpublished. Mrs. R.L.S. writes about the bad health of her husband and herself, and about Lloyd Osbourne's studies in Edinburgh. She makes generalizations about Englishmen, Frenchmen and Americans, and characterizations of Colvin, Symonds and Gosse.*

3854

[*March, 1885*]. Bonallie Tower, Bournemouth [*and Hyères*]. My dear Mrs Williams, I cannot tell you with what amusement I read Reardens views of my relations with professor Colvin and Symonds. *Signed:* Fanny V de G. Stevenson. 8 pp. *Unpublished. Mrs. R.L.S. writes about Colvin, Symonds, James Payn, Besant, Lang, Meredith and other writers. She tells of her work with Stevenson on* The Dynamiters, *and of her purchase of the house, Skerryvore, at Bournemouth for $9,000. She writes of Judge Rearden and of the maid, Valentine. The letter was begun in Bournemouth, and finished at Hyères where she went to close up affairs.*

3855

[*April or May, 1885. Skerryvore, Bournemouth*]. My dear Mrs Williams, We have just moved into our lovely house, of which I sent you a description. *Signed:* F V de G. Stevenson. 8 pp. *Unpublished. Mrs. R.L.S. writes of the house, Skerryvore; of Henry James and Sir Henry Taylor. Lloyd Osbourne's father has evidently made an offer to the boy to take care of him on a ranch at Sonoma, California. Regarding this Mrs. R.L.S. writes:* I should like his father to know that if he takes Sam [*i.e. Lloyd*] he also takes his maintenance and his future prospects upon his own shoulders and that I shall be no more responsible. *Mrs. Stevenson does not think her son would be happy on a ranch in California.*

1170

3856

[*October, 1885*]. Skerryvore, Bournemouth. My dear Mrs Williams, I have been waiting and waiting to get some photographs to send in return for your lovely ones. *Signed:* Fanny V de G. Stevenson. *4 pp. Unpublished. Mrs. R.L.S. writes of John S. Sargent's portrait of Stevenson and her, of Henry James, Sir Percy and Lady Shelley and Rosina Vokes. She believes that Lloyd Osbourne does not think favorably of his father's offer.*

3857

[*October or November, 1885*]. Skerryvore . . . Bournemouth. My dear Mrs Williams. Pray excuse this professional paper. I am writing in bed, the only spot where I can be certain of being alone for a moment. *Signed:* F. V de G. Stevenson. *6 pp. Unpublished. Mrs. R.L.S. writes of a severe hemorrhage Stevenson had in Exeter, of Thomas Hardy, Henry James, Katherine de Mattos, Lloyd Osbourne, and of photography.*

3858

[*April, 1886*]. London Chelsea. My dear Mrs Williams. I have been intending to write to you for a long time. *Signed:* F. V de G. Stevenson. *8 pp. Unpublished. Mrs. R.L.S. writes of stopping in Bath and elsewhere with Stevenson's father; of Lloyd Osbourne's losing his sight while taking examinations in Edinburgh and her fear of his continuing blindness; of Mr. Bloomer, an artist, and Henry James. Mrs. R.L.S. has brought her maid, Valentine, to London for treatment of the latter's jaundice.*

3859

[*January, 1887. Bournemouth*]. Dear Friend, In the face of such woful [*sic*] news what can I say? *Signed:* F. V de G. S. *4 pp. Unpublished. Mrs. R.L.S. sends her sympathy in the death of Virgil Williams, and mentions her premonition of the bad news contained in Mrs. Williams's letter two days before its arrival. She writes of her neuralgic rheumatism, and of her plan to come to America. She asks if Mrs. Williams could return to England with her.*

1171

3860

[*April? 1887. Bournemouth*]. Louis had got so far when he became too tired, and had to go to bed. *Signed: Fanny V. de G. Stevenson. 3 pp. Unpublished. Mrs. R.L.S. writes of her son, Lloyd's, preparations for expected increasing blindness, about R.L.S.'s health, and the devotion of the maid, Valentine. This is an addition to a letter by R.L.S.*

3861

[*April, 1887*]. Skerryvore Westbourne Bournemouth. My dearest Friend. My letter, in the face of that awful calamity, I fear came to you not as I meant it. *Signed: Fanny V. de G. Stevenson. 4 pp. Unpublished. Mrs. R.L.S. writes of her* neuralgic rheumatism of the heart, *which she fears may cause her early death. Because of R.L.S.'s bad health she has for the time given up plans for a visit to America. She writes further about Mrs. Williams's loss of her husband.*

3862

[*June, 1887*]. Skerryvore Westbourne Bournemouth. I should have written to you before, dear friend, but for a very sad reason. Louis's father died . . . *Signed: F. V. de G. Stevenson. 4 pp. Written on black-bordered stationery. Unpublished. Mrs. R.L.S. writes about the death, funeral and will of R.L.S.'s father; of plans to move to Colorado; of Lloyd Osbourne's dislike for his father. The thought of his father is a nightmare horror to him. R.L.S.'s Uncle George Balfour, a physician, says that Mrs. R.L.S. does not have rheumatism.*

3863

[*September, 1887. Newport, R. I.*] My dear Mrs Williams. Here we are at Newport, stopping with very delightful millionaires [*Mr. and Mrs. Charles S. Fairchild*], who are spoiling us beautifully. *Signed: Fanny V. de G. Stevenson. 2 pp. Unpublished. Mrs. R.L.S. writes of a bad Atlantic crossing and of her and Stevenson's illnesses.*

3864

[*November, 1887*]. Saranac Lake Adirondack Mountains. My dear Friend. This is just a word. You ask if you can do anything for me. *Signed:* Fanny V de G Stevenson. *3 pp. Written on black-bordered stationery. Unpublished. Mrs. R.L.S. asks Mrs. Williams to find out and let her know the state of Judge Rearden's health. She writes of an article by William Archer titled* Robert Louis Stevenson at "Skerryvore."

3865
[*April or May, 1888. Indianapolis*]. My dearest Friend, I have been wondering why we heard nothing from you; though, after all, I dont know why we should wonder as all the letters we write are lost. *Signed:* F. V. de G. Stevenson. *2 pp. Written on stationery of* The Bates House, Indianapolis. *Unpublished. Mrs. R.L.S. writes of a visit to her mother in Indianapolis, and of possible journeys in the future.*

3866
[*June, 1888*]. Yacht Casco [*Pacific Ocean*]. My dear Mrs Williams. It is not that I have anything to say that I write. *Signed:* Fanny. *2 pp. In pencil. Unpublished. Another word of farewell.*

3867
[*July, 1888*]. Anaho bay: Nouka-hiva Marquesas Islands. My dear friend. I do not suppose you will be able to make out where we are. *Signed:* Fanny V. de G. Stevenson. *8 pp. Unpublished. Mrs. R.L.S. writes about meetings with natives, food, health, etc.*

3868
Aug 20th [*1888*]. Taiohai Noukahiva. My dear Mrs Williams As you see, we have bidden goodbye to our beautiful Anaho and our savage friends. *Signed:* Fanny V. de G. Stevenson. *5 pp. Unpublished. Mrs. R.L.S. writes of farewells in Anaho, gifts, cannibalism, etc.*

3869
[*November, 1888*]. Tahiti. My dear friend, I parted with you, for so I feel the breaking off of a letter, just as we left Taiohae. *Signed:* Fanny V de G. Stevenson. *16 pp. Unpublished. Mrs. R.L.S. writes of their stay in Hiva Oa; their adoption by Hakaiki*

Paaeua, a chief; dinners, etc. with the new parents, and with Moipu, a cannibal; and a voyage among the Pernicious Isles.

3870

April 9th [*1889*]. Honolulu. My dear friend, I am just dead beat with business letters. *Signed:* Fanny V. de G. Stevenson. *4 pp. Unpublished. Mrs. R.L.S. writes of plans for further voyages, without R.L.S.'s mother who returns to Scotland; and about* The Wrong Box *which was in the publisher's hands.*

3871

June 18th [*1889*]. Honolulu. My dear friend. This is just a hasty note of goodbye. *Signed:* Fanny V. de G. Stevenson. *4 pp. Unpublished. Mrs. R.L.S. writes, while awaiting arrival of the* Equator *on which they were about to sail, about music produced by various members of the party, Ah Foo their Chinese cook, and Isobel Strong's illness.*

3872

[*December, 1889*]. Schooner Equator, off Samoa. My dear friend, I shall have so much to do immediately on our arrival in Samoa that I may not have time to get off a word to you by the first steamer. *Signed:* Fanny V. de G. Stevenson. *6 pp. Unpublished. Mrs. R.L.S. writes of passengers on the* Equator, *her husband's good health and the bad health of other members of the party.*

3873

[*Winter, 1889–1890. Samoa*]. My dear friend, I am unexpectedly told that my letters must be immediately ready or they will not catch the mail boat. *Signed:* Fanny V. de G. Stevenson. *1 p. Unpublished. Mrs. R.L.S. writes about pictures shipped from San Francisco, and her need of an American wood-burning stove.*

3874

[*January, 1891. Vailima*]. My dear Friend, I am very much obliged to you for the trouble you have taken about the stove. *Signed:* F V de G Stevenson. *9 pp. Unpublished. Mrs. R.L.S. writes about cooking; about Henry Simile, a native cook, who horsewhipped a troublesome white woman; about a visit from threatening drunken sailors.*

3875

[*March or April, 1891. Vailima*]. My dear friend. First business, I have received the invoice for the stove, but hear nothing of the article. *Signed: Fanny V. de G. Stevenson. 8 pp. Unpublished. Mrs. R.L.S. writes about the household and the new house at Vailima, about the mails, and about R.L.S.'s trip to Sydney from which he had recently returned in bad health.*

3876

[*April? 1891. Vailima*]. My dear friend. I am very tired, and it is late in the night, but just now I am so busy that I must seize any moment that is possible or I shall never get a letter written. *Unfinished and unsigned. 6 pp. Unpublished. Mrs. R.L.S. is annoyed at a newspaper report that Henry Adams and John La Farge were rebuffed at Vailima. She writes about a new stove that has arrived, about the difficulty of buying common household articles in Samoa, about eating arrangements.*

3877

[*1893. Samoa*]. Dear Friend Excuse haste, the steamer is just coming in. I was nearly killed coming down from Vailima on my horse. *Signed: F. V. de G. Stevenson. 2 pp. Unpublished. Mrs. R.L.S. asks Mrs. Williams to get her a divided riding skirt.*

3878

Oct 18th 1893. S. S. Monawai. My dear friend, You will be surprised, I know, at my whereabouts. *Signed: Fanny V de G Stevenson. 4 pp. Written on stationery of Union Steam Ship Company of New Zealand Limited. Unpublished. Mrs. Stevenson is following R.L.S. to Honolulu, where the latter is ill. She writes about a measles epidemic, and two young women (travelling companions) who would like to give concerts in San Francisco.*

3879

[*December, 1895*]. Hotel San[*sic*] Souci Waikiki Honolulu. My dear Dora, This is to introduce Mr Young, a friend of Louis's and ours. *Signed:* Fanny V. de G. Stevenson. *2 pp. Written on black-bordered stationery. With addressed envelope. Unpublished.*

3880

[*August, 1896*]. Vailima date unknown. My dearest friend, I do mean to write to you by every mail, but when the time comes something seems to always happen to prevent my doing so. *Signed:* Fanny. *8 pp. Written on black-bordered stationery. With addressed envelope. Unpublished. Mrs. R.L.S. writes about a trial in which she was defendant against Robert T. Chatfield, and acted as her own lawyer; about Lloyd Osbourne's and Mrs. Sanchez's illnesses; and about her (Mrs. R.L.S.'s) donkey.*

3881

Nov 2nd, 96. Vailima. My dear Dora. I have a headache this morning, and am doubtful whether I shall be able to write a long letter. *Signed:* Fanny. *8 pp. On black-bordered stationery. With addressed envelope. Unpublished. A medium has brought to Mrs. Williams a message which, it was claimed, came from R.L.S. Mrs. Stevenson advises Mrs. Williams to have nothing to do with mediums.*

3882

[*November, 1896. Vailima*]. My dear Dora, This is just a hasty note to say that one of the daughters of the chief justice will arrive in San Francisco on the same steamer that carries this letter. *Signed:* Fanny V. de G. Stevenson. *3 pp. Written on black-bordered stationery. With addressed envelope. Unpublished. Mrs. R.L.S. writes about Marjorie Ide, who is being sent to school in the United States against her will.*

3883

[*March, 1897*]. Vailima. My dearest Dora, I must write like lightning to get a word down before Lloyd goes off with the letters. *Signed:* Fanny V. de G. Stevenson. *4 pp. Written on*

*black-bordered stationery. With addressed envelope. Unpub-
lished. Mrs. R.L.S. gives a further reason for not wanting Mrs.
Williams to consult mediums; she writes also about her new
grandson, Alan Osbourne; and about a Mr. Brooks who had
recently been a visitor at Vailima.*

3884
August 28th 97. Vailima Samoa. My dearest Dora. This being
my last letter to you before I leave for S. F. I do not feel like
making it a very long one. *Signed:* Fanny. *2 pp. Written on
black-bordered stationery. Unpublished. Mrs. R.L.S., who has
gone barefoot for many years, asks to have shoes made for her:
wide with thin soles.*

3885
[*Postmarked:* Jan 24 . . . '98]. Occidental Hotel [*San Francisco*].
Dearest Dora, You see I am here, where you used to so kindly
come and sit and talk with me. *Signed:* Fanny V. de G. Stevenson. *4 pp. Written on black-bordered stationery, with motto:
Coelum non Solum. With addressed envelope and mounted
stamp. Unpublished. Mrs. R.L.S. asks about Mrs. Williams's trip
to North Carolina. She writes of the marriage of a mutual ac-
quaintance, and mentions her plan to go to the St. Charles
Hotel because R.L.S. and she were happy there.*

3886
April 7th [*1898. New York*]. My dearest Dora, A dozen times
I have sat down to write to you, and always I am interrupted
by company. *Signed:* Fanny V de G. Stevenson. *4 pp. With
addressed envelope and mounted stamps. Unpublished. Mrs.
R.L.S. writes about various family matters.*

3887
April 17th [*1898*]. Hotel Albert [*New York*]. My dearest Dora,
I am getting very anxious because I dont hear from you. *Signed:*
Fanny V. de G. Stevenson. *2 pp. With addressed envelope and
mounted stamp. Unpublished. Mrs. R.L.S. writes about the ill-
nesses of Isobel Strong and herself.*

3888

[*Postmarked:* Au 23 98. Dorking]. My dearest friend. It is a long time since I have written to you. *Unfinished and unsigned. 4 pp. With addressed envelope and mounted stamp. Unpublished. Mrs. R.L.S. explains her going barefoot in Samoa, her loose clothes and her smoking.*

3889

[*Postmarked:* Sp 16 98. Dorking]. My dearest Dora, I have just received your sweet letter. *Signed:* Fanny. *2 pp. With addressed envelope and mounted stamp. Unpublished. Mrs. R.L.S. writes of her imminent gall bladder operation.*

3890

[*Postmarked:* 13 Dez 1898 Funchal Madeira]. My dearest friend, I have only a few drops of ink, and, as you see, a very unsteady hand. *Signed:* Fanny V de G. Stevenson. *3 pp. Written on stationery of* Reid's New Hotel. *With addressed envelope and mounted stamp. Unpublished. Mrs. R.L.S. writes of suffering after her operation, and of a slow trip through France, Spain and Portugal.*

3891

[*Postmarked:* Sep 28 . . . 1901. San Francisco]. My dear friend, I have been wondering what had become of you. *Signed:* Fanny. *2 pp. With addressed envelope and mounted stamp. Unpublished. Mrs. R.L.S. is considering as a new gardener a man who knew Stevenson.*

3892

[*Postmarked:* Nov 5 . . . 1903]. The Judson Washington Square New York. My dear Dora. I have been too tired to write before, and indeed am too tired yet. *Signed:* Fanny V. de G. S. *3 pp. With addressed envelope and mounted stamp. Unpublished. Mrs. R.L.S. has just had a railway journey of six days from California in which seven engines broke down. She refers to a forthcoming celebration of Stevenson's birthday in San Francisco.*

3893

[*Postmarked:* Dec 13 1903 (?) New York]. The Judson Washington Square. My dear Dora, In wild haste, while plans begin, I do up, and send in this envelope a humble Christmas offering. *Signed:* Fanny. *1 p. With addressed envelope and mounted stamps. Unpublished.*

3894

[*December 13, 1905. Mexico*]. My dear Dora, I cannot bear being said goodbye to, so I went off without saying nothing to nobody. *Signed:* Fanny V. de G. Stevenson. *4 pp. With addressed envelope and mounted stamps. Unpublished. Mrs. R.L.S. writes about a cold and rheumatism, a story by Lloyd Osbourne titled* The Renegade, *and sends a check with which Mrs. Williams is asked to purchase a Christmas present for herself.*

3895

[*January, 1906*]. Ensenada Lower California Mexico. My dear Dora, I feel that I must reach out a hand to you over the grave of our beloved friend. *Signed:* Fanny V. de G. Stevenson. *3 pp. With addressed envelope and mounted stamp. Unpublished. A letter of commiseration over the death of an unidentified man.*

3896

[*Postmarked:* May 7 . . . 1906]. Gilroy . . . Cal. My dear Dora I couldn't understand where I was to write to you. *Signed:* Fanny V. de G S. *3 pp. With addressed envelope and mounted stamp. Unpublished. Mrs. R.L.S. writes about the saving of her house from destruction in the San Francisco earthquake and fire.*

3897

[*Postmarked:* May 10 . . . 1906]. Gilroy Cal. My dear Dora, You didn't give me a clear address in your note. *Signed:* Fanny V. de G. S. *4 pp. With addressed envelope and mounted stamp. Unpublished. Mrs. R.L.S. writes further concerning her experiences following the San Francisco disaster.*

1179

3898

[*1886. London*]. Dear Sir, My husband, Mr R. L. Stevenson, being unable, through illness, to answer letters, I take it upon myself to do so for him. *Signed:* Fanny V. de G. Stevenson. *1 p. Written on* British Museum *stationery. Unpublished. Mrs. R. L. S. writes that her husband intended* Dr. Jekyll and Mr. Hyde *to be an allegory, though he hoped it might interest as a tale.*

3899

Jun 21st [*1891*]. Vailima Apia. My dear Auntie[?], I should have written by the last steamer to thank you for your . . . presents. *Signed:* Fanny V. de G. Stevenson. *3 pp. Unpublished. Mrs. R.L.S. writes of the hardships at Vailima in the early days of their residence, of the arrival of her mother-in-law, etc.*

3900

[*December 2, 1895*]. Sans Souci Hotel Waikiki Honolulu. Dearest [*illegible name*] Here we are at the old place, very comfortably settled. *Signed:* Fanny. *4 pp. Written on black-bordered stationery. Unpublished. Mrs. R.L.S. writes of Lloyd Osbourne's and her recent poor scale of living in San Francisco and their present grand scale in Hawaii. She refers to R.L.S. as a real Christian.*

INDEX OF FIRST LINES
OF VERSES BY STEVENSON
WRITTEN IN HIS LETTERS

INDEX OF FIRST LINES
OF VERSES BY STEVENSON
WRITTEN IN HIS LETTERS

GENERAL INDEX

GENERAL INDEX

1187

*Five hundred copies printed on all-rag paper
and completed in July 1956.
Designed by Carl Purington Rollins.*

---

*Composition and presswork by Connecticut Printers, Incorporated.
Text in Caledonia type.
Collotypes by Meriden Gravure Company.
Binding by Russell Rutter.*